Collins Advanced Modular Sciences

Biology Core

Mike Bailey and Keith Hirst

Series Editor: Mike Coles

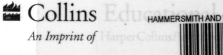
Collins Educational

An Imprint of HarperCollins

Northern
Modular Scier

Published by Collins Educational
An imprint of HarperCollins*Publishers*
77–85 Fulham Palace Road
Hammersmith
London
W6 8JB

© 1995 Mike Bailey and Keith Hirst

First published 1995
Reprinted 1996

ISBN 0 00 322381 7

Design by Ewing Paddock at Peartree Design

Edited by Eva Fairnell
Assistant Art Editor: Simon de Pinna

Picture research by Caroline Thompson

Illustrations by Barking Dog Art, Russell Birkett,
Tom Cross, Jerry Fowler, Hardlines

Printed in Hong Kong

Contents

To the student   5

1   Food for growing babies   6

2   Biological energy resources   16

3   Enzyme washing powders   28

4   Growing cells   34

5   Blood and sweat   46

6   The development dilemma   55

7   Controlling living systems   66

8   Genetic engineers   79

9   Sex and reproduction   92

10 Genes and disease   103

11 Introducing variation   120

12 Family trees   132

13 Food, farming and tigers   143

14 Greening the desert   157

15 Running to win   169

16 Balancing your sugar   181

17 Controlling the flow   192

18 Cleaning the blood   207

    Answers to questions   218

    Glossary   233

    Index   243

Acknowledgements

Text and diagrams reproduced by kind permission of:
Apple Press; BBC Wildlife Magazine; Blackwell Publishers; DHSS; The Guardian; Harvard University Press; Hodder Headline plc; Holt Saunders; Imperial Cancer Research Fund; The Independent; Michael Joseph Ltd; Junction Books; The Liverpool Echo; New Scientist, IPC Magazines Ltd; The Observer; Oryx, Flauna and Fauna Preservation Society; Panos Institute; Plymouth Health Authority; SMA Nutrition; Vegetarian Society; Wadsworth Publishing Co.; Weidenfeld and Nicholson; Wolfe Publishers; World Wildlife Fund for Nature UK, Data Support for Educational Services.

Crown copyright is reproduced with the permission of the Controller of HMSO.

Every effort has been made to contact the holders of copyright material, but if any have been inadvertently overlooked the publishers will be pleased to make the necessary arrangements at the first opportunity.

The publishers would like to thank the following for permission to reproduce photographs (T = Top, B = Bottom, C = Centre, L = Left, R = Right):

Allsport 51;
Allsport/Tony Duffy 46L;
Allsport/Gray Mortimore 66R;
Allsport/Simon Brutty 92;
Allsport/USA/Mike Powell 169;
Allsport/Chris Raphael 169L;
Sally Anne Thompson/Animal Photography 110CR, 133BL&C;
Francois Gohier/Ardea London 58TR&TL;
Jean-Paul Ferrero/Ardea London 62;
Biophoto Associates 17CL, 35, 36, 37, 38, 39, 41, 42, 43, 53, 85CR, 94C, 98T&R, 106CR, 154T, 164, 167, 183, 184CL&CR&R, 193, 209TL, 212;
Chris Bonington Picture Library 175;
British Sugar plc 79C;
J Allan Cash Photolibrary 28C, 31;
Bruce Coleman Ltd 11TR, 12, 55R, 58C, 60, 65, 70CL, 71, 85BL, 107CT&BR&C, 110TL&TR&CL, 123, 127, 128, 129, 133T&BR, 135, 136CR&TR&C, 140, 143L, 145CL, 150C, 154TR, 157, 161B, 190, 204, 216;

Gerry Cranham 67;
The Ronald Grant Archive 101B, 124R;
Sally & Richard Greenhill 45, 77, 173, 181C;
Sebastian Keep/Robert Harding Picture Library 16TL;
Nigel Cattlin/Holt Studios International 10, 79 (inset), 148, 150B, 152CL&CR&B&BL;
Inga Spence/Holt Studios International 148;
Andrew Lambert 49;
Steve McCurry/Magnum Photos Ltd 151, 168;
Fred Mayer/Magnum Photos Ltd 156L;
Tiddy Maitland-Titterton 68;
NHPA 40, 58BL&BR, 70C&CR, 132, 134, 136CL, 137, 141, 152C, 155, 156R, 161T, 162T, 191;
Robert Dowling/OSF 113;
R & J Kemp/SAL/OSF 145BL;
Max Gibbs/OSF 176;
LSF/OSF 179T;
PPL Therapeutics Ltd 79T;
Clive Barda/P.A.L. 179B;
Photos Horticultural 101CL;
Jonathan Scott/Planet Earth Pictures 99;
Popperfoto 115, 122;
Gareth Price 6TL&TR;

Range/Bettmann/UPI 143T;
Reading Buses/Reading Transport Ltd 23;
Tim Hall/Redferns 120;
Science Photo Library 7B, 11CR&L, 16TC, 20, 29, 34, 47, 52, 63, 66 (inset), 73, 80, 81, 83, 85BR, 86, 93, 94L, 98L, 100, 106CL, 118, 124 (inset), 126, 159, 162BL, 172, 181T, 184L&C, 196, 197, 198, 200, 207, 209CL;
Shout 192, 202;
Michael Gunther/Still Pictures 17C;
Herbert Giraudet/Still Pictures 55L;
Tony Stone Images 9C, 23, 106T, 130, 182, 211;
Thierry Orban/Sygma 203C;
C & S Thompson 9 (inset), 66L, 107BL, 108, 162BR, 181L;
John Walmsley 91;
Wander Ltd 46 (inset);
Wysoy 14B;
Zefa Pictures Ltd 7T, 26, 28T;

Cover photograph supplied by Science Photo Library.

This book contains references to fictitious characters in fictitious case studies. For educational purposes only, photographs have been used to accompany these case studies. The juxtaposition of photographs and case studies is not intended to identify the individual in the photograph with the character in the case study. The publishers cannot accept any responsibility for any consequences resulting from this use of photographs and case studies, except as expressly provided by law.

To the student

This book aims to make your study of advanced science successful and interesting. The authors have made sure that the ideas you need to understand are covered in a clear and straightforward way. The book is designed to be a study of scientific ideas as well as a reference text when needed. Science is constantly evolving and, wherever possible, modern issues and problems have been used to make your study interesting and to encourage you to continue studying science after your current course is complete.

Working on your own

Studying on your own is often difficult and sometimes textbooks give you the impression that you have to be an expert in the subject before you can read the book. I hope you find that this book is not like that. The authors have carefully built up ideas, so that when you are working on your own there is less chance of you becoming lost in the text and frustrated with the subject.

Don't try to achieve too much in one reading session. Science is complex and some demanding ideas need to be supported with a lot of facts. Trying to take in too much at one time can make you lose sight of the most important ideas – all you see is a mass of information. Use the learning objectives to select one idea to study in a particular session.

Chapter design

Each chapter starts by showing how the science you will learn is applied somewhere in the world. Next come learning objectives which tell you exactly what you should learn as you read the chapter. These are written in a way which spells out what you will be able to do with your new knowledge, rather like a checklist – they could be very helpful when you revise your work. At certain points in the chapters you will find key ideas listed. These are checks for you to use, to make sure that you have grasped these ideas. Words written in **bold type** appear in the glossary at the end of the book. If you don't know the meaning of one of these words check it out immediately – don't persevere, hoping all will become clear.

The questions in the text are there for you to check you have understood what is being explained. These are all short – longer questions are included in a support pack which goes with this book. The questions are straightforward in style – there are no trick questions. Don't be tempted to pass over these questions, they will give you new insights into the work which you may not have seen. Answers to questions are given in the back of the book.

Good luck with your studies. I hope you find the book an interesting read.

Mike Coles, Series Editor
University of London Institute of Education, June 1995

Food for growing babies

'I hope you are going to give up that vegetarian rubbish now. You have to eat for two now, you know. That baby will never grow healthily unless you eat properly.'

'You don't have to eat meat to stay healthy, mum. My diet is probably better than yours, with all that animal fat and artificial additives, because I make sure I eat a healthy, balanced diet. I'm not going to listen to old wives' tales for the next seven months.'

Natalie's parents had not approved of her eating habits, ever since she stopped eating meat in her teens. When she got married they stopped pestering her about her diet, but the expected arrival of the first grand-child had raised the whole issue once again.

" The fat end of the veg shocks experts "

Veggie kiddies have stunned scientists in Liverpool by being fat. Despite their apparently healthier high fibre and low fat diet, it has been found that many young vegetarians are overweight.

The discovery came during the study by nutrition experts at Liverpool John Moores University – the first research of its kind in Britain. They are following the progress of 120 children aged between 7 and 10, half of whom do not eat meat. The aim is to see whether the veggies grow up healthier.

Every six months their weight and height is measured and their body fat checked during the study.

Source: *The Liverpool Echo*, 9 April 1993

This scenario is becoming ever more common. Surveys show that more and more teenagers are turning to vegetarian or vegan (no animal products at all) diets. Nutritional issues often hit the headlines in news bulletins. Misinformation abounds!

Do you know what foods our bodies need, and why? Would an understanding of the structure and function of the molecules that make up food enable us to work out a balanced, healthy diet for ourselves and the rest of our family?

1.1 Learning objectives

After working through this chapter, you should be able to:

- **recall** the monomers that make up carbohydrates and proteins;

- **describe** how monomers combine by condensation reactions to form polymers;

- **recall** the structural formulae of biological monomers;

- **recall** which elements are present in carbohydrates, proteins and fats;

- **describe** how the tertiary structure of a protein gives the molecule a specific three-dimensional shape;

- **explain** that triglycerides have hydrophilic and hydrophobic chemical groups;

- **recall** the structure of phospholipids;

- **explain** how the structure of biological molecules is related to their function.

1.2 Food types

We need a variety of food to maintain a healthy diet.

Food is a mixture of chemicals. Since all food comes from living organisms the chemicals present in food are similar to the chemicals needed by living bodies. Food scientists classify these food chemicals into five groups:
- carbohydrates;
- proteins;
- fats;
- minerals;
- vitamins.

Minerals and vitamins are needed by the body in small amounts to help chemical reactions take place. Water is also needed because these reactions occur in solution.

Carbohydrates, proteins and fats are large molecules needed by the body in greater amounts. They have various functions. The body uses a series of chemical reactions to break down these large molecules from food into their smaller constituents. The body then manufactures what chemicals it needs from these constituents. Without suitable raw materials, or without the appropriate information, the body cannot assemble these chemicals and may suffer as a result.

1.3 Monomers and polymers

Carbohydrates and proteins are examples of a type of molecule called a **polymer**. A polymer is a molecule made up of repeating units, rather like links joined together in a chain. The individual units are called **monomers**, and the same type of unit can be used to build different kinds of chains – long, short, straight, branched.

The basis of both carbohydrate and protein monomers is the carbon atom. What is so special about carbon? Carbon atoms can join with each other to form long chains, and they can easily form links with atoms of many other elements (Fig. 1).

It is possible to join monomers into molecules of many sizes, shapes and complexity. Many of these carbon-based molecules have special properties, properties that make life on Earth possible.

Q 1 Why are carbon atoms found in every monomer?

Glucose is one of the simplest monomers. It is a sugar and contains atoms of three different elements: carbon, hydrogen and oxygen (Fig. 2).

Protein monomers always contain nitrogen atoms in addition to carbon, hydrogen and oxygen; some protein monomers also contain sulphur atoms, and others phosphorus atoms.

Fig. 1 Carbon chains

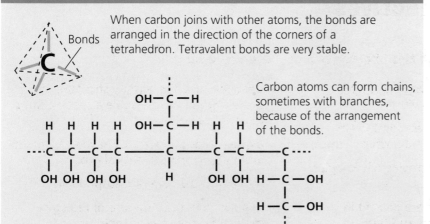

When carbon joins with other atoms, the bonds are arranged in the direction of the corners of a tetrahedron. Tetravalent bonds are very stable.

Carbon atoms can form chains, sometimes with branches, because of the arrangement of the bonds.

Fig. 2 A glucose molecule

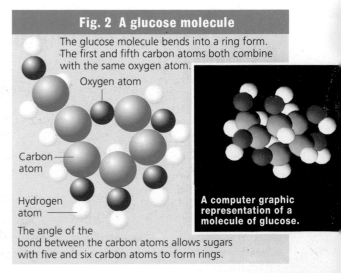

The glucose molecule bends into a ring form. The first and fifth carbon atoms both combine with the same oxygen atom.

Oxygen atom

Carbon atom

Hydrogen atom

The angle of the bond between the carbon atoms allows sugars with five and six carbon atoms to form rings.

A computer graphic representation of a molecule of glucose.

1.4 Carbohydrates

Plants are rich in carbohydrates: starches, cellulose and sugars. Sugars, such as glucose, are the monomers from which starch and cellulose are made up. Sugar monomers are small molecules that dissolve in water and taste sweet. They are called **monosaccharides**.

Glucose is a monosaccharide. It is the sugar found in animal blood. Fructose is another monosaccharide; it has the same formula as glucose but its molecule is a different shape. Honey is a good source of fructose.

Sucrose is the most common sugar in plants, and is a **disaccharide**. The sugar you put in your tea or coffee is sucrose. Disaccharides are formed when two monosaccharides join by a **condensation** reaction (Fig. 3). Glucose and fructose combine to form sucrose in a condensation reaction.

Carbohydrate polymers, such as starches and cellulose, are called **polysaccharides**. They are giant polymer molecules made up from many monomers joined together by condensation.

The properties of a polysaccharide depend on:
- the number of monosaccharide units;
- how they are joined together.

For example, the same monomer, glucose, can be joined in different ways to form the polymers starch, found in plants, and glycogen, found in animal muscle tissue (Fig. 4).

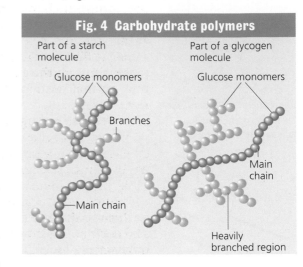

Fig. 4 Carbohydrate polymers

Part of a starch molecule

Glucose monomers

Branches

Main chain

Part of a glycogen molecule

Glucose monomers

Main chain

Heavily branched region

The glucose monomer in starch is called α-glucose. Cellulose is made from a slightly different glucose monomer: β-glucose (Fig. 5).

Q 2 Draw a diagram to show how three β-glucose molecules could be joined by condensation reactions to form part of a cellulose molecule.

Fig. 3 Condensation reactions

Two molecules of glucose can join by a condensation reaction to form a disaccharide. In a condensation reaction, an 'H' atom and an 'OH' group are removed from adjacent molecules, producing water as a by-product.

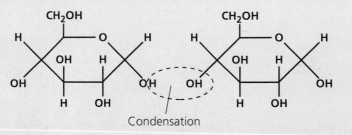

Condensation

Polysaccharides, with many monomers joined together, are often drawn diagrammatically like this.

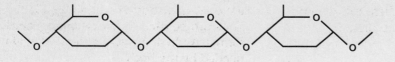

Fig. 5 α-glucose and β-glucose

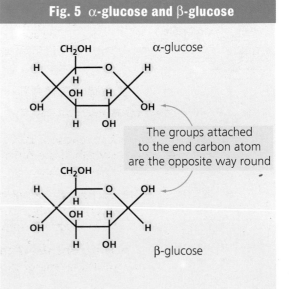

α-glucose

The groups attached to the end carbon atom are the opposite way round

β-glucose

Because the monomers differ, the polymer molecules have different shapes. The shape of each determines its function. The functions of carbohydrates include forming cell walls and storing energy.

Cellulose molecules form long straight chains that link together with weak chemical bonds to form bundles of molecules which form fibres. These fibres are part of most plant cell walls and give them strength. Most animals cannot digest cellulose fibre, but it gives bulk to food as it passes through the gut. This means the muscles that push food along the gut are not strained.

Starch and glycogen are carbohydrate polymers that act as energy storage compounds. Glycogen is the animal equivalent to starch. They have large molecules so are insoluble in water, and they have coiled and highly branched chains which give them a compact shape. The body breaks down starch into its sugar monomers (Fig. 6).

Since sugars are small molecules that are soluble in water, they can easily be moved around in the body to where they are required. Their main function is to transfer energy stored in the molecules to other essential chemical reactions. The reaction that does this is called respiration, which you can read about in Chapter 2. Sugars are also converted into other substances required for the growth and maintenance of the body.

3 List the important differences between typical sugars and starches.

Walkers and climbers eat sugary snacks to provide their bodies with instant energy.

Fig. 6 Use of carbohydrate

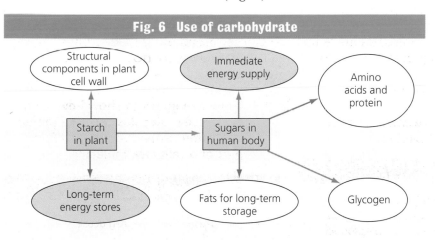

Key ideas

- The reaction used to build up all carbohydrate polymers is called condensation.

- Carbohydrate polymers include cellulose, starch and glycogen. They are made up from sugar monomers.

- The properties of these chemicals depend on the shape of their molecules.

- Cellulose molecules have long, straight chains, ideal for forming fibres.

- Starch and glycogen have compact, coiled and branched molecules suitable for their storage function.

- Sugars are small diffusible molecules that are easily transported around the body. They can be used to release energy and to form carbohydrates and other molecules needed by the body.

1.5 Proteins

While plant foods tend to be rich in carbohydrates, animal foods tend to be rich in protein and fat.

Natalie's parents are worried that she will not get enough protein from her vegetarian diet. What proteins will she get from her food? Natalie, like most informed vegetarians and vegans, knows that she has to eat pulses (peas and beans) and cereals (flour and rice) in her diet if she is to obtain all the **amino acids** she needs to keep her healthy.

Amino acids are the monomers from which the large polymers, proteins, are built up. In the gut, the body breaks down the large protein molecules in food into the smaller amino acids, which can then be absorbed in the bloodstream. Cells in the body can assemble these monomers into a large variety of protein polymers. The liver can also make some amino acids from sugars and other amino acids to help to build new proteins.

All proteins in the living world are made from a selection of only 20 naturally occurring amino acids. Plant proteins can therefore be broken down and reassembled as human protein. Although we can make most amino acids from sugars and other amino acids, there are eight amino acids that must be present in our diet if we are to be able to synthesise all the proteins we require for growth and repair.

These eight amino acids are known as **essential amino acids**. Meat has a very good balance of all the essential amino acids. Pulses are rich in all the essential amino acids except methionine; cereals are rich in all except lysine. By including both cereals and pulses in the diet, we can obtain all the essential amino acids.

All amino acids have an amino group and an acid group. They differ in the group attached to the central carbon atom. This group is given the general name 'R' (Fig. 7). Two amino acids join by condensation, as the sugar monomers do. The bond linking the two amino acids is a peptide bond and the resulting substance produced is a **peptide** (Fig. 7).

A soya bean is a pulse that is exceptionally rich in amino acids, except methionine.

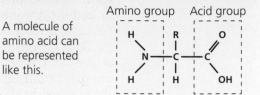
Fig. 7 Structural formulae of peptides

A molecule of amino acid can be represented like this.

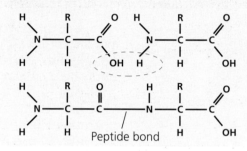

Two amino acid molecules join by a condensation reaction to form a peptide.

Peptide bond

4 a What is the difference between a non-essential amino acid and an essential amino acid?

b Draw the structural formula of a molecule of each of the three amino acids in Table 1.

Table 1. Different amino acids

Amino acid	R group
Glycine	H
Alanine	CH$_3$
Cysteine	CH$_2$SH

Proteins have a wide variety of functions and properties. These depend upon the type and order of amino acids in the protein molecule. There are over 10 000 different proteins in the human body; each of these proteins has its own, unique sequence of amino acids. This sequence is known as the **primary structure** of a protein.

The information required to sequence amino acids is contained in the genes in molecules called nucleic acids. How this information is translated into amino acid sequences in proteins is explained in Chapter 8.

Many proteins contain several short chains of amino acids. These chains are called **polypeptides**; the chains may form coils or take on a pleated appearance. The coiling or pleating of the polypeptide chains is known as the **secondary structure** of a protein (Fig. 8).

The polypeptide chains may be joined by weak chemical bonds to give a more complex three-dimensional shape. This shape is called the **tertiary structure** of a protein (Fig. 8).

A polarised light micrograph of a cross-section of horn from the Indian rhinoceros. The horn consists of keratin. Magnification × 50.

Fig. 8 Three-dimensional structure of proteins

A fibrous protein, showing a helical secondary structure

Polypeptide chain

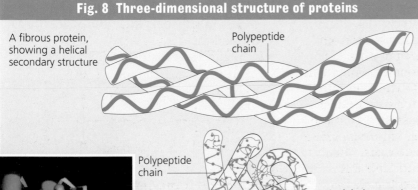

Polypeptide chain

A globular protein, showing a more complex tertiary structure

Source: adapted from Green et al., *Biological Science 1&2*, Cambridge, 1994

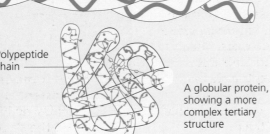

A computer graphic image of myoglobin.

The secondary structure is important for fibrous proteins, which have structural functions. For example, keratin has long straight molecules and forms part of structures like hair and horn. For globular proteins, the tertiary structure is more important. Many globular proteins are carrier molecules, e.g. myoglobin which transports oxygen in muscles.

Other globular proteins are known as enzymes, which act as catalysts for many of the reactions that take place in living organisms. All enzymes are proteins, and therefore proteins are involved in all the reactions that take place in living organisms, e.g. salivary amylase helps break down starch into smaller molecules. You can find out more about enzymes in Chapter 3.

5 How is such a variety of proteins possible? Explain in terms of the structure of proteins.

Key ideas

• Proteins are polymers made, by condensation reactions, from monomers called amino acids.

• Protein polymers have complex three-dimensional shapes that determine their function.

• Long, straight protein molecules form the basis of fibrous structures like hair.

• Globular polymers can be used as carrier molecules.

• Enzymes are proteins that catalyse many of the reactions in living cells.

1.6 Fats

The other group of chemicals the body needs in large amounts is fats, or **lipids**. Fats are not polymers like carbohydrates and proteins, but are large molecules made up of fatty acids and glycerol. Like carbohydrate and protein monomers, these smaller constituent molecules contain carbon, hydrogen and oxygen atoms, and are joined by condensation reactions. Most fat molecules have three fatty acids joined to one glycerol molecule; for this reason they are often called **triglycerides** (Fig. 9).

Some fatty acids have more hydrogen atoms in their molecules than others. Those with many hydrogen atoms are called **saturated**, and form fats that are usually solid at room temperature. Fatty acids with fewer hydrogen atoms are called **unsaturated**; they form fat molecules that are usually liquid at room temperature. Animal fats tend to be saturated and plant fats tend to be unsaturated (Fig. 9).

Fats have a number of uses in the body:
- the principal function of fats is to act as energy stores;
- some fats are stored in the skin, where they help to insulate the body;
- some fatty acids are used to produce other important molecules such as hormones and molecules in cell membranes;
- fatty acids can be used to release energy;
- many vitamins, such as vitamin D, are soluble in fats only, so if there are no fats in the diet, there is no vitamin D in the diet;
- some fats have a structural function.

Hibernating mammals use stores of fats in the body to provide the energy for necessary chemical reactions to take place.

It is the hydrocarbon tail and the high proportion of hydrogen that makes fats such good long-term energy stores.

A special type of fat, called a **phospholipid**, is the main constituent of cell membranes. Phospholipids have two fatty acids and one phosphate group attached to the glycerol (Fig. 10).

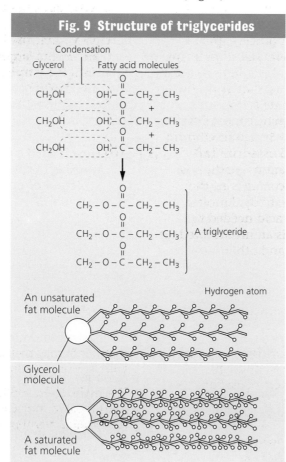

Fig. 9 Structure of triglycerides

A triglyceride

An unsaturated fat molecule

Glycerol molecule

A saturated fat molecule

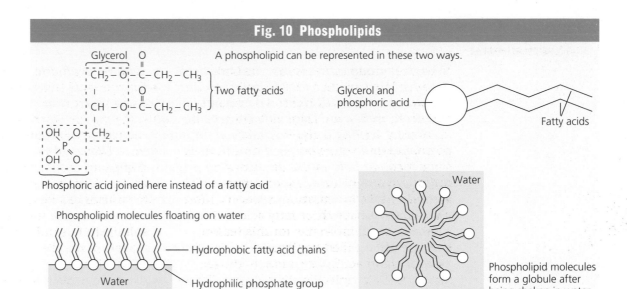

Fig. 10 Phospholipids

Glycerol

A phospholipid can be represented in these two ways.

Two fatty acids

Glycerol and phosphoric acid — Fatty acids

Phosphoric acid joined here instead of a fatty acid

Phospholipid molecules floating on water

— Hydrophobic fatty acid chains

Water

— Hydrophilic phosphate group

Water

Phospholipid molecules form a globule after being shaken in water

The phosphate group dissolves in water, but the two fatty acid chains do not. This means that the phosphate end of the molecule is **hydrophilic**, 'water-loving', while the other end is **hydrophobic**, 'water-hating'. Phospholipids float on the surface of water, with their tails in the air. When shaken in water, phospholipids cluster together with their tails all pointing inwards (Fig. 10). We shall see later that the globule shown here is very similar to the membranes found in all cells.

The body can manufacture most fatty acids but others can only be obtained from the diet. These are called **essential fatty acids**. As with essential amino acids, it is important that the diet contains all the fatty acids needed by the body. Linoleic acid is an essential fatty acid needed to make phospholipids. It is an unsaturated fat found in cereals, pulses and other vegetables.

6 a What types of food, animal and plant, are good sources of:
(i) carbohydrate;
(ii) essential amino acids;
(iii) essential fatty acids?
b Why does the body need carbohydrates, proteins and fats?
c Why does the body need to break down the larger molecules of food into the smaller constituent molecules?

Key ideas

- Fats called triglycerides are built by joining three molecules of fatty acids to one molecule of glycerol by condensation reactions. Substitution of one fatty acid by a phosphate group produces a phospholipid.

- The main functions of triglycerides are energy storage and insulation.

- Fatty acids may be used to release energy and to produce other molecules.

- The hydrophilic and hydrophobic nature of phospholipid molecules makes them ideal for forming membranes.

1.7 A complete diet

'I know breast feeding is best, but are there any options available for when I return to work? Is breast feeding essential or will powdered milk be all right? And I would like to use a vegetarian powdered milk – are these safe for growing babies?'

'Breast feeding is the best method for babies. However, modern powdered milks are very good and there is a range to choose from. Most formula baby milks are based on proteins from cow's milk, and many are suitable for a vegetarian diet. There are also some formula milks based on soya protein; they are for babies that are allergic to cow's milk protein or intolerant to lactose, the sugar found in cow's milk. An example is Wysoy™, which is also suitable for vegetarians. You need to decide what works best for you, the baby and your partner.'

Young babies are fed exclusively on milk and grow very rapidly. Breast milk obviously provides a complete and natural diet for a human baby. Synthetic milks such as Wysoy™ are carefully formulated so that they contain all the nutrients needed for healthy growth.

7 a Using Table 2 and Fig. 11, calculate the relative proportions of protein, carbohydrate and fat in Wysoy and in breast milk.

b Think about the functions of protein and carbohydrate and then suggest why there is much more carbohydrate than protein in both milks.

c Do you think the difference in the proportions of protein, carbohydrate and fat between Wysoy and human milk is significant? Explain your answer.

d Calculate the total mass of:
(i) vitamins;
(ii) minerals in 100 g Wysoy (1 μg = 0.001 mg).

Table 2. Nutrients in human breast milk						
Approximate content per 100 ml						
Energy	293 kJ	Manganese	Data unavailable	Riboflavin	31 μg	
Protein	1.3 g			Niacin	230 μg	
Fat	4.2 g	Sodium	15 mg	Pantothenic acid	260 μg	
Carbohydrate	7.4 g	Potassium	60 mg			
Calcium	35 mg	Chloride	43 mg	Vitamin B$_6$	5.9 μg	
Phosphorus	15 mg	Vitamin A	60 μg	Vitamin B$_{12}$	0.01 μg	
Magnesium	2.8 mg	Vitamin D	0.01 μg	Folic acid	5.2 μg	
Iron	0.076 mg	Vitamin E	0.35 mg	Biotin	0.76 μg	
Zinc	0.295 mg	Vitamin K	Data unavailable	Vitamin C	3.8 mg	
Copper	39 μg					
Iodine	7.0 μg	Thiamin	16 μg			

Source: DHSS, *The Composition of Mature Human Milk*, 1977

Fig. 11 Information from a Wysoy product

Approximate content per 100 ml (as fed)			
Energy	280 kJ	Vitamin A	75 μg
Protein	1.8 g	Vitamin D	1.1 μg
Fat	3.6 g	Vitamin E	0.74 mg
Carbohydrate	6.9 g	Vitamin K	10 μg
Calcium	67 mg	Thiamin	100 μg
Phosphorus	50 mg	Riboflavin	150 μg
Magnesium	6.7 mg	Niacin	900 μg
Iron	0.8 mg	Pantothenic acid	300 μg
Zinc	0.6 mg	Vitamin B$_6$	60 μg
Copper	33 μg	Vitamin B$_{12}$	0.2 μg
Iodine	15 μg	Folic acid	8.0 μg
Manganese	20 μg	Biotin	3.5 μg
Sodium	19 mg	Vitamin C	9.0 mg
Potassium	72 mg	*Source: SMA Nutrition,*	
Chloride	43 mg	1994	

Essential amino acids, sugars and essential fatty acids are just some of the chemicals needed to build a healthy body. We also need relatively small amounts of minerals and vitamins.

Minerals are vitally important for healthy growth and functioning of the body. For example, calcium is an important constituent of bones and teeth. It is also essential for some chemical reactions, such as the clotting of blood. Iron is an essential component of haemoglobin, the protein found in red blood cells whose function is oxygen transport.

Vitamins are equally important. Most of them are needed in very small quantities to work alongside enzymes in catalysing the chemical reactions which occur in the body. Water is needed by the body because all these chemical reactions take place in solution.

Vitamins and minerals cannot be made by the body, so must form part of the diet.

Vegans and vegetarians have to be careful to supplement their diet with vitamin B_{12} because this vitamin is not found in plant foods. Without it they suffer from a particularly serious type of anaemia in which enlarged and deformed red blood cells are produced. You will notice that Wysoy contains this vitamin.

The protein in Wysoy is mainly derived from soya beans, but includes all the essential amino acids needed to produce all the different proteins required by the body, so vegetarians could use this powder.

8 Who is right – Natalie or her parents? Are there any risks to health, particularly for young children, in having a diet with no animal products? What advice would you give to a young mother? Justify your advice by referring to the facts you have learned in this chapter.

Key ideas

- Minerals and vitamins are needed to ensure the healthy growth and functioning of the body.

- Water is needed as all chemical reactions within the body take place in solution.

2 Biological energy resources

Alternative fuels could also help prevent the smog that occurs over cities, such as Los Angeles.

In the mid-1970s, during the 'Middle East Oil Crisis', many governments funded research into finding alternative fuels for motor vehicles. One group of scientists investigated ways to use microscopic organisms called cyanobacteria, or blue-green algae, to produce hydrogen. In very bright light, cyanobacteria can 'split' water molecules to release hydrogen. The hydrogen could then be burned to provide energy. Although the process has not yet been used commercially, the research has given us a valuable insight into the way that plants photosynthesise – transfer energy from sunlight into food. It has also furthered our understanding of respiration – the process used by most organisms to release energy from food.

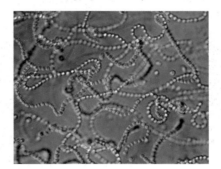

Further research into photosynthesis might allow us to grow fuels for cars and other uses. In a hundred years oil may be an interesting history topic. Can biologists solve the world's energy crisis?

A light micrograph of *Nostoc* sp., a filamentous cyanobacterium. Magnification × 150.

2.1 Learning objectives

After working through this chapter, you should be able to:

- **explain** the processes of oxidation and reduction;

- **describe** how photosynthesis uses energy in light to make organic molecules;

- **explain** how energy in light excites electrons in chlorophyll molecules;

- **describe** photolysis, the splitting of water which results in the release of oxygen;

- **explain** how energy from excited electrons is used to generate adenosine triphosphate (ATP) and reduced nicotinamide adenine dinucleotide phosphate (NADPH);

- **explain** how ATP and NADPH are used to 'fix' carbon dioxide to produce carbohydrates;

- **recall** that photosynthesis includes light-dependent and light-independent reactions;

- **recall** that respiration is the process by which energy in organic molecules is made available for other processes within a cell;

- **describe** how the process of glycolysis involves the oxidation of glucose to pyruvate with a net gain of ATP and reduced nicotinamide adenine dinucleotide (NADH);

- **explain** how pyruvate enters the Krebs cycle;

- **describe** how the Krebs cycle involves a series of oxidation reactions and the release of carbon dioxide, leading to the production of ATP and NADH;

- **explain** how oxidative phosphorylation generates ATP;

- **explain** the role of ATP as an intermediate energy carrier.

2.2 They changed the atmosphere

Cyanobacteria are primitive organisms, related to bacteria, that seem to have changed little in the last 3000 million years. They may well have been amongst the very first living organisms on Earth. They almost certainly helped to change the atmosphere from an inhospitable mixture of carbon dioxide, methane and ammonia into one containing enough oxygen to support animal life (Fig. 1).

Cyanobacteria contain molecules of the pigment **chlorophyll *a*** identical to those found today in almost all plants. Some cyanobacteria are remarkably similar in structure to the chloroplasts found inside the green cells of more modern plants (Fig. 2).

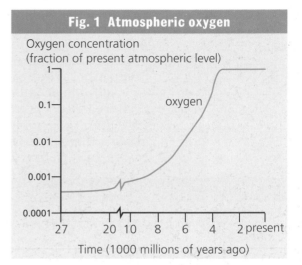

Fig. 1 Atmospheric oxygen

Oxygen concentration
(fraction of present atmospheric level)

oxygen

Time (1000 millions of years ago)

Fig. 2 Cyanobacteria and chloroplasts

Cyanobacteria are found in a range of environments, from hot water springs to solid snow.

Chloroplasts are found within plant cells.

As green plants have evolved, they have helped make an oxygen-rich atmosphere in which animals can live.

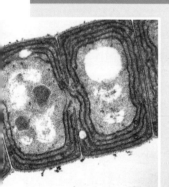

Electron micrograph of a cross-section of a cyanobacterium. Magnification × 20 500.

Electron micrograph of a cross-section of a chloroplast. Magnification × 15 000.

However, in bright light cyanobacteria behave differently from modern plants; they give off hydrogen gas as well as oxygen. The scientists who were trying to find alternative fuel sources grew cultures of cyanobacteria in small plastic containers. They calculated that a tank, 8 m × 2 m × 2 m, containing cyanobacteria could produce enough hydrogen to provide for the fuel needs of an average house. Energy from the Sun is 'free', and you might expect that this idea would have been developed further.

1 Suggest what difficulties there might be in using a tank of cyanobacteria to produce hydrogen fuel for a house.

Why do cyanobacteria produce hydrogen? Cyanobacteria release hydrogen when they photosynthesise, and to answer this question we need to understand the essential features of **photosynthesis**.

You probably already know the summary equation for photosynthesis.

$$6CO_2 + 6H_2O \rightarrow C_6H_{12}O_6 + 6O_2$$

Of course, in the real world, the reactions are much more complex. There are at least two groups of reactions:
- light-dependent reactions only occur in the light;
- light-independent recations occur all the time.

2.3 Reduction and oxidation

To understand photosynthesis you have to understand the structure of **atoms** and **compounds** (Fig. 3). You also need to understand the terms **oxidation** and **reduction**. When electrons, or hydrogen, are added to an atom or compound, it is **reduced**. Reduction is a very common reaction. The opposite reaction, oxidation, occurs when electrons or hydrogen are taken away from an atom or compound.

Atoms or compounds which supply electrons in a chemical reaction are called reducing agents. Oxidising agents take away electrons. Whenever a chemical is reduced (gains electrons) another must be **oxidised** (gives up electrons) (Fig. 4). This means oxidation reactions and reduction reactions always occur together and are often referred to as **redox** reactions.

Fig. 3 Atoms and compounds

A simple model of an atom, e.g. carbon, has a central nucleus, containing **protons** and **neutrons**, surrounded by orbits of **electrons**.

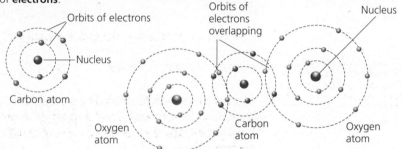

The molecule of a simple compound, e.g. carbon dioxide, is made up of different atoms whose electron orbits overlap. The areas where the orbits overlap are called **bonds** and help to hold the atoms together.

Fig. 4 Redox reactions

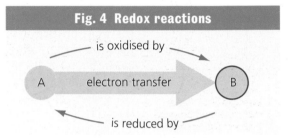

Carbon dioxide provides the carbon required to make the carbohydrate in photosynthesis. Before the carbon dioxide can be reduced, however, two other essentials are needed to drive the series of reactions involved in photosynthesis:
- a source of energy;
- a supply of electrons.

2.4 Light-dependent reactions of photosynthesis

The **light-dependent reactions** of photosynthesis provide the energy and electrons needed for later reactions. Light is the energy source. Chlorophyll *a* is one of a special group of compounds that can absorb light energy and use it to boost the energy level of electrons from the hydrogen atoms in water. Electrons can be compared to satellites orbiting Earth. To move a satellite into a higher orbit requires energy, e.g. from firing a booster rocket. Similarly, energy is required to boost an electron into a higher orbit around the nuclcus of an atom, from where it can be passed on to another atom (Fig. 5).

Water provides the supply of electrons. Water molecules can be split up in two different ways, one of which needs light energy and another that does not.

Fig. 5 Electron orbits

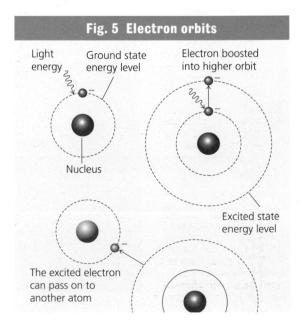

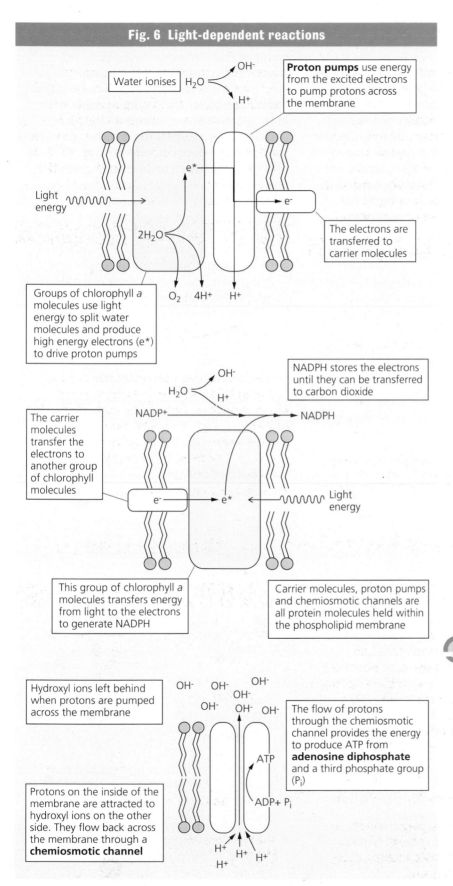

Fig. 6 Light-dependent reactions

Water ionises | H_2O

OH⁻

H⁺

Proton pumps use energy from the excited electrons to pump protons across the membrane

e*

Light energy

e⁻

The electrons are transferred to carrier molecules

$2H_2O$

O_2 $4H^+$ H^+

Groups of chlorophyll *a* molecules use light energy to split water molecules and produce high energy electrons (e*) to drive proton pumps

OH⁻

H_2O

H⁺

NADP⁺ ⟶ NADPH

NADPH stores the electrons until they can be transferred to carbon dioxide

The carrier molecules transfer the electrons to another group of chlorophyll molecules

e⁻ ⟶ e*

Light energy

This group of chlorophyll *a* molecules transfers energy from light to the electrons to generate NADPH

Carrier molecules, proton pumps and chemiosmotic channels are all protein molecules held within the phospholipid membrane

Hydroxyl ions left behind when protons are pumped across the membrane

OH⁻ OH⁻ OH⁻ OH⁻ OH⁻ OH⁻

The flow of protons through the chemiosmotic channel provides the energy to produce ATP from **adenosine diphosphate** and a third phosphate group (P_i)

ATP

Protons on the inside of the membrane are attracted to hydroxyl ions on the other side. They flow back across the membrane through a **chemiosmotic channel**

ADP + P_i

H^+ H^+ H^+
H^+

Water molecules **ionise** naturally to produce hydroxyl ions (OH⁻) and protons (H⁺).

$$H_2O \rightleftharpoons OH^- + H^+$$

This process does not need light and is happening all the time. A very small percentage of any volume of water, e.g. outside a cell membrane, is ionised, and removing either an OH⁻ or an H⁺ ion from that volume causes another molecule of water to become ionised.

Hydrogen atoms can also be split into protons (H⁺) and electrons (e⁻). Light energy trapped by chlorophyll *a* within a cell can be used to split water molecules to release electrons.

$$\text{water} \rightarrow \text{protons} + \text{electrons} + \text{oxygen}$$

$$2H_2O \rightarrow 4H^+ \quad + 4e^- \quad + O_2$$

This process is known as **photolysis**. There is an abundant 'free' supply of water that cyanobacteria can use as a source of electrons.

Unfortunately the electrons released from the water cannot react directly with carbon dioxide. So an acceptor molecule called **nicotinamide adenine dinucleotide phosphate** (NADP⁺) collects the excited electrons from the chlorophyll and transfers them to the carbon dioxide. NADPH is produced, and some of the energy of the excited electrons transfers to a temporary energy storage molecule called **adenosine triphosphate** (ATP).

2 Has the NADP⁺ been oxidised or reduced to NADPH? Explain.

The way in which NADPH and ATP are produced is quite complicated and involves a number of processes (Fig. 6). The photomicrograph of a cyanobacterium on page 17 shows phospholipid membranes that could be the ones in Fig. 6.

Green plants use all the hydrogen protons and electrons available to produce NADPH and ATP. However, in bright light cyanobacteria are unable to make full use of all the protons and electrons and the excess are released as hydrogen gas. It is as if the part of the reaction that splits the water is going too fast for the reaction that uses the electrons and hydrogen ions. The cell needs to get rid of the hydrogen ions, or the pH of the cell would fall. The easiest way is to combine the hydrogen ions and electrons to form hydrogen atoms and molecules. These can bubble off as gas. It is this hydrogen release that makes cyanobacteria potentially such a useful source of fuel.

Some projected designs of space ships intended for long voyages to the outer planets include tanks of cyanobacteria.

If there is an unusual amount of sunlight, cyanobacteria can grow abnormally. As well as giving off hydrogen, they can become very toxic to many organisms, including humans.

3 Explain how cyanobacteria might be useful on such a long voyage.

Green plants, and cyanobacteria in normal light intensities, release oxygen as a result of the removal of electrons from water molecules (Fig. 7). The importance of this reaction is staggering. All the oxygen in the atmosphere, the oxygen which makes animal life possible, comes from this reaction. The oxygen we breathe is a waste product of a reaction whose function is to provide the energy to operate a proton pump.

4a Write word equations for the two reactions that split water.
  b What happens to the products of the split water molecules?
  c From where is the energy obtained to operate proton pumps and chemiosmotic channels, and the energy to produce ATP?
  d Write an equation to show how protons and excited electrons are used to produce NADPH.

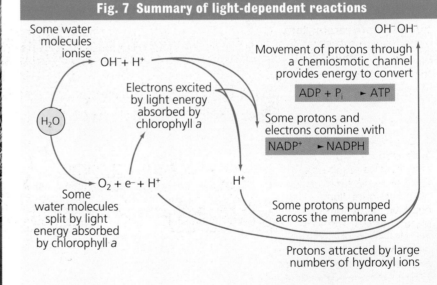

Fig. 7 Summary of light-dependent reactions

Some water molecules ionise

$OH^- + H^+$

$OH^- \, OH^-$

Electrons excited by light energy absorbed by chlorophyll a

Movement of protons through a chemiosmotic channel provides energy to convert

$ADP + P_i \rightarrow ATP$

H_2O

Some protons and electrons combine with

$NADP^+ \rightarrow NADPH$

$O_2 + e^- + H^+$

Some water molecules split by light energy absorbed by chlorophyll a

H^+

Some protons pumped across the membrane

Protons attracted by large numbers of hydroxyl ions

Key ideas

• In a light-dependent series of reactions chlorophyll a molecules absorb energy as light and use it to excite electrons which they obtain by splitting water.

• This reaction is the source of all of the oxygen in the Earth's atmosphere.

• The energy of some of the excited electrons is used to drive proton pumps. Other excited electrons are used to produce NADPH.

• The flow of protons through chemiosmotic channels in the phospholipid membranes provides the energy to produce ATP.

2.5 Light-independent reactions of photosynthesis

Light energy from the Sun is only available to plants during the day, limiting the time when the light-dependent reactions of photosynthesis can take place. There is a limited amount of $NADP^+$ available to reduce and a limited amount of ADP for conversion to ATP for energy storage. A more permanent store of energy is therefore required. The primitive atmosphere was very rich in carbon dioxide. The energy from ATP and the electrons from NADPH were used to reduce this carbon dioxide and build it into carbohydrate. This carbohydrate could provide a longer term store of energy or be used as building blocks to produce all the other **organic** molecules (molecules containing hydrogen and carbon atoms) needed for growth.

The method developed by cyanobacteria to reduce carbon dioxide into carbohydrate is used, unchanged, by modern plants. The method involves the **light-independent reactions** (Fig. 8). In cyanobacteria these reactions occur within the solution inside the cell. In plants they occur within the solution inside a chloroplast.

5 **Name two carbohydrate polymers that can be produced from glucose. What use can these polymers be put to in plants?**

Fig. 8 Light-independent reactions

1. Almost all photosynthetic organisms use **ribulose bisphosphate carboxylase** to join carbon dioxide and water to **ribulose bisphosphate.**

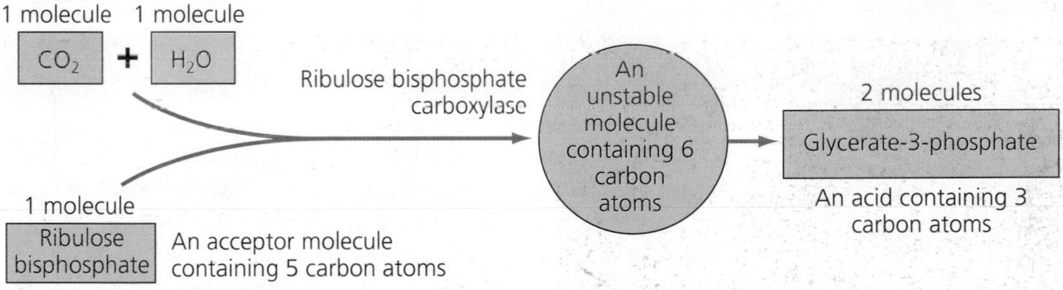

2. To convert **glycerate-3-phosphate** into carbohydrate requires both the ATP and the NADPH produced in the light-dependent reactions of photosynthesis. The ATP and NADPH force electrons into the glycerate molecule in a series of reduction reactions. This oxidises the ATP and NADPH. The ADP + P_i and $NADP^+$ return to the site of the light reactions.

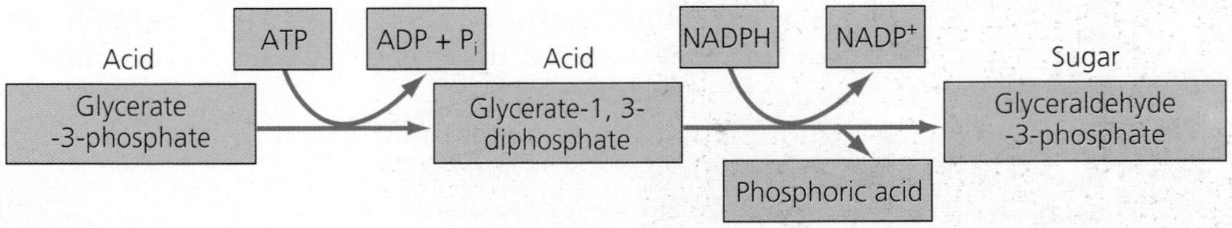

3. Glyceraldehyde-3-phosphate is a sugar converted into a whole series of other sugars, including glucose. Glyceraldehyde-3-phosphate can also be used to synthesise lipids and proteins. In order to produce large quantities of glyceraldehyde-3-phosphate, plants need a constant supply of ribulose bisphosphate. Chemical pathways regenerate ribulose bisphosphate from some of the glyceraldehyde-3-phosphate.

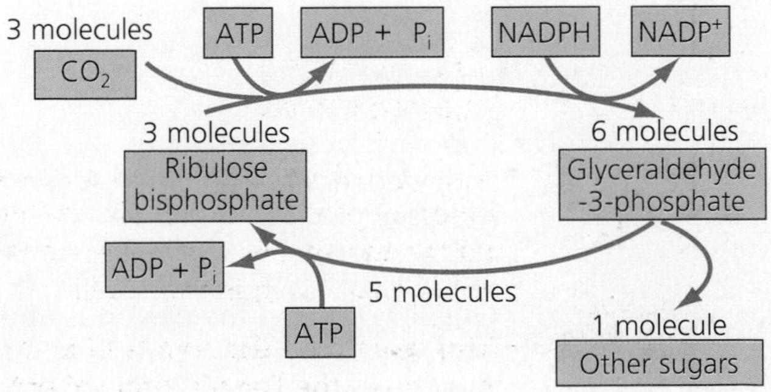

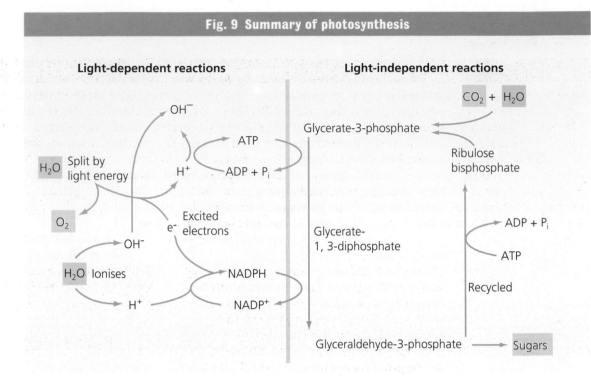

Fig. 9 Summary of photosynthesis

Light-dependent reactions

H_2O Split by light energy

OH^-

ATP

H^+ ADP + P_i

O_2

Excited e^- electrons

OH^-

H_2O Ionises

H^+

NADPH

NADP$^+$

Light-independent reactions

CO_2 + H_2O

Glycerate-3-phosphate

Ribulose bisphosphate

ADP + P_i

ATP

Glycerate-1, 3-diphosphate

Recycled

Glyceraldehyde-3-phosphate ⟶ Sugars

6 a What proportion of the glyceraldehyde 3-phosphate produced in photosynthesis is recycled to produce acceptor molecules for carbon dioxide?

b Researchers have discovered a chemical that stops the production of the enzyme ribulose bisphosphate carboxylase. Cyanobacteria treated with this chemical cannot produce the enzyme. How will this affect the rate of:
(i) growth of the cyanobacteria;
(ii) evolution of hydrogen?
Explain both of your answers.

The light-dependent reactions use light energy to excite electrons and drive the two reduction reactions forming ATP and NADPH (Fig. 9). The light-independent reactions use the ATP and NADPH to drive a series of reduction reactions to produce carbohydrates.

7 The light-independent reactions used to be called the dark reactions. This name is not often used now. Why do you think light-independent is a better name?

Key ideas

- Photosynthesis is made up of a series of light-dependent and light-independent reactions.

- In the light-independent series of reactions NADPH provides the electrons and ATP the energy to reduce the carbon atoms in carbon dioxide to carbohydrates, effectively storing the energy from sunlight in the carbohydrate.

- This series of reactions is the source of most of the food materials required by living organisms.

2.6 Respiration

" Grow your own diesel "

Three buses in Reading will today become Britain's first to run on rapeseed oil instead of diesel. They will use a fuel called 'Diesel-Bi', produced by Novamont, an Italian company, for the next three months as an experiment.

The manufacturers say the oil, which has been refined from rapeseed oil, harms the environment much less than conventional fuels. It generates no sulphur dioxide, one of the principal components of acid rain, and emission levels of black particles and smoke are lower. It is biodegradable, so spillages cause little damage. It could also help reduce levels of carbon dioxide emission. During the growth period of the rapeseed, carbon dioxide is absorbed from the atmosphere, so the net emission from the fuel is zero.

The oil can be used in diesel engines without any modification. There are already a number of similar experiments in Italy, France, Austria and Germany

Source: adapted from an article by Christian Wolmar, *The Independent*, 3 November 1992

Photosynthesis produces a store of energy in a fuel–oxygen system. The fuel can be in the form of glucose, starch, or even rapeseed oil. The energy in fossil fuels, which we burn in our fires, power stations and vehicle engines, was transferred into the original plants by photosynthesis. The energy can be recovered from these compounds by burning them in oxygen and breaking down the fuel–oxygen system. Carbon burned in oxygen forms the gas carbon dioxide. Adding oxygen to an atom or compound is another way of describing an oxidation reaction.

Living organisms do not burn carbohydrates. Instead they use a series of oxidation reactions known as **respiration** that transfers the energy from the fuel–oxygen system into ATP, with some energy lost as heat. Again you probably remember the equation for respiration.

Reading Transport are experimenting with rapeseed oil as fuel for their buses.

$$C_6H_{12}O_6 + 6O_2 \rightarrow 6CO_2 + 6H_2O + \text{energy}$$

Animals depend on plants for their energy supplies. Some animals eat plants to obtain the energy-store materials. They then oxidise these materials to release energy. Other animals eat animals to obtain their energy-store materials.

Respiration and combustion depend on the oxygen in the atmosphere. Cyanobacteria were possibly the first organisms to release oxygen into the atmosphere; modern plants maintain the oxygen levels in the atmosphere.

During respiration carbon is oxidised. Four electrons are removed from each atom of carbon – exactly the opposite of photosynthesis (Fig. 10). Whereas energy is required to add electrons to organic molecules in photosynthesis, removing

Fig. 10 Comparing photosynthesis and respiration

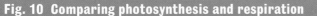

Photosynthesis

H_2O → $O_2 + H^+ + e^-$

Electron donor

Given off

Electrons forced into carbon dioxide – reduction

e^-

Carbohydrate

Respiration

H^+

H_2O

O_2

Electron acceptor

e^-

Electrons removed from carbohydrate – oxidation

electrons in respiration releases energy. In photosynthesis NADPH acts as an electron donor to the carbon. In respiration a similar compound, **nicotinamide adenine dinucleotide** (NAD+) accepts high energy electrons from carbon, becoming reduced to NADH in the process. NADH therefore contains a great deal of energy. This energy can be released by transferring the electrons to oxygen. The electrons are not transferred from NADH to oxygen directly; the series of oxidation reactions that transfer the electrons makes up the major part of respiration.

Glycolysis is the first stage of respiration (Fig. 11). The conversion of glyceraldehyde 3-phosphate to pyruvate is an oxidation reaction. Electrons are removed from the glyceraldehyde and transferred to NAD+. The energy released is used to convert ADP + P_i to ATP.

The end products of glycolysis are pyruvate and NADH. NADH is generated at several stages in respiration; we shall consider the fate of all the NADH produced later in this section.

The next two stages in respiration both involve two processes:
- oxidation – removal of electrons by NAD+ or a similar molecule called **flavine adenine dinucleotide** (FAD);
- decarboxylation – removal of a molecule of carbon dioxide.

During the **oxidative decarboxylation** of pyruvate, carbon dioxide is removed, and electrons transferred from pyruvate to NAD+, forming NADH. Pyruvate is oxidised while NAD+ is reduced. **Coenzyme A** enables the reaction to take place, and the resulting decarboxylated fragment of pyruvate is called **acetylcoenzyme A**.

8 What is the net gain of ATP per molecule of glucose during glycolysis?

9 How many carbon atoms are there in the decarboxylated fragment of pyruvate?

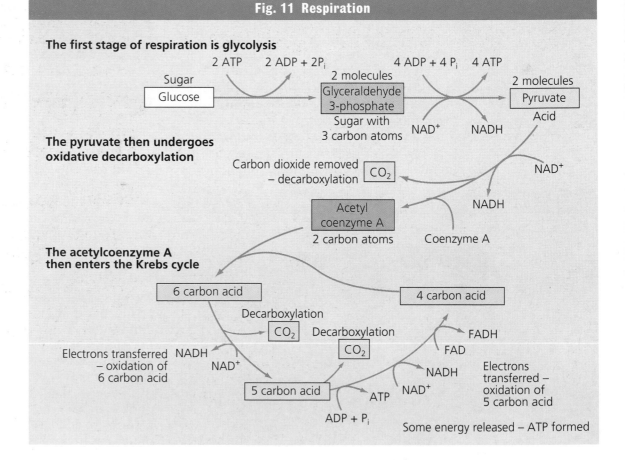

Fig. 11 Respiration

The first stage of respiration is glycolysis

2 ATP → 2 ADP + 2P_i 4 ADP + 4 P_i 4 ATP

Sugar
Glucose → 2 molecules Glyceraldehyde 3-phosphate → 2 molecules Pyruvate Acid

Sugar with 3 carbon atoms NAD+ NADH

The pyruvate then undergoes oxidative decarboxylation

Carbon dioxide removed – decarboxylation CO_2

NAD+

Acetyl coenzyme A
2 carbon atoms

NADH

Coenzyme A

The acetylcoenzyme A then enters the Krebs cycle

6 carbon acid

4 carbon acid

Decarboxylation CO_2 Decarboxylation CO_2

FADH

FAD

Electrons transferred – oxidation of 6 carbon acid NADH NAD+

NADH

Electrons transferred – oxidation of 5 carbon acid

5 carbon acid ATP NAD+

ADP + P_i

Some energy released – ATP formed

The acetylcoenzyme A then enters a cyclic series of reactions called **Krebs cycle** (Fig. 11), after the scientist who discovered the sequence. The acetylcoenzyme A joins onto a four-carbon acid to form a six-carbon acid. Two molecules of carbon dioxide are then removed from this acid, and the resulting four-carbon acceptor acid is recycled. Several electrons are also transferred to NAD^+ and FAD , reducing them to NADH and FADH, respectively.

The three decarboxylation reactions together with the removal of electrons mean that all three carbon atoms of the pyruvate end up in carbon dioxide. However, all the electrons that have been removed from these carbon atoms are now in NADH or FADH molecules.

The next stage uses the energy of these electrons to produce ATP – the whole purpose of respiration.

You should not be surprised by now to learn that the way in which the energy of the electrons is transferred to ATP uses the same mechanisms as that in photosynthesis – proton pumps and chemiosmotic channels (Fig. 12).

NADH and FADH transfer their electrons to a chain of electron carrier molecules situated in the phospholipid membranes, similar to those which hold the electron carriers of photosynthesis. The two carriers are different but their function is the same. When NADH or FADH transfer electrons, protons are transferred at the same time. The energy from the electrons is used to pump protons (H^+) across the membrane. This leaves behind a higher concentration of hydroxyl ions (OH^-). These hydroxyl ions attract the protons. At intervals in the membrane are chemiosmotic channels similar to those described in the section on photosynthesis, that will allow protons to flow through.

As the protons flow through these channels, attracted by the hydroxyl ions, they provide the energy to attach a third phosphate (P_i) group to ADP to form ATP.

The passage of one pair of electrons along the chain of carriers provides enough energy to move sufficient protons to produce three molecules of ATP.

The final carriers in the chain transfer electrons to oxygen atoms (Fig. 13). Each of these oxygen atoms picks up two protons to produce a molecule of water.

$$2e^- + 2H^+ + O \rightarrow H_2O$$

Fig. 12 ATP production

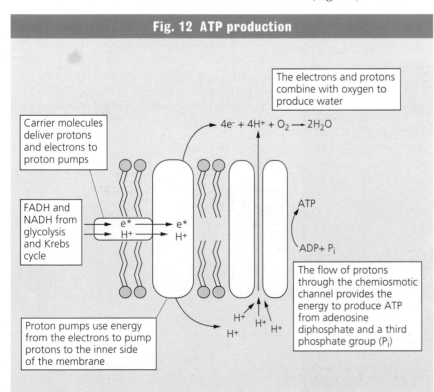

The electrons and protons combine with oxygen to produce water

Carrier molecules deliver protons and electrons to proton pumps

$4e^- + 4H^+ + O_2 \longrightarrow 2H_2O$

FADH and NADH from glycolysis and Krebs cycle

ATP

ADP+ P_i

Proton pumps use energy from the electrons to pump protons to the inner side of the membrane

The flow of protons through the chemiosmotic channel provides the energy to produce ATP from adenosine diphosphate and a third phosphate group (P_i)

Fig. 13 Summary of respiration

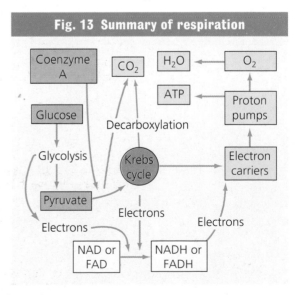

Coenzyme A

CO_2

H_2O

O_2

ATP

Glucose

Decarboxylation

Proton pumps

Glycolysis

Krebs cycle

Electron carriers

Pyruvate

Electrons

Electrons

Electrons

NAD or FAD

NADH or FADH

2.7 The role of ATP

Why go to all this trouble to make ATP? It is an energy carrier molecule that is used to provide energy for synthetic reactions and to work in most types of living cells (Fig. 14).

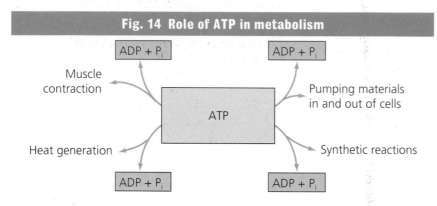

Fig. 14 Role of ATP in metabolism

Scientists now think that all living organisms possess proton pumps. The energy to operate the proton pumps is either transferred from light energy in the case of photosynthesis, or from the energy stored in sugars in the case of respiration in both animals and plants. These proton pumps allow all living organisms to produce ATP.

Q 10 a Scientists have discovered a chemical which uncouples the Krebs cycle from the electron transport chain. How will this affect the production of ATP?

b Some researchers think this chemical would be a perfect 'slimming pill'. Why do they think this? What dangers would there be to this kind of pill?

The oldest reaction

Three thousand million years ago primitive organisms called cyanobacteria evolved a system that could trap and then use light energy. This system consists of pigments and enzymes bound together on phospholipid membranes. The reactions are known as photosynthesis. Respiration is essentially the reverse of photosynthesis. These energy transfer mechanisms have remained virtually unchanged for 3000 million years and are used by almost every type of living organism.

All life as we know it depends on these reactions. Photosynthesis traps light energy from the Sun and stores it as carbohydrate. Other organisms obtain this stored energy from their food. Respiration makes the energy from the carbohydrate available as ATP. Cells then use the energy stored in ATP as necessary.

Scientists have unravelled the mechanisms that living organisms use to transfer energy from sunlight into organic compounds which can be used as fuels. Does that mean we are closer to becoming energy sufficient or do we still face a future with diminishing supplies of fossil fuels or increased risks from the proliferation of nuclear power stations?

We can use the energy available as ATP to be as active as we like!

Key ideas

- Energy can be released from carbohydrates by a series of reactions called respiration.

- Respiration is the reverse of photosynthesis.

- Carbon atoms in carbohydrates are oxidised to carbon dioxide.

- The energy from the electrons from the carbon atoms is used to operate proton pumps similar to those in photosynthesis.

- The flow of protons through chemiosmotic channels in phospholipid membranes provides the energy to generate ATP.

- The electrons are finally transferred by carrier molecules to oxygen atoms. These oxygen atoms pick up protons to form water molecules.

- ATP is an energy carrier molecule.

- The mechanisms that produce ATP are similar in both photosynthesis and respiration.

Enzyme washing powders

A wooden boat that could be susceptible to marine worm damage.

The marine worm *Spirorbis borgalis*.

An enzyme from a mollusc will create a cleaner wash. The Agriculture Research Service in Peoria, USA, announced the discovery of a bacterium which produces an enzyme that may well find an important role in biological washing powders. The bacterium is found in the digestive gland of the marine shipworm – not a true worm, but an elongated mollusc which can bore into woodwork, often of ships. The enzyme produced by the bacterium may help to make washing powders more environmentally friendly. The Peoria researchers have a second application for their new enzyme. It is highly effective in removing the protein which accumulates on contact lenses. And, unlike existing proteases used for this purpose, it remains active in the presence of the disinfectant hydrogen peroxide. A single solution can thus be used in place of the conventional two solutions for cleansing and sterilising.

For many years sodium tripolyphosphate has been used in washing powders to prevent various forms of dirt from adhering to fabrics. But as it has come under suspicion as a cause of the deadening of lakes and rivers by eutrophication, this chemical has been removed from commercial laundry detergents, or at least drastically reduced in concentration. The new formulations tend to be relatively alkaline, a condition in which existing proteases are less effective. But the activity of the new shipworm enzyme is not impaired in this way.

Source: adapted from an article by Bernard Dixon, *The Independent*, 12 July 1993

3.1 Learning objectives

After working through this chapter, you should be able to:

- **explain** how enzymes lower the activation energies of reactions;

- **recall** that enzymes enable the chemical reactions that support life to proceed sufficiently quickly within a reasonable temperature range;

- **explain** how enzymes act by forming enzyme–substrate complexes;

- **explain** the effects of change in temperature, pH, substrate concentration, competitive and non-competitive inhibition on the rate of enzyme action in terms of their tertiary structure.

3.2 Detergents

The white foam is mainly composed of phosphates from detergents used at a nearby campsite. The phosphates cause the growth of plants such as duckweed, the green layer above the foam, which kills all other plants normally living in the water by preventing light reaching them.

Food stains such as blood and egg are proteins. These proteins are insoluble in water, which is why they are difficult to remove. Removing protein stains involves breaking down the food-stain proteins into amino acids, which will dissolve in water. Biological detergents contain **proteases** – protein-digesting enzymes – that break down proteins into soluble amino acids.

There are, however, problems with some enzymes in current use; they only work slowly in cold water and some of the additives needed to make them work effectively, such as phosphates, have proved to be detrimental to the environment. The enzyme from the 'worm' may overcome many of these problems: scientific research often leads unexpectedly to discoveries with great benefits.

The reaction that breaks down proteins is called **hydrolysis**, which means 'breaking down using water'. Hydrolysis is the reverse of the condensation reaction that you studied in Chapter 1. Molecules are split apart with the addition of water. But peptide bonds are difficult to break down; even if you soaked stained clothing in water for days, the stain would still be there. Until biological detergents came onto the market, the only way to remove biological stains was to boil the clothes, but boiling damages most modern fabrics.

3.3 Activation energy

Why then do the peptide bonds break down in boiling water but not in cold water? In order to break down the peptide bonds, the electron orbits of the atoms in the water molecules must overlap with the electron orbits of the atoms which form the peptide bonds. But electron orbits repel each other (because they are both negatively charged). To make the reaction possible the water molecules have to be moving so quickly that this repulsion is overcome. Moving molecules have **kinetic energy**; the faster they are moving the more kinetic energy they have. The kinetic energy of water molecules can be increased by heating them.

The minimum kinetic energy needed to overcome the repulsion between molecules is called the **activation energy** of the reaction (Fig. 1a). The molecules that react are called **substrate molecules**.

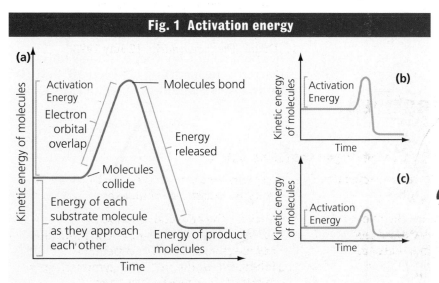

Fig. 1 Activation energy

1 a Would the substrate molecules in Fig. 1b react? Explain your answer.
b The substrate molecules in Fig. 1c have less energy than the substrate molecules in Fig. 1b, but they still react. Explain why.

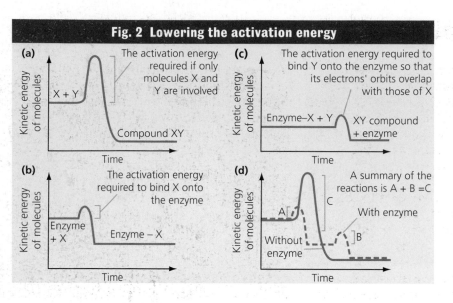

Fig. 2 Lowering the activation energy

(a)

Kinetic energy of molecules

X + Y

The activation energy required if only molecules X and Y are involved

Compound XY

Time

(b)

Kinetic energy of molecules

Enzyme + X

The activation energy required to bind X onto the enzyme

Enzyme – X

Time

(c)

Kinetic energy of molecules

The activation energy required to bind Y onto the enzyme so that its electrons' orbits overlap with those of X

Enzyme–X + Y

XY compound + enzyme

Time

(d)

Kinetic energy of molecules

A summary of the reactions is A + B =C

A

C

With enzyme

Without enzyme

B

Time

The activation energy of a reaction cannot be changed. However, **enzymes** have the same effect as lowering the activation energy by splitting the reaction into stages, each with a lower activation energy (Fig. 2). This is vitally important for living organisms. Enzymes ensure that the reactions vital to their existence can proceed rapidly at the temperatures that exist inside their bodies. Once the reaction is completed, the enzyme is free to bind with another of the first molecule in the reaction. Enzymes are a type of **catalyst**, compounds that affect the rate of chemical reactions but are not changed at the end of the reaction.

3.4 Enzyme structure

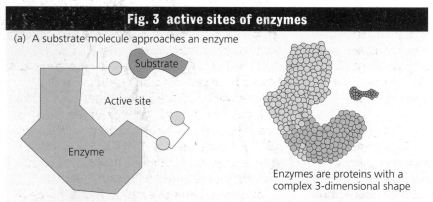

Fig. 3 active sites of enzymes

(a) A substrate molecule approaches an enzyme

Substrate

Active site

Enzyme

Enzymes are proteins with a complex 3-dimensional shape

(b) The shape of the enzyme is distorted by the substrate as the substrate is 'locked' in place, forming the enzyme–substrate complex

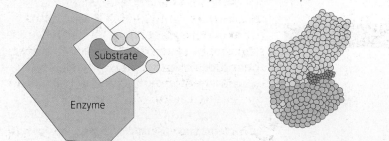

Substrate

Enzyme

Source: adapted from Salisbury and Ross, *Plant Physiology*, Wadsworth 1992

An enzyme molecule is a globular protein with a complex tertiary structure. Weak chemical bonds between the polypeptide chains maintain the shape of the enzyme. Substrates can be attached to a particular part of the enzyme molecule. The combination of an enzyme with substrate molecules is called an **enzyme–substrate complex**. The part of the enzyme onto which a substrate molecule fits is called the **active site** (Fig. 3).

The enzyme holds the substrate molecules together for the minute fraction of a second the molecules need to react. The products are then released. The active sites on the enzyme are now ready to receive more substrate molecules. This happens so quickly that enzyme-catalysed reactions are anything between 10^8 and 10^{20} times faster than uncatalysed reactions at $20°C$.

Key ideas

- Because they are proteins with a complex tertiary shape, enzymes are able to form complexes with substrate molecules.

- These complexes bring substrate molecules close together to allow reactions to happen more quickly.

3.5 Effect of temperature on enzyme activity

In North America washing machines use hot water from the tap – this usually has a temperature of 50–60°C. In Western Europe washing machines are fitted with heaters, some of which heat the water to 95°C. The proteases in most biological washing detergents have been developed to work best at 55–60°C.

In most countries in the world, clothes are washed in cold water. Often the washing is done in rivers that could also be the only supply of fresh water.

 2 a What is the main disadvantage of washing clothes in cold rather than hot water?
b In what ways could biological washing detergents pollute fresh water?

The temperature at which an enzyme works best is known as the **optimum temperature** for that enzyme. Most chemical reactions are affected by temperature in the same way as enzymes, in the range 10–40°C.

 3 a Using the graph in Fig. 4, what is the optimum temperature for the washing powder protease?
b Calculate from Fig. 4 by how much the reaction rate will increase for a 10°C rise in temperature.

These women, at Teresina, Piani, Brazil, use the local river to do their washing.

The protease in Fig. 4 does not work at all at temperatures higher than 75°C. This is because enzymes are also proteins. Higher temperatures cause the atoms in the molecule to vibrate so rapidly that the weak bonds between the polypeptide chains break down and the molecule unravels. The shape of the active site depends on the bonds that maintain the tertiary structure of the protein molecule. If there are no active sites, the enzyme cannot function. The enzyme is said to be **denatured**.

Most enzymes in the human body have an optimum temperature between 35°C and 40°C and are denatured by temperatures above 45°C. Temperatures below 35°C do not affect the tertiary structure of enzyme molecules. However, the molecules move so slowly that few substrate molecules reach active sites and the reaction is therefore very slow.

 4 Sketch an activity/temperature graph for an enzyme from the human body.

The shipworm enzyme is highly active and stable at temperatures between 25°C and 50°C. Its high activity at cool temperatures means the shipworm is well adapted for life in the cool sea water. This means that it will work well in the energy-conserving cold-water detergents that are being developed.

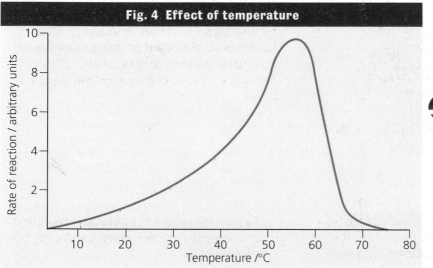

Fig. 4 Effect of temperature

Rate of reaction / arbitrary units vs Temperature /°C

3.6 Effect of pH on enzyme activity

As well as having an optimum temperature, enzymes have an **optimum pH**. Most enzymes are denatured in solutions that are strongly acidic or strongly alkaline. Again, denaturation alters the shape of the enzyme so that active sites are no longer available. Extremes of pH are rarely found inside the cells of living organisms.

Activity/pH graphs for different enzymes vary much more than the corresponding activity/temperature curves.

5 **What is the advantage of using an enzyme with a curve similar to B in Fig. 5 rather than one similar to A, in washing powders?**

Many enzymes have a bell-shaped curve similar to curve A on Fig. 5. The shipworm enzyme has a curve similar to curve B.

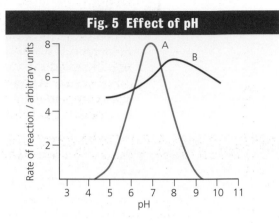

Fig. 5 Effect of pH

3.7 Effect of concentrations on enzyme activity

Enzymes only work when they form enzyme–substrate complexes with the substrate. The reaction rate depends on the

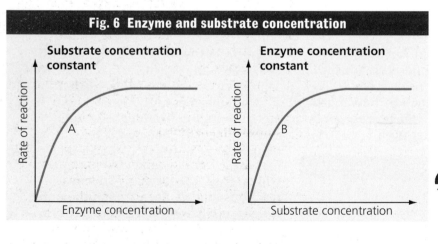

Fig. 6 Enzyme and substrate concentration

number of substrate molecules that bind to enzyme molecules. Clearly, the more enzyme molecules in the solution, the greater the chance of a substrate molecule finding an active site and the greater the rate of reaction. Similarly, the more substrate molecules in a solution, the greater chance of forming an enzyme–substrate complex and the greater the rate of reaction. The curves for the effects of enzyme concentration and of substrate concentration on the rate of reaction are very similar (Fig. 6).

6 **Explain in terms of active sites why the curves start to flatten out at A and B in Fig. 6.**

Key ideas

- Raising the temperature increases the rate of an enzyme reaction, a 10°C rise doubling the rate of reaction. Enzymes have an optimum temperature. High temperatures denature enzymes by destroying their tertiary structure.

- All enzymes also have an optimum pH. Extremes of pH denature enzymes.

- Increasing the enzyme concentration increases the rate of reaction until the substrate concentration becomes limiting.

- Increasing the substrate reaction increases the rate of reaction until the enzyme concentration becomes limiting.

3.8 Inhibition of enzyme activity

Many enzymes have a high substrate specificity. This means that only one particular substrate molecule is able to attach to the active site. Other enzymes have a low substrate specificity, which means molecules with a similar shape to the usual substrate can attach to the active site. If more than one possible substrate molecule are present in the same solution they compete for the active sites – they are **competitive inhibitors** (Fig. 7a).

Some competitive inhibitor molecules do not react with the active site. They do not destroy, or denature, the enzyme but no reaction will take place until the inhibitor molecule is released and the usual substrate molecule can combine with the enzyme.

Q 7 What would be the effect on the rate of a competitively inhibited enzyme reaction of increasing the usual substrate concentration?

Other molecules inhibit enzyme reactions in a different way. They do not attach themselves to active sites, but to a different part of the enzyme. This alters the shape of the enzyme molecule so that the active site can no longer bind with a substrate molecule. These molecules are called **non-competitive inhibitors** (Fig. 7b). Once attached to an enzyme, some non-competitive molecules are very difficult to remove – the enzyme can be destroyed. This is why heavy metals such as mercury and lead are so poisonous; they are non-competitive inhibitors that effectively prevent many of the body's reactions taking place.

Enzymes allow reactions in organisms to proceed quickly at environmental temperatures. Information about the shipworm enzyme has led us towards understanding further the key features of enzyme action. Research is developing that will do the same for many chemical reactions that we need around the home, e.g. doing the weekly wash, or even in industry. Many other living organisms could harbour secrets like the shipworm.

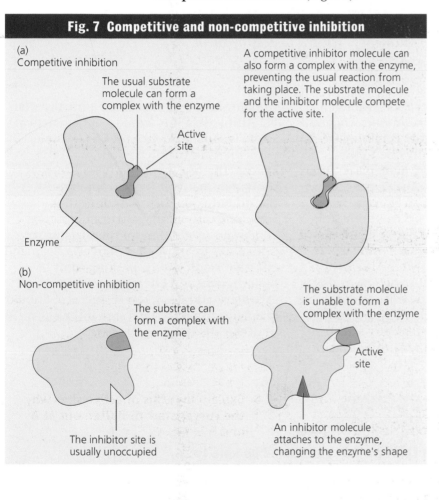

Fig. 7 Competitive and non-competitive inhibition

(a)
Competitive inhibition

The usual substrate molecule can form a complex with the enzyme

Active site

Enzyme

A competitive inhibitor molecule can also form a complex with the enzyme, preventing the usual reaction from taking place. The substrate molecule and the inhibitor molecule compete for the active site.

(b)
Non-competitive inhibition

The substrate can form a complex with the enzyme

The inhibitor site is usually unoccupied

The substrate molecule is unable to form a complex with the enzyme

Active site

An inhibitor molecule attaches to the enzyme, changing the enzyme's shape

Key ideas

- Competitive inhibitors affect the rate of enzyme action because they have similar shapes to the substrate molecules and compete with them for the active sites on the enzymes.

- Non-competitive inhibitors affect the shape of enzyme molecules so that the active site can no longer bind with substrate molecules.

4 Growing cells

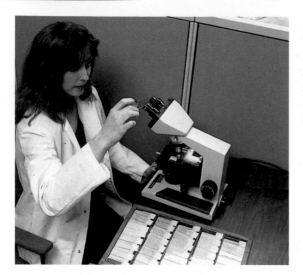

'I work for a screening programme – a different approach to medical care. Instead of waiting for people to feel ill, screening programmes aim to detect diseases in the early stages – sometimes before patients know that anything is wrong. The earlier a disease is detected, the better the chance of treatment being successful. I am examining cervical smears – cells gently scraped from the lining of the neck of the womb. I am looking for cells that are not in themselves cancerous, but which often lead to the development of cancer. If I find any, the patient will have a smear taken regularly for the rest of her life; and if the cells become cancerous, immediate treatment is started to destroy them.'

Cervical cancer kills over 2000 women in Britain each year. But the number of deaths from this cancer is steadily declining by about 5% per year, mainly due to the screening programme. In some places, such as British Columbia in Canada, the screening programme is so effective that cervical cancer only occurs in immigrants or women that were too old to benefit from the screening programme when it was introduced. Do you know how the use of the light and electron microscopes and centrifugation have made this screening possible?

In Britain, women are usually screened every 3 years. Many doctors think that all women should be examined annually. Can you think why this would not be practical? There is some evidence linking lifestyle, particularly sexual behaviour, with this cancer. The test is voluntary and surveys show that many of those women most at risk do not come forward for testing. Screening only needs a light microscope and an understanding of the structure of cells. Early treatment is relatively cheap and effective. Radical surgery, long-term radiotherapy and aftercare are very expensive and less likely to succeed. Should people be forced to be tested if their lifestyle puts them at greater risk?

4.1 Learning objectives

After working through this chapter, you should be able to:

- **explain** how the electron microscope has increased our knowledge of the fine structure of organelles;

- **recognise** certain cell organelles as seen in electron micrographs (nucleus, endoplasmic reticulum and ribosomes, cell membrane, mitochondrion, chloroplast, cell wall) and recall their functions;

- **explain** how differential centrifugation has contributed to our increased knowledge of the function of organelles;

- **recall** the structure of typical eukaryotic animal and plant cells;

- **recall** the structure of prokaryotic cells of cyanobacteria and bacteria;

- **explain** the differences between eukaryotic and prokaryotic cells.

4.2 Seeing cells through microscopes

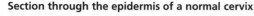
Fig. 1 Cervical smears

These light micrographs of cervical smears have been specially stained to show the nuclei.

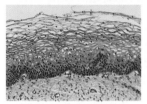

Section through the epidermis of a normal cervix

Cells form a normal layer

Only cells in this layer divide

Section through the epidermis of a cervix which shows the early stage of possible cancer

Abnormal cells with large nuclei

A wider layer of dividing cells

This patient would receive treatment.

Section through epidermis with developing cancer

Developing cancer – all the cells are dividing, out of control

Normal epidermis can be seen on the left

This patient would receive treatment.

You may have examined cells from the lining of your cheek. These look very similar to normal cervical cells (Fig. 1). The staining techniques you used probably showed the nucleus as a 'blob' and did not show up any other structures inside the cell. We now know that cells contain a large number of structures called **organelles**, each of which has its own specific function. Medical screening depends on our understanding of the way cells work. Even a simple **light microscope** can show the changes in a cell that might be the beginning of cancer.

Organisms are organised on a cellular basis. Some organisms are only one cell, others consist of many cells. Within multicelled organisms, cells with similar functions group together to form **tissues**. Some tissues may then form **organs**. Organs are structures that perform specific functions.

Q 1 Explain how knowing the function of cell organelles helps us to understand how organs work.

4.3 Resolving power

The largest single organelle in most cells is the nucleus. Scientists working in the 1950s and 1960s found that nuclei play a vital role in the control of cell activities. The nucleus became the focus of research for many cancer scientists. They desperately needed to know more about the internal structure of these organelles. But light microscopy could give them no more information – light microscopes had reached the limit of their **resolving powers**.

Resolving power is literally the power to distinguish between two objects. Think of a car at night; when it is a long distance away the two headlights appear as a single light. As the car gets nearer you can see that there are two headlights – you have resolved the one light into two lights. By using binoculars you could resolve the light into two headlights while the car was further away. A powerful lens can resolve

individual dots on a photograph and show that the whole image is just made up of a pattern of dots. However, even the most powerful lens cannot resolve two dots that are closer together than 250 nm. This is to do with the light rather than the lens. Two dots must be further apart than one half the wavelength of the light used to view them.

To resolve the internal structure of cell membranes or cell organelles something with a shorter wavelength than light is needed. The **electron microscope** uses a beam of electrons with a wavelength of approximately 0.005 nm.

Q 2 What is the theoretical limit of an electron microscope's resolving power?

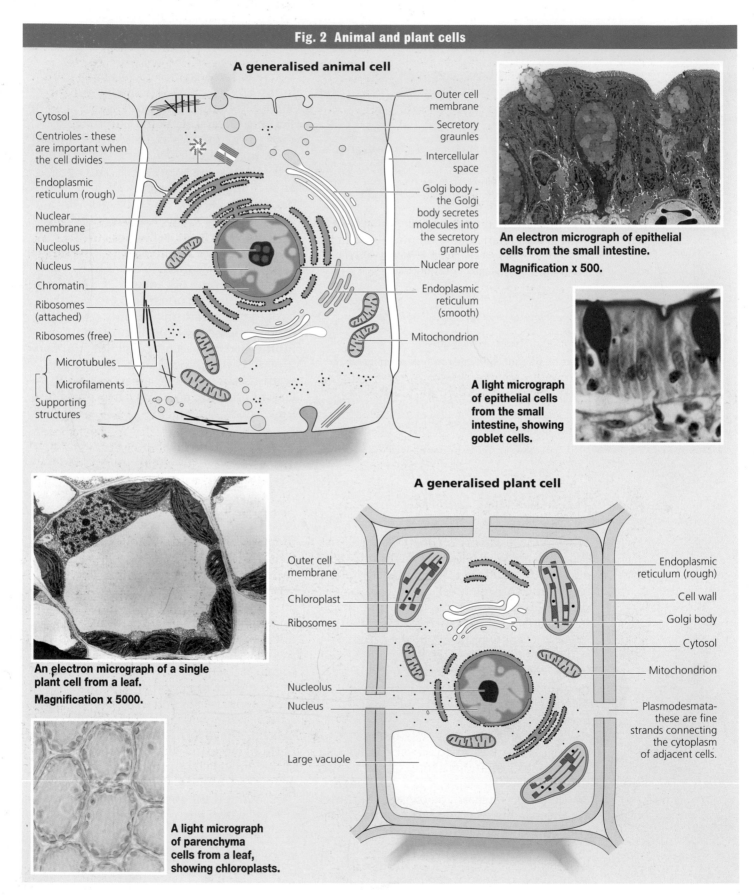

Fig. 2 Animal and plant cells

A generalised animal cell

Cytosol

Centrioles - these are important when the cell divides

Endoplasmic reticulum (rough)

Nuclear membrane

Nucleolus

Nucleus

Chromatin

Ribosomes (attached)

Ribosomes (free)

Microtubules

Microfilaments

Supporting structures

Outer cell membrane

Secretory graunles

Intercellular space

Golgi body - the Golgi body secretes molecules into the secretory granules

Nuclear pore

Endoplasmic reticulum (smooth)

Mitochondrion

An electron micrograph of epithelial cells from the small intestine.
Magnification x 500.

A light micrograph of epithelial cells from the small intestine, showing goblet cells.

An electron micrograph of a single plant cell from a leaf.
Magnification x 5000.

A light micrograph of parenchyma cells from a leaf, showing chloroplasts.

A generalised plant cell

Outer cell membrane

Chloroplast

Ribosomes

Nucleolus

Nucleus

Large vacuole

Endoplasmic reticulum (rough)

Cell wall

Golgi body

Cytosol

Mitochondrion

Plasmodesmata - these are fine strands connecting the cytoplasm of adjacent cells.

Preparing a specimen for an electron microscope is different from preparing a cheek cell smear (Fig. 2). Different stains are used and the specimen has to be smaller and thinner than can be used on a light microscope. But the results are well worth the effort.

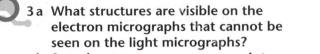

3 a **What structures are visible on the electron micrographs that cannot be seen on the light micrographs?**
   b **Sort the structures you can see into:**
     (i) those in plant and animal cells;
     (ii) those in plant cells only;
     (iii) those in animal cells only.

Key ideas

- Animal and plant cells contain a number of organelles. Some of these organelles can be seen with a light microscope but, with the exception of nuclei, nothing can be seen of their internal structure.

- Electron microscopes can resolve smaller objects than light microscopes because the beam of electrons has a shorter wavelength than light rays.

4.4 The nucleus

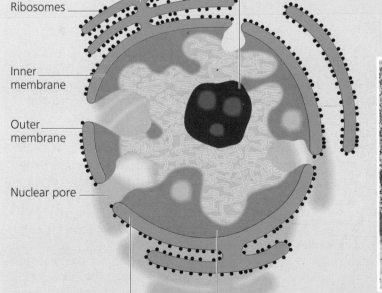

Fig. 3 A cell nucleus

Nucleolus
The **nucleolus** is concerned with producing RNA for the manufacture of ribosomes.

Endoplasmic reticulum

Ribosomes

Inner membrane

Outer membrane

Nuclear pore

Nuclear membrane
The **nuclear membrane** is a double phospholipid membrane. It has large pores not found in any other phospholipid membranes, which allow the large RNA molecules to pass through it.

Chromatin
When a cell is not dividing, the DNA molecules of the chromosomes form **chromatin**, which stains darkly. Chromatin takes on an abnormal appearance in the first stage of cervical cancer.

The **nucleus** (Fig. 3) contains the information required to control the activities of the cell. This information is carried in molecules called nucleic acids. There are two types of nucleic acid – DNA and RNA. Their functions are described in Chapter 8, and the processes which allow each cell to have a full complement of information are described in Chapter 9.

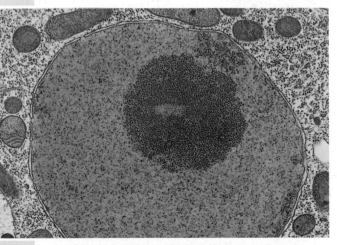

A false colour electron micrograph of a cell nucleus.
Magnification × 16 500.

4.5 Endoplasmic reticulum and ribosomes

Fig. 4 Endoplasmic reticulum and ribosomes

Ribosomes

Ribosomes are the smallest organelles in the cell. They are composed of protein and RNA. The RNA in ribosomes is produced in the nucleolus. Ribosomes build proteins. Endoplasmic-bound ribosomes are attached to the rough endoplasmic reticulum.

Cytosol

The **cytosol** is a solution containing enzymes involved in glycolysis and in synthetic reactions. Cytosol also contains fat globules, a range of granular inclusions including pigment molecules, food storage compounds, waste products about to be expelled, and oil globules.

Rough endoplasmic reticulum

The **rough endoplasmic reticulum** consists of sheets of phospholipid membrane supporting ribosomes.

Smooth endoplasmic reticulum

The **smooth endoplasmic reticulum** is a tubular phospholipid membrane not supporting ribosomes.

Intracisternal (lumenal) phase

The **endoplasmic reticulum** (Fig. 4) is a series of phospholipid membranes continuous with both the outer membrane of the cell and the nuclear membrane. The spaces between these membranes are filled with fluid and form a possible transport system for materials throughout the cell. The endoplasmic reticulum also increases the surface area of the cell, which helps with exchange of materials between the cell and its environment.

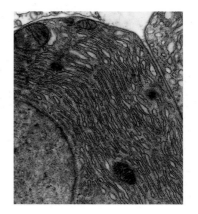

An electron micrograph of endoplasmic reticulum and ribosomes. Magnification × 7500.

4.6 Cell membranes

One fact which may have struck you from the electron micrographs is that a number of the organelles appear to contain double membranes similar in appearance to the outer membrane of the cell.

All these membranes have one thing in common – they consist of two layers of phospholipid molecules (Fig. 5). You first met phospholipids in Chapter 1. In a membrane the two layers of phospholipids are arranged with the fatty acid chains pointing inwards. They arrange themselves like this because the fatty acid chains are hydrophobic.

Q 4 What does hydrophobic mean?

You have already come across intrinsic membrane protein molecules in Chapter 2. These are the molecules that hold the chlorophyll molecules in place in the membranes and which form the channels through the membranes for the proton pumps.

Phospholipid membranes have two main functions:
- in all organelles they control the transport of materials from one side to the other;
- in chloroplasts and mitochondria they keep pigments and carrier molecules in fixed positions.

You can find out more about the transport functions of phospholipid membranes in Chapter 5. Here we shall be more concerned with the molecules bound to their surfaces.

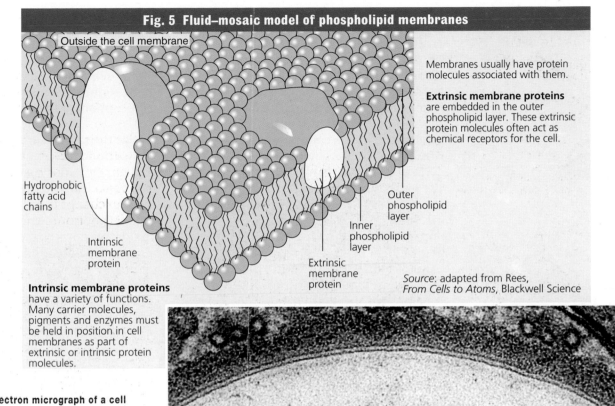

Fig. 5 Fluid–mosaic model of phospholipid membranes

Outside the cell membrane

Membranes usually have protein molecules associated with them.

Extrinsic membrane proteins are embedded in the outer phospholipid layer. These extrinsic protein molecules often act as chemical receptors for the cell.

Hydrophobic fatty acid chains

Intrinsic membrane protein

Outer phospholipid layer

Inner phospholipid layer

Extrinsic membrane protein

Source: adapted from Rees, *From Cells to Atoms*, Blackwell Science

Intrinsic membrane proteins have a variety of functions. Many carrier molecules, pigments and enzymes must be held in position in cell membranes as part of extrinsic or intrinsic protein molecules.

An electron micrograph of a cell membrane.
Magnification × 190 000.

4.7 Centrifugation

Centrifugation

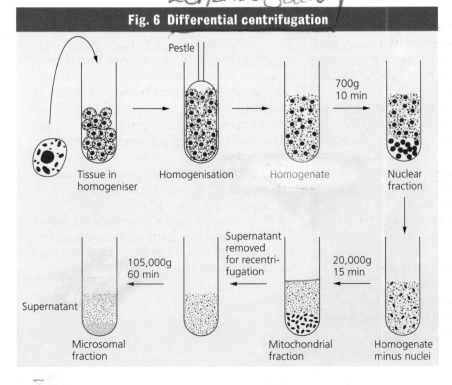

Fig. 6 Differential centrifugation

Pestle

700g 10 min

Tissue in homogeniser

Homogenisation

Homogenate

Nuclear fraction

105,000g 60 min

Supernatant removed for recentrifugation

20,000g 15 min

Supernatant

Microsomal fraction

Mitochondrial fraction

Homogenate minus nuclei

The detail available from light microscope observations was all that was available to the biochemists who first tried to work out the sequence of reactions in photosynthesis and respiration. There were so many different reactions that it seemed unlikely that they could all be occurring at the same time in every part of the cell. Perhaps different organelles were responsible for different processes? Perhaps the function of an organelle was to keep the enzymes and carriers involved in one process, e.g. respiration, separate from those from another process, e.g. photosynthesis? The only way to find out was to break down cells, separate the organelles and investigate what they did. To do this successfully they needed to keep the enzymes and other molecules intact inside the organelles. The apparatus that made this possible was the **centrifuge** (Fig. 6). This research technique allows scientists to research functioning rather than structure.

If a mixture of particles of different sizes is spun at high speed in a centrifuge, the larger particles tend to accumulate at the bottom of the tube. Since organelles are quite different in size, this principle can be used to separate them. Cells are broken up in a **homogeniser**, a device rather like a kitchen blender, that breaks down the outer membrane of the cells but leaves the organelles intact. The **homogenate** is then spun at relatively slow speed. The nuclei, the largest organelles in the cell, collect at the bottom of the tube. The suspension above the cells is known as the **supernatant**. This supernatant is then spun at a higher speed. This time the mitochondria separate out. The process is repeated at higher centrifuge speed to separate out the ribosomes.

5 From what you have seen in Fig. 2, at which stage in the process would you expect the chloroplasts in plant cells to separate out? Explain your answer.

In 1937 Robin Hill separated the chloroplasts from leaf cells and was able to show that these isolated chloroplasts, when illuminated, could carry out the light-dependent reactions of photosynthesis – they did not need the other parts of the cell to carry out their function.

6 What are the end products of the light-dependent reactions of photosynthesis?

In the same year Hans Krebs separated mitochondria from animal cells and was able to work out the sequence of reactions involved in the oxidative decarboxylation of pyruvate in respiration. He found that the enzymes and carriers involved in oxidative decarboxylation were all located inside the mitochondria. The series of reactions has been named the Krebs cycle in his honour.

7 Very active cells have many more mitochondria than cells which are not active. Suggest a reason for this difference.

The next stage was to use the electron microscope to look inside the cell organelles in more detail than was possible with the light microscope.

4.8 Chloroplasts

We and other animals depend on the oxygen-rich atmosphere that plants have helped form as a result of photosynthesis.

In the cyanobacteria you read about in Chapter 2, the phospholipid membranes holding the molecules needed for the light-dependent reactions of photosynthesis are spread throughout the cell. In green plants the membranes are gathered together in **chloroplasts** (Fig. 7). The membranes in both cyanobacteria and plants are called **thylakoids**.

8 From your work in Chapter 2, what important substance is formed when the protons flow back through the thylakoids?

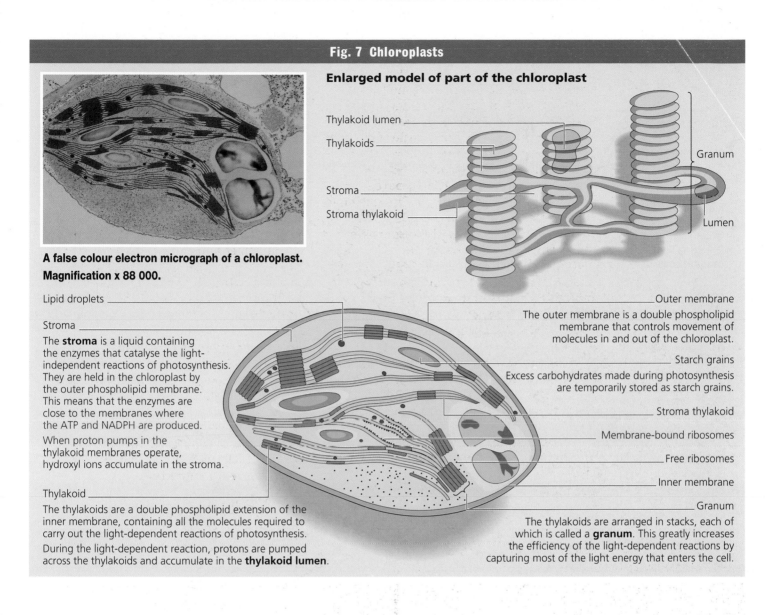

Fig. 7 Chloroplasts

Enlarged model of part of the chloroplast

Thylakoid lumen

Thylakoids

Stroma

Stroma thylakoid

Granum

Lumen

A false colour electron micrograph of a chloroplast.
Magnification x 88 000.

Lipid droplets

Stroma

The **stroma** is a liquid containing the enzymes that catalyse the light-independent reactions of photosynthesis. They are held in the chloroplast by the outer phospholipid membrane. This means that the enzymes are close to the membranes where the ATP and NADPH are produced.

When proton pumps in the thylakoid membranes operate, hydroxyl ions accumulate in the stroma.

Thylakoid

The thylakoids are a double phospholipid extension of the inner membrane, containing all the molecules required to carry out the light-dependent reactions of photosynthesis.

During the light-dependent reaction, protons are pumped across the thylakoids and accumulate in the **thylakoid lumen**.

Outer membrane

The outer membrane is a double phospholipid membrane that controls movement of molecules in and out of the chloroplast.

Starch grains

Excess carbohydrates made during photosynthesis are temporarily stored as starch grains.

Stroma thylakoid

Membrane-bound ribosomes

Free ribosomes

Inner membrane

Granum

The thylakoids are arranged in stacks, each of which is called a **granum**. This greatly increases the efficiency of the light-dependent reactions by capturing most of the light energy that enters the cell.

4.9 Mitochondria

In the cyanobacteria the membranes containing the electron carriers used in respiration are also spread throughout the cell. In **mitochondria** electron carriers are gathered together on the inner membrane (Fig. 8).

In the cells of organisms that have evolved more recently than cyanobacteria, there is division of labour. The membranes of the mitochondria hold the enzymes needed for the electron transfer stages of respiration. The energy transfer stages of photosynthesis are bound to the membranes in the chloroplasts. In both cases protons are pumped into an enclosed space before they flow back through the membrane to generate ATP. This leads to much greater efficiency of energy transfer than in cells where there is no enclosed space into which to pump the protons.

9 a Look back at Chapter 2. Which molecules donate electrons to the electron carriers in the cristae?

b Give four similarities in structure between mitochondria and chloroplasts.

c How are mitochondria and chloroplasts similar in function?

Fig. 8 Mitochondria

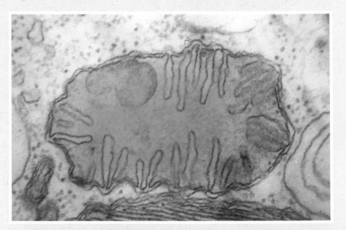

DNA
The DNA threads contain the information required for the mitochondria to replicate.

Intermembrane space

Ribosomes

Outer membrane
The outer membrane controls the passage of materials in and out of the mitochondrion.

Inner membrane
The inner phospholipid membrane is highly folded to form **cristae.** These increase its surface area. The proton pumps in the cristae pump protons from the liquid matrix into the lumen (space) of the cristae. As the protons flow back through the membrane into the matrix, ATP is generated.

Matrix
The matrix contains all the enzymes required for oxidative decarboxylation reactions (Krebs cycle), so they are near the electron carriers in the cristae. Hydroxyl ions accumulate here when proton pumps are operating during aerobic respiration.

Respiratory assemblies
Collections of molecules concerned with respiration.

The enzymes for glycolysis are found in the liquid that surrounds the mitochondria.

Crista
The cristae contain the electron carrier molecules (which carry electrons to oxygen) and the molecules involved in proton pumps and ATP generation. The **lumen** of the cristae is where protons accumulate when the proton pumps operate during respiration.

An electron micrograph of mitochondria.
Magnification x 18 000.

A false-colour electron micrograph of a mitochondrion, showing the folded cristae clearly.
Magnification x 144 000.

Key ideas

- Electron microscopy has shown that most organelles are made up of phospholipid membranes. These membranes control the entry and exit of materials to the organelles. They also support enzymes and electron carriers.

- Differential centrifugation can separate the organelles from homogenised cells and allow study of the function of organelles.

- Organelles compartmentalise the various sets of chemical reactions that occur within cells. This leads to much greater efficiency.

4.10 The cell wall

Roughly 25% of a young plant cell wall, known as the **primary cell wall**, is the carbohydrate polymer cellulose. This is arranged in sheets of **microfibrils** (Fig. 9). The microfibrils are embedded in a supportive framework of other compounds, the most common being complex carbohydrates called **hemicelluloses**. These make up approximately 50% of the wall. Hemicelluloses are polysaccharides similar to cellulose but with shorter, branched chains. Other soluble polysaccharides called **pectins** make up the remainder.

The function of the primary cell wall is to control the growth and shape of the cell. The shape of this wall is determined by the arrangement of the cellulose microfibrils. The primary wall may help to support young plants by providing a pressure called pressure potential, which is discussed in Chapter 5.

When the cell has completed growth it may, depending on its location, develop a **secondary cell wall.** Wood is made up of xylem cells. The secondary walls of these cells become impregnated with a tough, waterproof material called lignin which gives them great strength. This waterproofing results in the death of the mature xylem cells. Cork cells which form the outer layer of tree bark become impregnated with a fatty material called suberin, which is also waterproof.

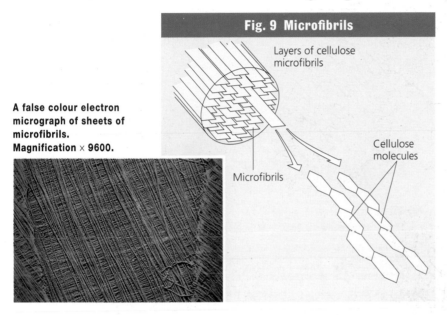

Fig. 9 Microfibrils

Layers of cellulose microfibrils

Cellulose molecules

Microfibrils

A false colour electron micrograph of sheets of microfibrils. Magnification × 9600.

4.11 Are all cells the same?

In Chapter 2 you were introduced to cyanobacteria, primitive cells that were very important in the evolution of many of the energy transfer systems found in modern organisms. Cyanobacteria belong to a group of organisms called **prokaryotes**, which means 'before the nucleus' (Fig. 10). Prokaryotes possess nucleic acids, but these are not held within a nuclear membrane. Instead there are strands of DNA collectively known as the **nucleoid** in the centre of the cell.

Organisms whose nucleic acids are contained by nuclear membranes are called **eukaryotes.** There are other differences between prokaryotes and eukaryotes.

The cell walls of prokaryotes contain polysaccharides, but not cellulose. They also contain protein and lipids. Many prokaryotes also secrete a protective capsule outside the cell wall; cyanobacteria secrete a gelatinous layer. Some prokaryotes have a long whip-like structure called a **flagellum** which allows them to move.

Prokaryotes increase the area of their internal membranes in two ways: bacteria have infoldings of the cell membranes called **mesosomes**, cyanobacteria have thylakoids.

 11 a Which organelle in higher organisms has internal projections similar to the mesosomes in bacteria?
  b From your work in Chapter 2, what is the function of thylakoids in cyanobacteria?

 10 Using Table 1 and comparing Figs 2 and 10, which organelles present in eukaryotes are absent in prokaryotes?

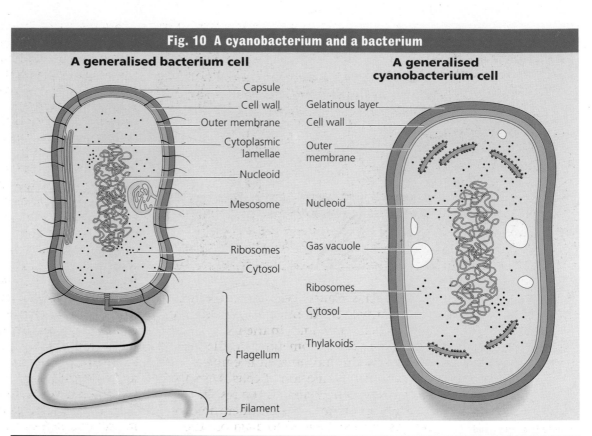

Fig. 10 A cyanobacterium and a bacterium

A generalised bacterium cell

- Capsule
- Cell wall
- Outer membrane
- Cytoplasmic lamellae
- Nucleoid
- Mesosome
- Ribosomes
- Cytosol
- Flagellum
- Filament

A generalised cyanobacterium cell

- Gelatinous layer
- Cell wall
- Outer membrane
- Nucleoid
- Gas vacuole
- Ribosomes
- Cytosol
- Thylakoids

Table 1. A comparison of prokaryotic and eukaryotic cells

Feature	Prokaryotic cell	Eukaryotic plant cell	Eukaryotic animal cell
Cell wall	Polysaccharide, but not cellulose	Cellulose	No cell wall
Phospholipid membranes	Present	Present	Present
DNA	Not enclosed in nucleus	Enclosed in nucleus	Enclosed in nucleus
Chloroplasts	Not present	Present	Not present
Mitochondria	Not present	Present	Present
Ribosomes	Present	Present	Present

Prokaryotes are important organisms. You will see in Chapter 6 how bacteria are involved in the decay of dead organisms and the cycling of nutrients. Some bacteria and cyanobacteria can 'fix' atmospheric nitrogen – in effect make fertilisers without the need for factories and their associated pollution. Bacteria have become vital tools in genetic engineering – a process which will have as big an impact on our future as the discovery of radioactivity did at the beginning of this century. Chapter 10 deals with genetic engineering in more detail, but no progress would have been possible in these developments without an understanding of the structure of bacteria gained from electron microscopy and centrifuge techniques.

Cancer

In developed countries cancer is rapidly becoming a dominant cause of death – from childhood leukaemia to prostate cancer in elderly men. The fundamental difference between cancer cells and normal cells is that the mechanisms which control cell division fail to operate in cancer cells. This is controlled within the nucleus by the

Regular visits to a Well Woman Clinic can greatly improve detection rates. Cancer begins to develop in approximately 50-60% of cases where abnormal cells are detected by cytologists. Cervical cancer develops relatively slowly from these cells, usually over several years, so there is a very good chance the abnormal cells, once spotted, can be treated successfully.

removing a small piece of tissue from the body so that a cytologist can examine the cells in more detail under a microscope. Cytologists who know the normal appearance of cell organelles can spot the abnormal organelles – the early stage of cancer. These cytological tests can be carried out very quickly – often whilst a patient is still on the operating table – with immediate feedback to the surgeon who can then decide how much tissue to remove. Confirmation of cancer almost always requires the judgement of a cytologist. The chance of survival from cancer frequently improves from 5% to 80% if the cancer is detected and treated in its early rather than later stages.

nucleic acids. Cancer cells can also differ from normal cells in other ways – often in appearance, sometimes in their biochemistry, and sometimes in the number of chromosomes in the nucleus. If the normal organisation of cells is changed in any way, cancer may be the result.

The appearance of cells under the light microscope can be used to diagnose the early stages of cervical cancer. Many other forms of cancer can be detected in their early stages by biopsy. This involves

Cancerous cells, tissues or organs are treated or removed. Research into the causes of cancer involves the use of a wide range of technology, including biochemistry, differential centrifugation and electron microscopy. These techniques have narrowed down the search to the cell nucleus and in particular to the malfunctioning of nucleic acids. Cures are perhaps not too far away.

Key ideas

- The genetic material of animal and plant cells is enclosed within a nuclear membrane.

- Organisms whose cells have a nuclear membrane and organelles such as mitochondria and endoplasmic reticulum are known as eukaryotes.

- Cyanobacteria and bacteria have no nuclear membrane, mitochondria or endoplasmic reticulum. They are known as prokaryotes.

- Prokaryotes have less compartmentalisation of reaction pathways than eukaryotes, and are therefore less efficient.

Blood and sweat

'I would never take drugs, that's really stupid. I'm not so desperate to win that I'd risk my health. But most of my friends are convinced that these new sports drinks improve performance – by keeping the body fluids in balance. I might use them – if I knew more about how they are supposed to work.'

Isostar Sport™ is one of several drinks that have recently become very popular with people who do aerobics or athletics.

Sports drinks all have one thing in common: they claim to be 'isotonic' and to provide replacement fluids and minerals that 'restore the body's balance'. Many athletes buy these drinks, which cost about 10% more than ordinary soft drinks, because advertisements stress the need for providing a balanced replacement of salts. But are they worth the extra money?

5.1 Learning objectives

After working through this chapter, you should be able to:

- **explain** that diffusion is the passive movement of substances along a concentration gradient;

- **explain** how osmosis is a special case of diffusion, depending on differences in water potential;

- **recall** the factors that affect the rate of diffusion;

- **use** the water potential equation to predict the net movement of water between two systems when the water potential of each is known;

- **explain** how the structure of a cell from the small intestine of a mammal enables it to absorb digested food products;

- **explain** how the structure of cell membranes relates to their ability to control the movement of substances;

- **explain** that active transport involves the movement of molecules or ions against a concentration gradient;

- **recall** the relationship between active transport and respiration;

- **explain** how the structure of a leaf enables the raw materials of photosynthesis to reach the chloroplasts in the leaf cells.

5.2 Sweating

During aerobics or athletics the body loses a lot of sweat. The loss of large quantities of sweat decreases athletic performance. Why does sweat have this effect?

Sweat is formed from the fluid part of blood – the **blood plasma**. The fluid lost in sweat needs to be replaced. However, it is not just water that is lost in sweat, mineral ions such as sodium (Na^+) and chloride (Cl^-) are lost too. Sweat tastes salty. If you have ever cut your lip you will know that blood tastes salty too.

All sports drinks contain similar amounts of mineral ions. The concentration of Na^+ and Cl^- ions in these drinks is very similar to the concentration of the ions in blood plasma (Table 1).

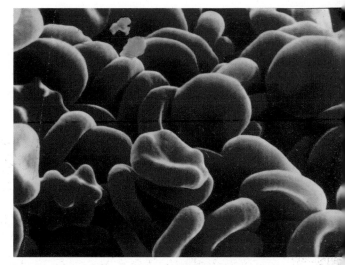

The shape of red blood cells depends on the concentration of ions in the blood plasma. The optimum biconcave shape provides the maximum surface area for the exchange of molecules. A high concentration of ions causes the red blood cells to become star-shaped. Magnification × 2800.

Table 1. Mineral ions			
Mineral ion	Na^+	Cl^-	K^+
Concentration in blood plasma (%)	0.35	0.35	0.02
Concentration in sweat (%)	0.15	0.2	0.02
Concentration in Isostar (%)	0.4	0.39	0.17

Isotonic drinks aim to replace the mineral ions lost from the blood plasma as a result of sweating, as well as the water. One of the reasons for doing this is to keep the red blood cells working efficiently. Red blood cells carry oxygen to the muscles – a drop in their efficiency could mean the difference between a gold medal and fourth place! This may explain why the level of hydration in the body affects performance.

1 Using Fig. 1, what is the relationship between the concentration of sodium chloride (NaCl) in the external solution and the volume of red cells?

A solution of concentration A (Fig. 1) will not cause any change in red blood cell volume. The solution is **isotonic** with the cell. Changes in the volume of the red blood cell are caused by differences in the rates at which water molecules enter and exit the cell. To work properly, the volume of red blood cells needs to be kept as constant as possible.

Fig. 1 Red cells and salt

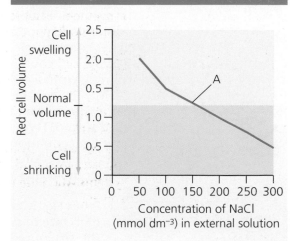

Red cell volume

Cell swelling

Normal volume

Cell shrinking

2.5
2.0
0.5
1.0
0.5
0

A

0   50 100 150 200 250 300

Concentration of NaCl ($mmol\ dm^{-3}$) in external solution

5.3 Osmosis and diffusion

The outer membrane of red blood cells lets some substances pass through it but not others. For example, water molecules can pass in but larger **solute** (dissolved) molecules such as glucose cannot. This means the membrane is a **differentially permeable membrane**. Where water passes from a region of higher concentration of water molecules to a region of lower concentration of water molecules through a differentially permeable membrane, the phenomenon is known as **osmosis** (Fig. 2). The water molecules pass through the membrane in both directions, but with a net movement towards the region of lower concentration. The larger molecules in the cell cannot move outwards through the membrane to balance the inflow of water.

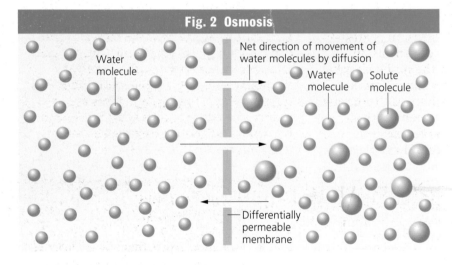

Fig. 2 Osmosis

Water molecule

Net direction of movement of water molecules by diffusion

Water molecule

Solute molecule

Differentially permeable membrane

We can begin to explain the change in the volume of the red blood cells in terms of osmosis. **Hypotonic** solutions have a higher concentration of water molecules than the cell contents so water molecules will move into a cell faster than out of the cell. This means the cell will swell. A cell that is full of water but has not burst is called **turgid**. **Hypertonic** solutions have a lower concentration of water molecules than the cell contents so the net movement of water molecules will be out of the cell.

 2 From Fig. 3, can you explain how a high rate of sweating might affect the size of red blood cells?

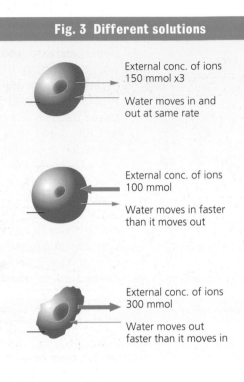

Fig. 3 Different solutions

External conc. of ions 150 mmol x3

Water moves in and out at same rate

External conc. of ions 100 mmol

Water moves in faster than it moves out

External conc. of ions 300 mmol

Water moves out faster than it moves in

In all liquids all the molecules are in constant, random motion. Solute molecules make weak chemical bonds with water molecules. Solutions with a large number of solute molecules will bind most of the water molecules. However, a solution with few solute molecules will only be able to bind a few water molecules – there are not enough solute molecules to go round. Water molecules bound to solute molecules move more slowly than free water molecules. This means that, in an area where some water molecules are free and others are bound, the free molecules will spread evenly throughout the area. We can see this effect as a net movement of water molecules from a region of high concentration of water molecules to a region of low concentration of water molecules.

The difference in concentration between two areas is called a **concentration gradient**. The movement of molecules along a concentration gradient is called **diffusion** (Fig. 4). Gases and molecules in solution move by diffusion. The movement of water by osmosis is a special type of diffusion.

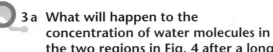

Q 3 a What will happen to the concentration of water molecules in the two regions in Fig. 4 after a long period of time?
b Explain the differences between osmosis and diffusion.

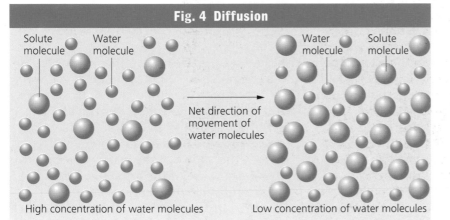

Fig. 4 Diffusion

Solute molecule Water molecule

Water molecule Solute molecule

Net direction of movement of water molecules

High concentration of water molecules

Low concentration of water molecules

The flavour and colour from tea diffuse through water.

Diffusion is a passive process, i.e. it requires no energy input from the cell for it to happen. The rate of diffusion is affected by the steepness of the concentration gradient and the size of the molecules that are diffusing. The greater the difference between two concentrations of a molecule, the quicker the net movement of those molecules from the area of high concentration to the area of low concentration.

The time taken for diffusion is quite short over microscopic distances, but over larger distances it is a different story. If a cell was 1 mm wide it would take a small molecule at least 4 minutes to get to the centre. Some cells, e.g. in the human gut and within plant leaves, have special adaptations to allow diffusion to happen quickly. Often these adaptations are to reduce the distance over which diffusion has to occur. There are examples later in this chapter.

Table 2. Diffusion distances and time	
Diffusion distance (μm)	Time required for diffusion by small molecules
1	0.4 ms
10	50 ms
100	5 s
1000 (1 mm)	8.3 min
10 000 (1 cm)	14 hours

Q 4 a From Table 2, calculate the speed of diffusion in cm s^{-1}:
(i) over 10 μm;
(ii) over 1 mm.
b How long will it take for an oxygen molecule to diffuse from the cell membrane to the centre of a cell 25 μm in diameter (this being the average size of a human body cell)?

Key ideas

- Solutions that are isotonic with red blood cells cause no change in volume. Solutions that are hypertonic make red blood cells lose water and shrivel up. Solutions that are hypotonic make red blood cells gain water and swell.

- Osmosis is a special type of diffusion.

- Molecules diffuse along concentration gradients, from regions of high concentration to regions of low concentration.

- The rate of diffusion can be increased by increasing the concentration gradient and decreasing the distance travelled.

5.4 Water potential

In order to predict whether water will diffuse into or out of cells by osmosis we need to give a numerical value to the effect of the solute molecules on the rate of diffusion of water molecules. You already know that when they form bonds with solute molecules, water molecules are less able to move than water molecules in pure water. The ability of water molecules to move is known as their **water potential**; the symbol for water potential is ψ. The water potential of pure water at atmospheric pressure is given the value 0. Since the water molecules in solutions cannot move as easily as in pure water, the water potential of solutions is always less than 0, i.e. the value of a solution is always negative. Water molecules always move to regions where the water potential is relatively more negative, i.e. has a lower water potential (Fig. 5). Why?

Fig. 5 Water potential

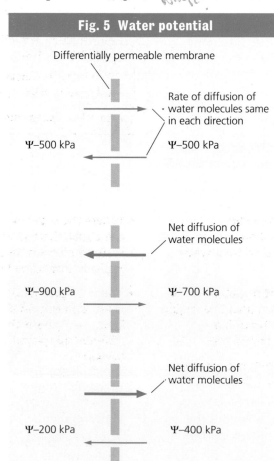

Differentially permeable membrane

Rate of diffusion of water molecules same in each direction

ψ–500 kPa ψ–500 kPa

Net diffusion of water molecules

ψ–900 kPa ψ–700 kPa

Net diffusion of water molecules

ψ–200 kPa ψ–400 kPa

The unit for potential is the kilopascal (kPa), which is a measure of the pressure acting upon the water molecules.

The water potential of a cell is affected by two factors:
• the concentration of solutes inside the cell;
• the pressure exerted on the cell contents by a stretched cell membrane or cell wall.

The concentration of solutes inside the cell is called the **solute potential** and is given the symbol ψ_S. It always has a negative value because the solute molecules reduce the ability of the water molecules to move – because of the attractive forces between solute and water molecules. The pressure exerted on cell contents is called the **pressure potential** and is given the symbol ψ_P. Pressure potential usually has a positive value. This is because the membrane or wall exerts a force on the cell contents to increase the concentration of water molecules in the cell. In effect it squeezes on the water, trying to push the water molecules out of the cell. We can calculate the value of the water potential of a cell by using the water potential equation.

$$\begin{aligned}\text{water potential of a cell} &= \text{solute potential} + \text{pressure potential}\\ \psi &= \psi_S + \psi_P\end{aligned}$$

This equation allows us to predict the direction of the net movement of water molecules between systems with different water potentials, for example between a red blood cell and a hypotonic solution (Fig. 6).

Fig. 6 Water potential equation

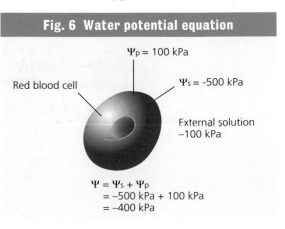

$\psi_P = 100$ kPa

Red blood cell

$\psi_S = -500$ kPa

External solution –100 kPa

$$\begin{aligned}\psi &= \psi_S + \psi_P\\ &= -500 \text{ kPa} + 100 \text{ kPa}\\ &= -400 \text{ kPa}\end{aligned}$$

The net movement of water molecules in this instance would be from outside the cell to within the cell, through the cell membrane.

5 If a solution had a ψ of –600 kPa, and a cell had a ψ_S of –500 and a ψ_P of 100, in what direction would the net movement of water be?

Our body cells only function normally if the water potential of the fluids surrounding them is kept relatively constant. When the blood plasma becomes a hypertonic solution due to loss of water by sweating, performance suffers. The American College of Sports Medicine recommends frequent drinks containing water, mineral ions and glucose for long distance runners (Table 3).

6 a Why do they recommend that the maximum concentration of sodium in the drink should be 200 mg per litre?
   b Why do the runners need sugar?

A runner in the London Marathon takes a drink from a 'water station' to help his performance.

Table 3. Guidelines for distance running

- It is the responsibility of the race sponsors to provide fluids which contain small amounts of sugar and mineral ions (less than 200 mg of sodium per litre of solution).

- Runners should be encouraged to ingest fluids frequently during competition.

- Race sponsors should provide 'water stations' at 3–4 km intervals for all races of 16 km or more.

Source: Fox, *Sports Physiology*, Holt Saunders, 1973

Key ideas

- Water molecules have less ability to move when in a solution than when in pure water. Their ability to move is called their water potential.

- Osmosis is the movement of water from a region of higher water potential to a region of lower water potential through a differentially permeable membrane.

- Water molecules always move to a region with a more negative water potential.

- Where the water potentials of two regions are equal, there is no net movement of water molecules because water molecules move in both directions at the same rate.

- The net movement of water molecules can only be predicted if the water potentials of both the systems that are separated by a differentially permeable membrane are known.

5.5 Specialised absorbing cells

The molecules of water and glucose and the ions in isotonic drinks are small and soluble. They are absorbed by cells lining the gut and passed into the blood plasma, where they are needed to help maintain performance. Most of the absorption takes place in the small intestine. The cells which line the small intestine are highly specialised to do this.

Q 7 Explain how folding the surface membrane helps intestinal cells to carry out their function.

Each of the three types of molecule – water, mineral ions and glucose – is absorbed in a different way through the membrane of the intestine cells. To understand how, you need to know the structure of the outer membrane of these cells.

The bulk of a cell membrane is made up of a double layer of phospholipids (Fig. 7). Molecules that are insoluble in lipids are not able to diffuse across the phospholipid regions of the membrane unless they are small enough to pass between the phospholipid molecules. Water molecules can diffuse between these phospholipid molecules.

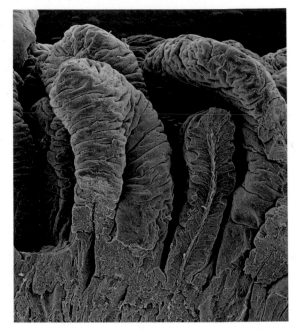

False colour scanning electron micrograph of a section through the wall of the human intestine showing many folded villi. Food molecules come into contact with the villi. Magnification × 70.

Intrinsic protein molecules within the phospholipid membrane provide transmembrane 'channels' through which small, water-soluble molecules such as glucose can diffuse (Fig. 8). Each substance probably has its own specific intrinsic protein molecule in the cell membrane. The proteins probably recognise their molecules by their shape – rather like enzymes can recognise substrate molecules. Since these protein molecules help other molecules to diffuse through the membrane, the process is known as **facilitated diffusion**. Like diffusion, facilitated diffusion only occurs down a concentration gradient and does not need a transfer of energy. Glucose and amino acids, which are insoluble in lipids, are examples of molecules that can diffuse through membranes in this way.

Mineral ions, however, usually do not pass through membranes in this way. The movement of ions across membranes is more complicated because of the charges they carry and because the cell often requires the ions to move against their concentration gradient.

Fig. 7 Phospholipid membranes

Outside the cell membrane

Intrinsic membrane proteins

Inside the cell membrane

Extrinsic membrane protein

Glycoprotein – a carbohydrate chain attached to a protein

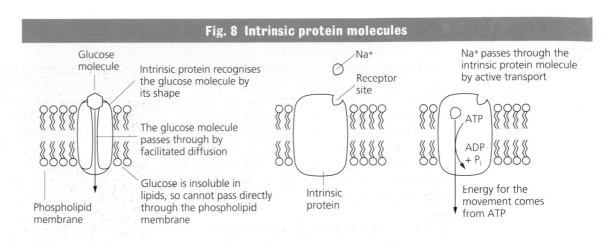

Fig. 8 Intrinsic protein molecules

Glucose molecule

Intrinsic protein recognises the glucose molecule by its shape

The glucose molecule passes through by facilitated diffusion

Glucose is insoluble in lipids, so cannot pass directly through the phospholipid membrane

Phospholipid membrane

Na+

Receptor site

Intrinsic protein

Na+ passes through the intrinsic protein molecule by active transport

ATP

ADP + P$_i$

Energy for the movement comes from ATP

Some intrinsic protein molecules act as molecular pumps, and allow the cell to accumulate ions against the concentration gradient, i.e. in the opposite direction to diffusion (Fig. 8). This is known as **active transport** and requires transfer of energy. The energy is provided by ATP, which is produced by cell respiration.

There are similar molecular pumps in the membrane for non-ionic substances such as glucose when these also need to be moved against a concentration gradient, such as the drink from a 'water station' which contains a low concentration of glucose.

8 Absorbing cells in the intestine have large numbers of mitochondria. Explain how this helps them to function efficiently.

5.6 Resourcing photosynthesis

Fig. 9 Leaf specialisations

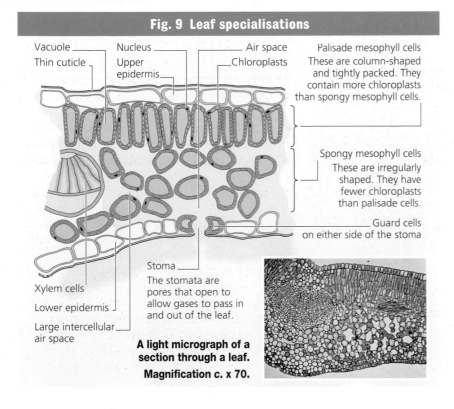

Vacuole

Thin cuticle

Nucleus

Upper epidermis

Air space

Chloroplasts

Palisade mesophyll cells
These are column-shaped and tightly packed. They contain more chloroplasts than spongy mesophyll cells.

Spongy mesophyll cells
These are irregularly shaped. They have fewer chloroplasts than palisade cells.

Guard cells on either side of the stoma

Stoma
The stomata are pores that open to allow gases to pass in and out of the leaf.

Xylem cells

Lower epidermis

Large intercellular air space

A light micrograph of a section through a leaf. Magnification c. x 70.

Plant cells also use diffusion and active transport to move molecules across their membranes. Plants make their own sugars, so they do not have the problem of absorbing sugars. But they do need to absorb the raw materials from which they make sugars. You will remember the overall equation for photosynthesis.

carbon + water + light → carbohydrate + oxygen
dioxide   energy

This process takes place in chloroplasts, mainly in the leaf cells. The structure of a leaf is adapted to get the raw materials to the chloroplasts, and to transport the sugar products away as efficiently as possible.

A plant leaf usually has a large surface area to absorb light and carbon dioxide, and is thin in order to reduce the distance over which carbon dioxide has to diffuse from the stoma to the chloroplasts. The light and carbon dioxide can therefore reach the chloroplasts quickly and easily.

9 How do the differences between palisade and spongy mesophyll layers enable the palisade layer to carry out more photosynthesis than the spongy mesophyll layer?

The water for photosynthesis moves from tubes called xylem vessels in the veins into the mesophyll cells by osmosis. The water in the xylem vessels has a lower concentration of mineral ions dissolved in it. Sugars are pumped from the mesophyll cells, against the concentration gradient, into phloem cells by active transport.

Other specialised absorbing cells in animals and plants also usually have both an increased surface area to allow an increase in the rate of diffusion and abundant mitochondria to provide, from respiration, the ATP to power the molecular pumps involved in active transport.

The water potential of fluids surrounding the cells of plants and animals needs to be kept within narrow limits in order for absorption, by diffusion, facilitated diffusion, osmosis and active transport, to work efficiently. Any disruption in the environment of a cell will cause a drop in its efficiency, as the concentration gradients will be altered. For plants this could mean reduction in growth rate due to reduced uptake of water and minerals. For athletes this could mean a reduction in performance and the last place in a race due to the loss of water and mineral ions in sweat.

We certainly need to replace the mineral ions and water that we lose through sweating, but it is the water that is the most important. The water potential of a system determines the net direction of movement of water and other molecules. You lose comparatively much more water than mineral ions in sweat. Is it really worth the extra money for the tiny amount of mineral ions in isotonic drinks?

Key ideas

- Most water-soluble molecules pass through specific intrinsic protein molecules in cell membranes by facilitated diffusion.

- Mineral ions are usually pumped across membranes against concentration gradients through other intrinsic protein molecules called molecular pumps.

- Active transport is the movement of ions and molecules against the concentration gradient. It requires energy.

- Organs may be modified for exchanging materials by diffusion.

- Cells may be specialised for absorbing materials by diffusion.

The development dilemma

Clearing areas for cattle ranching is destroying much of the rainforest in Brazil.

❝ Cutting edge ❞

Amazonia is at the cutting edge of the development dilemma, where northern money threatens southern lives and livelihoods. Western tax-payers who finance multinational lending agencies are being urged to question whether submerging the world's tropical forests under reservoirs, or encouraging indiscriminate burning to make vast, unproductive cattle ranches, is a good use of their money. The total effect of deforestation in Amazonia is equivalent to the intensity of 100 volcanoes, and accounts for a tenth of the world's atmospheric pollution.

Source: adapted from an article by Susan Griggs, *The Independent*, 26 July 1988

Why is deforestation in Amazonia so important to countries elsewhere in the world? Do you know why rainforests have such an impact on global climate, as well as on local climate and soil fertility? These rainforests are very productive and diverse, and the relationships between all the species very complex. Can this productivity be used sustainably?

❝ Diversity of life ❞

Hot, humid jungle has been standing on the world's equator for tens of millions of years. This very stability may be one of the causes of the almost unbelievable diversity of life that exists there today. The numbers are astounding. In one hectare of jungle, it is common to find well over a hundred different kinds of tall tree. And this richness is not restricted to plants. Over 1600 species of bird live in the jungles of the Amazon and the number of insects there is almost beyond computation. Entomologists in Panama collected over 950 species of beetle from just one species of tree.

Source: Attenborough, *The Living Planet*, Collins, 1984

This Atlantic rainforest in Rio de Janeiro State, Brazil, is full of life.

6.1 Learning objectives

After working through this chapter, you should be able to:

- **recall** that photosynthesis is the route by which energy enters ecosystems;

- **describe** the carbon cycle;

- **explain** how energy transfers through trophic levels in food chains and food webs and is dissipated;

- **recall** the relationship of pyramids of number, biomass and energy to their corresponding food chains and webs;

- **interpret** energy flow diagrams;

- **explain** how organic molecules are broken down in an ecosystem by microorganisms and how the materials in them are recycled;

- **know** the importance of nitrate, phosphate and magnesium in plants;

- **recall** the role of microorganisms in the carbon and nitrogen cycles;

- **understand** the relationships between organisms involved in nitrogen fixation.

6.2 The importance of rainforests

The timber from tropical rainforests is familiar all over the world, but the rainforests are also home to a wide variety of other useful species. These are essential to the local people and are the origin of many products manufactured and used daily in more developed countries. More than 50% of modern medicines come from the natural world, and many of these are from rainforest plants. Yet, less than 1% of rainforest plants have been screened for potentially useful products. As rainforests are cut down for timber or unsustainable agriculture, many species become extinct. How many of these species might contain a new drug for cancer treatment or a cure for AIDS?

Because the climate at the equator is hot and humid with plenty of sunlight, tropical rainforests are very productive. The sunlight provides a high energy input all year round that can be used by trees and other plants. The climate has also been stable for a very long time, allowing many species to evolve. The relationships between all the different species in a rainforest are very complex, and can be analysed in a variety of ways. The consequences of disturbing these relationships can harm the rainforest species directly, but it can also affect areas elsewhere in the world. For example, tropical rainforests help regulate climate and soil fertility, as well as providing an immense source of genetic diversity.

1 **Why do you think it is important to preserve rainforests, from a local and global point of view?**

6.3 The carbon cycle

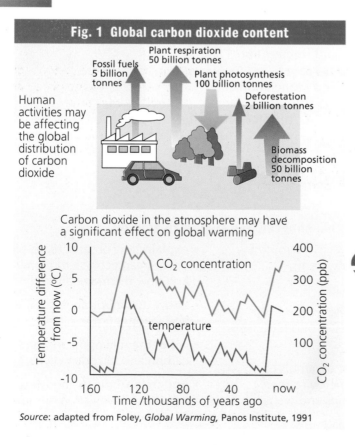

Fig. 1 Global carbon dioxide content

Plant respiration 50 billion tonnes

Fossil fuels 5 billion tonnes

Plant photosynthesis 100 billion tonnes

Deforestation 2 billion tonnes

Human activities may be affecting the global distribution of carbon dioxide

Biomass decomposition 50 billion tonnes

Carbon dioxide in the atmosphere may have a significant effect on global warming

CO_2 concentration

temperature

Source: adapted from Foley, *Global Warming*, Panos Institute, 1991

Trees are approximately 50% carbon. This carbon is the result of photosynthesis. Using energy from the Sun, trees absorb large quantities of carbon dioxide from the atmosphere, to make carbohydrate and other organic molecules. Carbon dioxide is an important **greenhouse gas**, that may be affecting the world's atmosphere by trapping heat and raising temperatures. This is known as **global warming**. Photosynthesis and respiration help keep the global content of carbon dioxide in equilibrium, but human activity may be upsetting that balance (Fig. 1).

2 **From Fig. 1, calculate the proportion of the increase in atmospheric carbon dioxide due to deforestation.**

The annual increase in the carbon dioxide content of the atmosphere for the whole planet is not as serious as Fig. 1 suggests. Phytoplankton are microscopic algae that live in the seas and oceans of the Earth. They take up carbon dioxide for photosynthesis and, even allowing for the amount lost by respiration, fix 4 billion tonnes per year. However, if we pollute the oceans and cause a drop in the size of the phytoplankton populations, this surplus may not be maintained. Increasing the level of carbon dioxide in the atmosphere may lead to a change in climate patterns.

The movement of carbon through living organisms can be summarised as the 'carbon cycle' (Fig. 2).

The death and excretion components in Fig. 2 are the same as the **biomass** decomposition in Fig. 1. Biomass is the mass of biological material of organisms. The microorganisms that are responsible for decomposition play a crucial role in the recycling of essential nutrients, and are mentioned in more detail later in this chapter. It is their respiration that releases much of the carbon back into the atmosphere as carbon dioxide.

3 An increase in the level of CO_2 in the air can increase the rate that carbon dioxide is taken out of the atmosphere. Explain why.

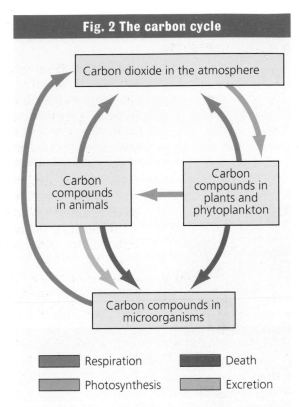

Fig. 2 The carbon cycle

Carbon dioxide in the atmosphere

Carbon compounds in animals

Carbon compounds in plants and phytoplankton

Carbon compounds in microorganisms

- Respiration
- Photosynthesis
- Death
- Excretion

Key ideas

- Energy enters ecosystems via photosynthesis.

- Carbon enters ecosystems via photosynthesis.

- Most of this carbon is eventually returned to the atmosphere through the respiration of plants, animals and microorganisms.

- Burning fossil fuels and deforestation increase the release of carbon dioxide back into the atmosphere.

6.4 Food chains and food webs

The carbon cycle gives an overview of the way in which carbon dioxide is fixed by plants, then transferred to animals. In the study of a particular ecosystem, e.g. a rainforest, we need to know exactly what eats what in order to work out the cycling of carbon and other minerals and the flow of energy.

We can represent the feeding relationships of organisms such as those in the photographs by means of **food chains**.

One food chain taken from the scenes below is:

> tree fruits → squirrel monkey → margay

The trees are called **producers** because, as a result of photosynthesis, they provide a source of food for other organisms. Producers are the only organisms in the food chain that fix carbon dioxide and give out oxygen. Our global atmosphere depends on the activity of the producers. The monkeys are **primary consumers** or **herbivores**, as they eat the producers directly. Margays are **secondary consumers** or **carnivores**, as they obtain their supply of food by eating primary consumers. The arrows in the food chain represent the flow of energy from the tree fruits to the monkey and finally to the margay.

A tamandua anteater feeds on termites.

A black-headed squirrel monkey feeds on tree fruits.

A margay hunts for prey such as monkeys and birds.

A great fruit-eating bat feeds on large fruit from trees.

A violet-eared humming bird visits a hibiscus flower for its nectar.

4 **Use information in the photographs to draw other food chains.**

We can link food chains into **food webs** (Fig. 3) in order to show the interrelationships between the organisms in different chains within the same ecosystem.

Some organisms can be both a primary consumer and a secondary consumer, or both a secondary consumer and a **tertiary consumer**, by being part of more than one food chain. **Omnivores** can eat either producers or consumers.

Fig. 3 Food webs

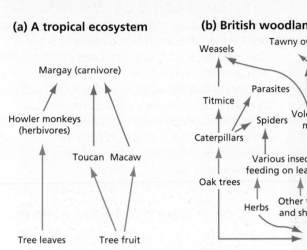

(a) A tropical ecosystem

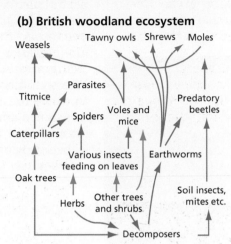

(b) British woodland ecosystem

5 a **Connect the food chains you drew in question 4 to form other food webs like that in Fig. 3a.**
  b **Use the information in Fig. 3b to draw food chains containing:**
     (i) four organisms;
     (ii) five organisms;
     (iii) six organisms.

6.5 Ecological pyramids

To compare food webs for different habitats we can ignore the different species and simply group together organisms that obtain their energy in similar ways – as producers, and primary, secondary and tertiary consumers. The levels of the pyramid are called the **trophic levels** of a food chain, trophic level 1 being the producers, trophic level 2 being the primary consumers, etc.

6 a **List the organisms at each level in the food webs for:**
     (i) tropical rainforest;
     (ii) British woodland.
  b **Write down any trends in the numbers of organisms at each level.**

Energy transfers from one trophic level to the next, but some is lost as heat at each level. There is therefore less energy available at each level.

When we include the numbers of plants in a trophic level, two major patterns of trophic level are found in natural ecosystems. Where the producers are small in size, they must be numerous if they are to support the larger primary consumers which feed on them. This gives a pyramid shape (Fig. 4). Where the producers are large, e.g. trees, and can support many, smaller primary consumers, the first trophic level is small, representing one plant, but above the producer level there is the normal pyramid shape (Fig. 4).

Fig. 4 Ecological pyramids

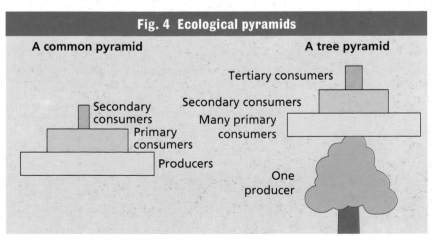

A common pyramid

Secondary consumers
Primary consumers
Producers

A tree pyramid

Tertiary consumers
Secondary consumers
Many primary consumers
One producer

Exceptions to these patterns in trophic levels may occur with parasites. For example, a few Buddleia plants may support large numbers of caterpillars. Ichneumon wasps lay several eggs in each caterpillar and the eggs hatch into larvae which feed as parasites inside the caterpillars. The ichneumon larvae themselves are often infested with large numbers of still smaller wasp larvae.

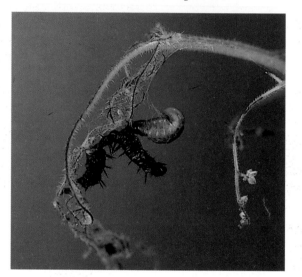

A larva and cocoon of an ichneumon wasp emerged from a peacock butterfly.

Buddleia → caterpillars → ichneumon larvae → wasp larvae

7 **Draw a pyramid of numbers for the parasitic food chain described above.**

Pyramids of numbers have their limitations when used to compare different ecosystems. It is not very useful to equate the number of grass plants in a meadow with the number of oak trees in a forest, nor the numbers of sticklebacks in a pond with the number of whales around Antarctica! One way of overcoming this problem is to use the biomass of all the organisms of one trophic level. The biomass is usually determined as dry mass (the mass after all the water in the organisms has been removed by gentle heating).

8 **Draw pyramids of biomass for the food chains outlined below.**

Oak tree → greenfly → ladybirds → blue tits
Buddleia → caterpillars → ichneumon larvae → wasp larvae

You might expect that all pyramids of biomass would have the shape of an upright pyramid and, in fact, most do. The exceptions are those from ecosystems based on phytoplankton. At certain times of the year these pyramids have an inverted shape. This is because of the sampling technique. Weighing the algae gives information only about the mass present at the instant the sample was taken. It gives no indication of the rate at which energy is being absorbed by the algae, nor of the rate at which it is being passed on to the consumers. Many of the algae are consumed almost as quickly as they are produced; one estimate of the life expectancy of an algal cell in summer is one day.

When the total amount of energy used by the different feeding types is calculated even phytoplanktonic systems give an upright pyramid – a pyramid of energy (Fig. 5).

Fig. 5 Pyramid of energy

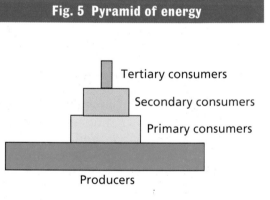

This type of pyramid enables us to compare the amount of energy that flows through different ecosystems. The more energy that flows through an ecosystem, the more productive it is. **Productivity** is the rate at which the energy entering an ecosystem is stored, and **net productivity** is the amount that is available to other trophic levels as food materials. Tropical rainforests are amongst the most productive ecosystems on Earth.

6.6 Energy flow

We can use an energy flow diagram to show what happens to the energy that flows through an ecosystem. **Net primary productivity** (NPP) is the amount of energy fixed in photosynthesis minus the amount lost by plant respiration.

$$\text{NPP} = \text{plant photosynthesis} - \text{plant respiration}$$

Although tropical rainforests have a very high productivity (Fig. 6), most of the energy fixed by the plants ends up as dead organic matter, much of which is fallen leaves. The energy then flows through the rest of the food chain. If tropical rainforest is replaced by grassland for feeding cattle, the energy flow is different.

Initially, it looks as though grassland is an improvement over rainforest because more of the energy from the plants is transferred to grazers. However, the NPP of the two systems is very different: 2200 g m^{-2} year^{-1} for the rainforest compared with 900 g m^{-2} year^{-1} for grassland in the first year after clearing the rainforest. Thereafter the productivity of the grassland decreases each year until it is no longer feasible to raise cattle there. Comparing shapes of energy flow diagrams is only useful if we know the value of the NPP.

Energy flow diagrams can also be constructed for individual animals (Fig. 7).

Fig. 7 Energy flow in animals

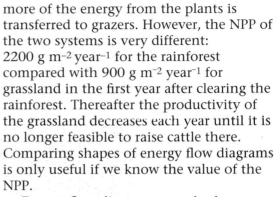

I = Intake
R = Respiration
A = Absorbed from food
F = Lost in Faeces
P = Passed on to next trophic level

Fig. 6 Energy flow in ecosystems

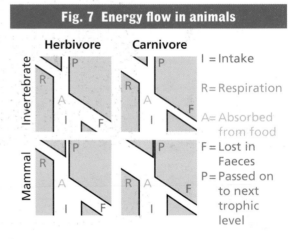

NPP = Net primary productivity
DOM = Dead organic material

9 List the major differences in energy flow through the two systems shown in Fig. 6.

10 a Can you suggest why the proportions of energy lost in the faeces and in respiration vary between herbivores and carnivores, invertebrates and mammals?

b Can you explain why there are seldom more than two stages involving vertebrate carnivores in a food chain?

Key ideas

- Feeding relationships can be summarised in food chains, food webs, pyramids of number and pyramids of biomass.

- All the energy that enters an ecosystem flows through each trophic level and is ultimately transferred to the environment.

- Trophic levels reflect the order of organisms within any food chain, web or pyramid.

- Energy flow through a community can be represented by pyramids of energy and energy flow diagrams.

6.7 Nutrient cycles

Rainforest trees can stand for over a hundred years, but eventually they will fall, whether or not at the hands of humans. Old branches and trunks become weakened by mould, fungi and the work of insects. Storms can cause the final fall, due to the volume of rain or a strike of lightning. Once on the ground, the fallen trunk becomes home to a variety of organisms, many of them invertebrates. Beetles, adult and larvae, will feed on the decaying wood, as will termites. The organisms that live on dead matter are called **detritivores**.

Fungi help a fallen tree decay in a subtropical rainforest in Australia.

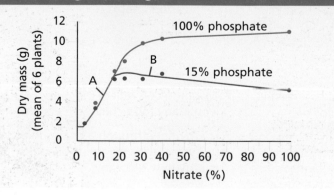

Dead plant tissue contains a large percentage of cellulose. Cellulose is the carbohydrate that makes up the plant cell walls and is very difficult to digest. Most detritivores cannot digest the cellulose because they cannot produce the enzyme cellulase. They often have microorganisms within their gut that do have the ability to break down the cellulose into its sugar monomers, which the detritivores can then absorb.

The climatic conditions of the rainforest also help the process of decay. The air is hot and humid, ideal for growth of bacteria, mould and fungi. Decomposition is therefore extremely rapid. It takes just 6 weeks for a leaf from a rainforest tree to decay completely, whereas an oak leaf in a temperate forest can take years. As decomposition occurs, the energy flowing through the system is used by respiration in microorganisms to break down complex organic molecules into carbon dioxide, water and inorganic ions. These nutrients can then be used by plants for photosynthesis to start the cycle again.

Q 11 Suggest some of the nutrients that are released during the decay process.

In order for trees and other plants to grow, they need:
• nitrate for amino acid production;
• phosphate for the production of amino acids and molecules such as ATP and $NADP^+$;
• magnesium for chlorophyll production.

Magnesium is usually absorbed from the soil as the Mg^{2+} ion. It forms part of the chlorophyll molecule; the first symptom of its deficiency is therefore chlorosis – yellowing of the leaves. It also activates many enzymes needed for photosynthesis.

Phosphorus is also usually absorbed from soil as the phosphate $H_2PO_4^-$ ion. Phosphates are involved in photosynthesis and respiration and form part of DNA and RNA molecules. Different concentrations of phosphate can limit how a plant absorbs nitrate (Fig. 8).

Fig. 8 Limiting effect of nutrients

100% phosphate

15% phosphate

Dry mass (g) (mean of 6 plants)

Nitrate (%)

Q 12 a What is limiting the growth of the plants at point A on the graph in Fig. 8, and at point B?
 b Why is this information useful to a farmer?

Nitrogen is found in all amino acids and proteins. Because enzymes are proteins, essential reactions may not occur if enzymes are not synthesised because of nitrogen deficiency.

Faeces, dead animals and dead plants all contain nitrogen compounds, but most of these compounds are insoluble and not available for immediate use. They are converted into soluble nitrates by a wide range of soil bacteria and fungi. These organisms secrete enzymes which convert the nitrogenous materials into soluble compounds, including ammonium compounds (Fig. 9).

Where soils are waterlogged and therefore there is no oxygen available for respiration, **denitrifying** bacteria use NO_3^- rather than oxygen as an electron acceptor for respiration. This reaction releases nitrogen gases into the atmosphere, i.e. nitrates are effectively lost from the soil.

Some prokaryotes, such as cyanobacteria and bacteria, can reduce N_2 to NH_3 by a process called **nitrogen fixation**. This process is carried out by bacteria such as *Azotobacter* in the soil and by bacteria living in symbiotic relationships with plants, particularly by *Rhizobium* which lives symbiotically inside the roots of legumes such as clover (Fig. 10). Nitrogen fixation occurs within the bacteria inside the plant cells. This effectively keeps the nitrates within the food web. The association between legumes and *Rhizobium* is an example of **mutualism**. In mutualism both organisms benefit from the relationship.

Q 13 Suggest ways in which each organism in Fig. 10 benefits from the relationship.

Fig. 10 Nitrogen fixation

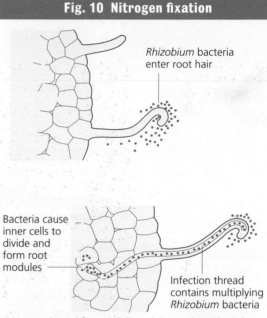

Rhizobium bacteria enter root hair

Bacteria cause inner cells to divide and form root modules

Infection thread contains multiplying *Rhizobium* bacteria

Source: adapted from Salisbury & Ross, *Plant Physiology*, Wadsworth, 1992

From respiration in bacteria

$$\text{Nitrogen in the atmosphere} \quad N_2 \xrightarrow{\substack{ATP \to ADP+P_i \\ NADH \to NAD^+}} NH_3 \quad \text{Ammonia now available for use by the plants}$$

From respiration in bacteria

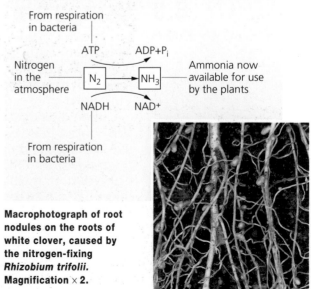

Macrophotograph of root nodules on the roots of white clover, caused by the nitrogen-fixing *Rhizobium trifolii*. Magnification × 2.

Fig. 9 Ammonification and nitrification

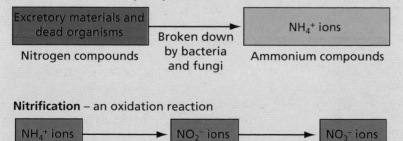

Nitrogen is usually absorbed by plants from the soil as nitrate (NO_3^-) or ammonium (NH_4^+) ions.

Ammonification – a hydrolysis reaction

Excretory materials and dead organisms	Broken down by bacteria and fungi	NH_4^+ ions
Nitrogen compounds		Ammonium compounds

Nitrification – an oxidation reaction

NH_4^+ ions	Nitrosomonas (bacteria)	NO_2^- ions	Nitrobacter (bacteria)	NO_3^- ions
Ammonium		Nitrite		Nitrate

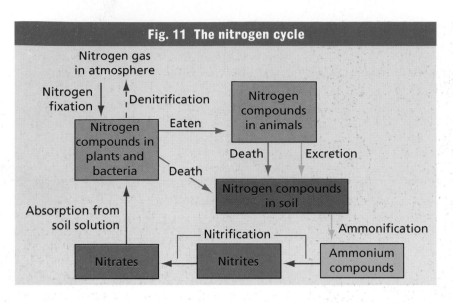

Fig. 11 The nitrogen cycle

The processes involved in the circulation of nitrogen are summarised by the nitrogen cycle (Fig. 11).

Rainforests and nutrients

The energy flowing through an ecosystem depends on the primary producers – the green plants. These plants need a good supply of energy, moisture and mineral nutrients to grow and transfer energy from sunlight into energy in plant tissues. Photographs of the rainforest always show lush green vegetation, and this often makes people think rainforest soil is very fertile.

However, rainforests grow in areas of very poor soil. How can we explain this?

When a leaf falls from a rainforest tree it decays very rapidly in the warm, wet conditions in the forest. The mineral ions in the dead leaf pass into the soil and are taken up by growing plants. So, most of the available minerals are locked up in the growing plants – the biomass. This is very different from forests in colder areas where decay can take much longer. Plants growing in these areas need a much higher level of mineral ions in the soil while they wait for dead leaves to decay. Rainforests cycle their minerals very rapidly and so can tolerate poor soil quality.

The climatic conditions in tropical rainforests also mean that the nutrients released by decomposition could be easily washed away into streams and rivers by the tropical rain storms. These mineral ions would then be lost to the ecosystem. In healthy, productive rainforest, younger trees with a dense mat of roots close to the surface of the soil absorb the released nutrients from the soil before they can be washed away. So trees keep these mineral ions in the ecosystem.

14 Suggest why the productivity of the grassland declines drastically in the years following rainforest clearance.

6.8 Using rainforests

As you can see, tropical rainforests are very important, not only to the species that live there, but on a worldwide scale. They act as 'sinks' that store carbon, reducing the level of carbon dioxide in the atmosphere. They also control drainage, soaking up rain fall like a sponge, and then releasing the water more slowly into the rivers. After deforestation, there are no trees to stop the torrential rain sweeping away the soil and the nutrients in it and flooding the rivers. The trees keep the mineral ions in the ecosystem, so they can provide the nutrients and energy to maintain the high productivity and diversity of species.

Destruction of the tropical rainforests means loss of the productivity of the

ecosystem, and loss of biodiversity, as well as affecting the soil fertility and climate. This productivity can be harvested sustainably, allowing the rainforests to continue to grow and flourish. Western money, for example, could be used to finance sustainable projects to ensure a healthy crop of latex from the rubber tree. Rubber is one of the most important materials in the industrialised world. Over half of the crop is used for making tyres, but some is also used in bubble gum and in other parts of the food industry. If we want to continue to eat Brazil nuts, sustainable projects must be developed to preserve the rainforest. The brazil nut tree is fertilised by a complex interrelationship between many

A rubber latex extractor at work with a rubber tree in the Amazonian rainforest.

animal and plant species. It cannot survive on plantations. The variety of other species that we rely on, e.g. cocoa and coffee, which can be found in rainforests needs to be conserved to safeguard the survival of plantations, and the flavour of the products! The people who live within the rainforests also need to be saved from extinction, as they know far more of the secrets of the rainforests than other humans.

There is a delicate balance between organisms and materials in an ecosystem. Human interference can upset this balance with potentially disastrous consequences both for the ecosystem and the whole planet. This does not just apply to tropical rainforests. Other forests and peatbogs (ancient, compressed plant remains), and the oceans, are all as important for diversity and climatic stability. Disrupting the flow of energy or recycling of nutrients in one ecosystem could affect others on a global scale.

 15 Explain why peatbogs are important in carbon cycling.

Key ideas

- Nitrogen and mineral ions are cycled between organisms and the environment.

- Microorganisms play a vital role in the cycling of carbon, nitrogen and mineral ions within ecosystems.

- In tropical rainforests, most of the mineral ions are stored in trees.

Controlling living systems

'An Olympic Gold-winning horse is worth a fortune in stud fees to its owner. I need to train the horses so that they can still win in hotter climates than they are used to, without coming to harm.'

Winning horses and hormone medicine depend on an understanding of control systems.

Virginia Leng on 'Murphy Himself' at the 1988 Badminton Horse Trials.

Most mammals have developed sophisticated controlling and regulating systems to maintain a constant internal environment. There is big money in applying an understanding of these systems. For example, an understanding of the working of the nervous system helps trainers to prepare their horses for competitions in hot climates.

Knowing how one set of hormones works to control the process of reproduction has lead to the development of the birth control pill. The birth control pill has provided big profits for its developers, and altered the control that women have over their lives. But how far should we go in artificially controlling body processes – in interfering with nature?

7.1 Learning objectives

After working through this chapter, you should be able to:

- **explain** why mammals use control systems to respond to the external environment;

- **explain** homeostasis, i.e. how control systems operate in mammals to maintain a constant internal environment;

- **explain** how mammals control their body temperature;

- **recall** that nervous communication involves the initiation of a nerve impulse;

- **recall** that nerve impulses often travel from a receptor to an effector via a coordinator;

- **interpret** behaviour in terms of stimulus, receptor, coordinator, effector and response;

- **recall** that hormones are chemicals secreted by endocrine glands and that they affect physiological activities;

- **explain** how luteinising hormone, follicle-stimulating hormone, oestrogens and progesterone regulate the mammalian oestrous cycle.

7.2 Cooling down

Intense heat and humidity could provide one test too many for horses at the Olympic Games in Atlanta in 1996. Researchers are desperately trying to find ways of keeping the horses cool.

Atlanta in July is the wrong time and place to hold an event in which horses gallop around a 7-kilometre cross-country course at an average speed of 34 kilometres an hour. The daytime temperatures can reach 30°C with humidities of up to 80%. There is just one compulsory rest of ten minutes after trotting and steeplechasing before the cross-country section.

Because of its size, the horse has a low surface area compared with the volume of its body. Each square metre of body surface must disperse the heat from about 100 kg of body tissue, compared with about 40 kg in human athletes.

Without some means of getting rid of this heat, the horse's body temperature would theoretically go up by 1°C every minute. The horse copes with this heat load through a phenomenal ability to sweat, losing up to 20 litres of fluid per hour. But in humid conditions this sweat may simply drip off rather than evaporating and cooling the horse.

To make matters worse, the fluid loss by sweating may cause dehydration, and the horse would quickly lose its ability to control its body temperature. From its normal level of 38°C, a horse's body temperature can rise safely to 42°C, but if it goes much higher signs of heat stress would appear. The horse would begin to stagger around and become a physical danger to itself and those around it. If left unchecked, the horse could lapse into a coma and die.

Source: adapted from an article by John Bonner, *New Scientist*, 26 March 1994

To cause this amount of suffering to a horse would be unacceptable. The financial loss to the owner would also be enormous! Should horses be made to compete if dehydration is the likely outcome? Can an understanding of temperature control mechanisms help to prevent such a tragedy?

Mammals try to keep a high, constant body temperature so that the enzyme-controlled reactions in their bodies always proceed at the optimum temperature.

1 From your work in Chapter 3, what will happen to the enzymes if the internal body temperature becomes too high?

In Chapter 5 you learned that loss of body fluids through sweating affects the performance of athletes. In the extract above you have just learnt that an exercising horse may lose up to 20 litres of sweat in one hour.

2 What serious effects can this excessive sweating have on the performance and health of the horse?

On a cool day mammals transfer energy as heat to the surroundings by convection and radiation (the amount of energy transfer by conduction is negligible). If the surrounding air is warmer than the mammal, energy transfers to the mammal in exactly the same way. One way a mammal can cool itself under these conditions is to produce sweat, which cools the body as it evaporates. If the conditions are too humid for the sweat to evaporate the mammal gets hotter and hotter and then suffers from heat stress.

These horses racing in Santa Anita, California have to be able to cope with the hot conditions.

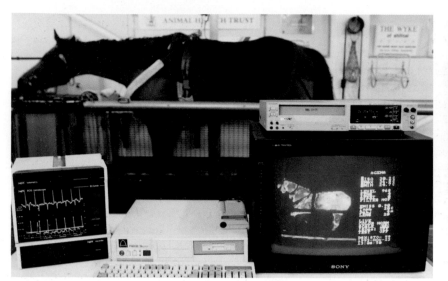

'Risky' on a treadmill at the Animal Health Trust.

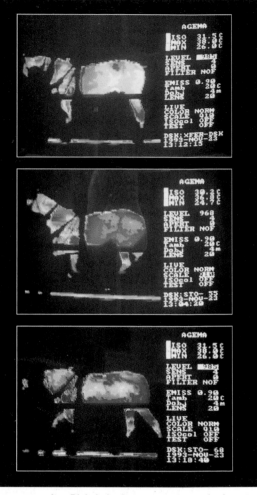

Cameras monitor Risky's body temperature as he is put through his paces on the treadmill.

Scientists at the Animal Health Trust at Newmarket, Suffolk, UK have been using a treadmill to investigate temperature regulation in horses. They have confirmed that in humid conditions horses produce enormous amounts of sweat, but still cannot cool easily between bursts of activity. They have also shown that there is a dramatic increase in the temperature of the skin as the horse attempts to lose energy. This is caused by an increase in the amount of blood flowing through the surface layers of the skin. This blood has been warmed as it passed through the muscles of the horse. Eighty per cent of the energy produced by the muscles during exercise is transferred to the blood as heat.

 3 a **Describe any patterns you can see on the monitors in the way that Risky's skin warms up during exercise.**
   b **Suggest an explanation for the patterns you have described.**

Mammals react to changes in the external environment, such as a rise in temperature, in order to keep their internal environment within safe limits. The process used to maintain the internal environment is known as **homeostasis**. Homeostasis involves a variety of control mechanisms. Sweating and increased skin temperature are switched on by homeostatic control mechanisms when the horse's body temperature rises.

The nervous system provides one mechanism for homeostatic control. At the base of the brain is a region called the **hypothalamus** (Fig. 1). This can be

Fig. 1 The hypothalmus

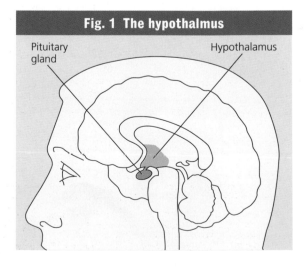

Pituitary gland

Hypothalamus

compared to the thermostat in a central heating system. There is an important difference, however. A room thermostat simply switches the circulating pump on when the room temperature falls, and off when the room temperature reaches the thermostat setting. So a thermostat can control the transfer of energy as heat into a room but it can do nothing to cool the room down on a hot day. In contrast, the hypothalamus has two regions:

- the **heat loss centre**, which switches on both sweating and increased blood flow through the skin surface if the body temperature rises;
- the **heat gain centre**, which can initiate responses to prevent the body cooling down too much.

The hypothalamus contains special nerve cells that monitor the temperature of the blood. These cells are known as temperature **receptors**. When an increase in blood temperature stimulates these cells, they send nerve impulses along nerve cells called **afferent** fibres. Afferent fibres carry nerve impulses to certain parts of the brain. They end in the heat loss and heat gain centres in the hypothalamus.

The heat loss centre is a special group of cells at the front of the hypothalamus. This centre is known as a **coordinator** because it coordinates what happens next. Nerve impulses are sent along nerve cells called **efferent** fibres. Efferent fibres take impulses away from the brain, to **effectors**. Effectors bring about a change or response. In this case the effectors are the sweat glands in the skin and the blood vessels that supply the skin. When these nerve impulses arrive, the sweat glands increase their production of sweat and the blood vessels widen. The widening of blood vessels is a process known as **vasodilation** (Fig. 2). Sweating and vasodilation are both processes to help the body cool down.

Q 4 Draw a flow chart that shows the sequence of events as a horse heats up beyond its normal body temperature.

To replace the fluid lost from the blood as sweat, the horse draws on the water present in its huge gut – up to 10% of a horse's weight is the water in its gut. However, this does little to replace the loss of vital mineral ions and it is the loss of these ions that causes most of the problems of heat stress.

In horses that have drawn too much water from the gut, movement of food materials through the gut stops. A veterinary can detect this using a stethoscope. Another useful indicator might be congestion in the mucous membranes of the nose and other air passages.

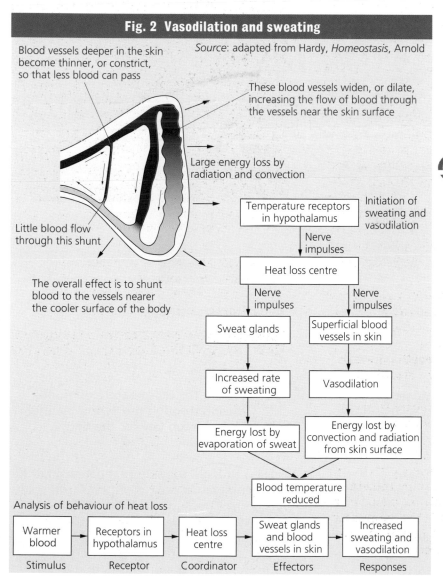

Fig. 2 Vasodilation and sweating

Source: adapted from Hardy, *Homeostasis*, Arnold

Blood vessels deeper in the skin become thinner, or constrict, so that less blood can pass

These blood vessels widen, or dilate, increasing the flow of blood through the vessels near the skin surface

Large energy loss by radiation and convection

Little blood flow through this shunt

The overall effect is to shunt blood to the vessels nearer the cooler surface of the body

Temperature receptors in hypothalamus → Initiation of sweating and vasodilation

Nerve impulses

Heat loss centre

Nerve impulses → Sweat glands → Increased rate of sweating → Energy lost by evaporation of sweat

Nerve impulses → Superficial blood vessels in skin → Vasodilation → Energy lost by convection and radiation from skin surface

Blood temperature reduced

Analysis of behaviour of heat loss

Warmer blood	Receptors in hypothalamus	Heat loss centre	Sweat glands and blood vessels in skin	Increased sweating and vasodilation
Stimulus	Receptor	Coordinator	Effectors	Responses

At the University of Sydney, Australia, David Hodgson has been looking at ways of rehydrating horses. His initial studies have shown that warm isotonic fluid is absorbed the quickest. A horse could absorb between 6 and 8 litres of this fluid into the blood during the compulsory ten-minute rest period. However, the horses may need special training to encourage them to drink at this stage in a competition.

5 Why is isotonic fluid better than water?

Some fur-covered mammals like dogs and cats often do not possess sweat glands.

To lose energy these animals breathe rapidly but shallowly; the rapid passage of air cools the blood in the blood vessels surrounding the mouth and lungs. This process is called **thermal panting**.

6 a Suggest a reason why fur-covered mammals often do not possess sweat glands.
b How will licking saliva over its body help a kangaroo rat cool down?
c How does wallowing help a hippopotamus to cool down:
(i) whilst in the water;
(ii) once back on the river bank?

A dog may pant up to 300 times a minute on a hot day.

A hippopotamus takes a bath when it is too hot.

The kangaroo rat produces a lot of saliva on a hot day – then licks this all over its body.

7.3 Keeping warm

So far we have only considered what happens when mammals such as horses overheat. In winter most mammals have the opposite problem: they need to conserve body energy.

Again, it is receptors in the hypothalamus that detect a fall in blood temperature. This time the receptors send nerve impulses along afferent fibres to the heat gain centre in the rear of the hypothalamus.

7 A fall in the temperature of blood flowing through the hypothalamus might be too late for the body. Explain why.

Receptors in the skin that detect a fall in skin temperature are called peripheral cold receptors. They are probably more important than the receptors in the hypothalamus. When stimulated by a fall in skin temperature they send nerve impulses along afferent fibres to the heat gain centre. This centre coordinates the responses to the cold conditions. It inhibits the heat loss centre and passes impulses to a range of effectors across the body:

- muscles in the tiny arteries supplying the superficial blood vessels;
- the hair erector muscles;
- the skeletal muscles;
- the brown fat tissue;
- the adrenal and thyroid glands.

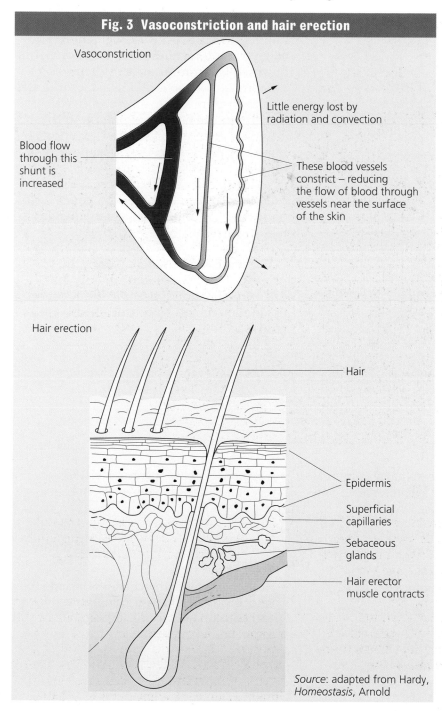

Fig. 3 Vasoconstriction and hair erection

Vasoconstriction

Little energy lost by radiation and convection

Blood flow through this shunt is increased

These blood vessels constrict – reducing the flow of blood through vessels near the surface of the skin

Hair erection

Hair

Epidermis

Superficial capillaries

Sebaceous glands

Hair erector muscle contracts

Source: adapted from Hardy, *Homeostasis*, Arnold

Impulses reaching the tiny arteries that supply the superficial blood vessels cause them to constrict. This process is known as **vasoconstriction** (Fig. 3).

Each hair in mammalian skin has a muscle attached near its base (Fig. 3). When a nerve impulse arrives from the hypothalamus, the hair is pulled upright. This process is known as **hair erection**. You have probably noticed this on your own skin – a 'goose pimple' is a part of the skin where a hair has been pulled upright. The effect of all the hairs in the skin being pulled upright is to trap a layer of air next to the skin. Air is a poor conductor of heat, so the layer of trapped air acts as an insulator, reducing energy transfer by radiation and convection. This method of conserving energy is only important in fur-covered mammals – it is of little value to humans. But in mammals such as the arctic fox, the insulation provided by the trapped air is so efficient that the animal does not begin to increase heat production until the temperature drops to –40°C.

Arctic foxes can survive a temperature of –80°C for up to an hour without a drop in core blood temperature; a human would be dead in minutes.

Impulses reaching the skeletal muscles cause them to contract spasmodically. We call this shivering. Cell respiration produces heat as a waste product. Shivering muscles have a high rate of respiration to release the energy for muscle contraction. The extra heat released transfers to the blood passing through the muscles.

Some mammals, including some humans, have layers of a special tissue called brown fat situated under the skin. When impulses arrive from the hypothalamus, the cells in this tissue rapidly oxidise fatty acids to release energy as heat. The position of this tissue – just under the skin – means that it acts rather like an electric blanket. Many hibernating mammals can switch on this 'electric blanket' during particularly cold weather to prevent frostbite or freezing to death.

The adrenal gland and the thyroid gland are both **endocrine glands**. Endocrine glands pass their secretions, chemicals called **hormones**, directly into the blood system. Hormones are chemicals that are transported by the blood to other parts of the body, where they affect physiological processes.

The adrenal and thyroid glands are important in temperature regulation. The adrenal gland secretes many hormones, one of which is **noradrenaline**. When noradrenaline reaches body tissues it causes an almost immediate, but short-lived, increase in the rate of respiration in the cells. The energy released in respiration is transferred as heat to the blood passing through these tissues.

The thyroid gland secretes a hormone called **thyroxine**. This has the same effect on the rate of respiration as noradrenaline, but the effect is slower and more prolonged.

All these responses are part of the process of **thermoregulation** (Fig. 4). Thermoregulation is a homeostatic process used by mammals to control their body temperature.

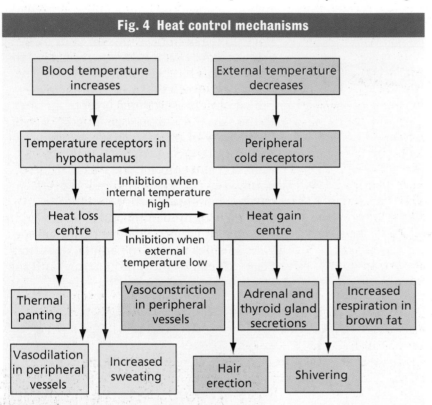

Fig. 4 Heat control mechanisms

Source: adapted from Hardy, *Homeostasis*, Arnold

Key ideas

- The body responds to external and internal stimuli in order to keep the internal environment within close limits.

- Homeostasis is the maintenance of a constant internal environment.

- The hypothalamus contains the coordinators for temperature regulation.

- Receptors send nerve impulses to a coordinator in the brain; the coordinator sends nerve impulses to the effector.

- Effectors may include endocrine glands and/or muscles.

- A response usually involves stimulus → receptor → coordinator → effector → response.

- Energy-loss mechanisms include increased rate of sweating, vasodilation and thermal panting.

- Heat-conservation mechanisms include vasoconstriction, hair erection, shivering and hormone-induced increased rate of respiration in the tissues.

- Endocrine glands secrete hormones that help control body processes.

7.4 Control of the oestrous cycle

Despite its unrivalled popularity as a contraceptive, the pill remains a variation on a now antiquated theme. Developed in 1951 it has become the Morris Minor of pharmaceuticals. Yet compared to other methods of contraception, this ageing product of post-war chemistry still looks positively high-tech.

The lack of progress since 1951 cannot be blamed on the indifference of scientists. In recent years, researchers have developed new hormone-based methods that would be safer and more pleasant to use than today's option. A 'male' pill is now a real possibility. In low doses the compound RU486, infamous as the controversial 'abortion pill', looks promising as a new contraceptive for women. And both men and women could benefit from novel contraceptive pills that work by interfering with gonadotrophin, a hormone released inside the brain that acts to control fertility.

But without the wholehearted backing of the pharmaceutical industry, none of these developments will ever reach the market. And that is the problem. Most of the leading pharmaceutical companies have stopped investing in contraceptive research and development. Nowhere is that more obvious than in the USA, where companies have been scared off contraception research by the vigorous campaigning of pro-life activists and the prospect of having to pay out millions of dollars to women who claim that a contraceptive product made them ill. The powerful 'right-to-life' movement in the USA has opposed those advocating RU486 as an abortion pill. The drug's image is now so tarnished that it may never see the light of day there as a contraceptive.

There have been many reactions to the 'combined oral contraceptive' that was introduced more than 40 years ago. This cocktail of oestrogen and progestogen – a synthetic version of the natural progesterone – prevents the monthly release of a fertiliseable egg and has been taken by millions of women. But over the years it has been, albeit controversially, linked to potentially fatal blood clots and cancers. The spectre of a fresh set of law suits inspired by a male hormonal contraceptive or a new female one fills drug companies with horror.

However, if scientists are right about new contraceptives that are being developed, they may not only be safer than the old ones but may even enhance health by reducing the risk of cancer or heart disease. This is what most frustrates biologists about the loss of nerve in the drug industry. It is also the reason why some of them are persevering.

Source: adapted from an article by Gail Vines, *New Scientist*, 30 April 1994

Contraceptive pills contain one or more synthetic female sex hormone.

Endocrine glands and the hormones they secrete are also involved in the control and coordination of the oestrous cycle of mammals. Research into how these hormones work has lead to the manufacture of birth control pills. However, controversy exists about the moral and physiological effects of the pill.

Q8 The original contraceptive pill was first tested on poor women in Puerto Rico – a developing country. Why do you think these women were chosen? What is your opinion on the ethics of this testing?

Female fertility is controlled naturally by hormones. In humans, the hormones cause an egg to mature and then be released from an ovary once every month. This occurs from puberty through to menopause.

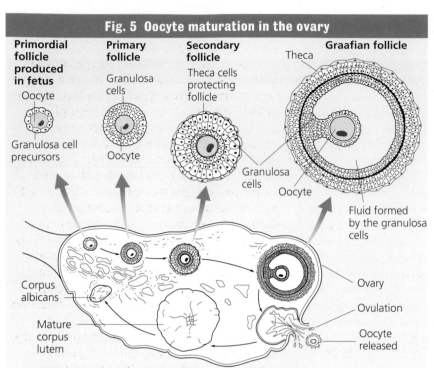

Fig. 5 Oocyte maturation in the ovary

Primordial follicle produced in fetus
Oocyte
Granulosa cell precursors

Primary follicle
Granulosa cells
Oocyte

Secondary follicle
Theca cells protecting follicle
Granulosa cells
Oocyte

Graafian follicle
Theca
Oocyte
Fluid formed by the granulosa cells

Corpus albicans
Mature corpus lutem

Ovary
Ovulation
Oocyte released

Source: Berne and Levy, *Principles of Physiology*, Wolfe, 1990

The eggs develop from cells in the ovaries called **primary oocytes** (Fig. 5). At the beginning of puberty a female human has about 400 000 oocytes in her ovaries. However, not all these develop.

Follicle cells that surround an oocyte divide, grow and eventually cause the release of the oocyte. After the release of the oocyte, these follicle cells continue to develop into the **corpus luteum** – a hormone-secreting structure that is very important during pregnancy. All these events are controlled by hormones. Hormonal contraceptive pills seek to disrupt the natural processes so that the oocyte is not released. To understand how this works, we must consider how the changing concentration of natural hormones in the blood brings about the release of an egg.

The menstrual cycle in the 'average' woman lasts 28 days (although very few women have a cycle that lasts exactly 28 days). This menstrual cycle is divided into three phases:
- follicular, where the follicle cells divide, grow and produce hormones;
- ovulatory, where the oocyte is released;
- luteal, where hormone production by the follicle cells increases.

Follicular phase

A rise in the plasma concentration of a hormone called **follicle-stimulating hormone** (FSH) starts this phase (Fig. 6). The rise in plasma FSH concentration begins one day before menstruation starts and continues until half way through the follicular phase. FSH is secreted by the **pituitary gland**, which is situated at the base of the brain under the hypothalamus. Look back at Figure 1 on page 68 to see how closely the hypothalamus and pituitary are linked. It is the hypothalamus that stimulates the secretion of FSH when it produces a hormone called **gonadotrophin-releasing hormone** (GnRH). The pituitary gland and the hypothalamus are both endocrine glands.

FSH stimulates a group of follicle cells, in one ovary, to grow and divide. Some of these follicle cells, the **granulosar cells**, begin to secrete ever increasing amounts of hormones called **oestrogens**.

The pituitary gland responds to the rising levels of oestrogens in the plasma by:
- inhibiting the production of FSH;
- stimulating the production of another hormone, **luteinising hormone** (LH).

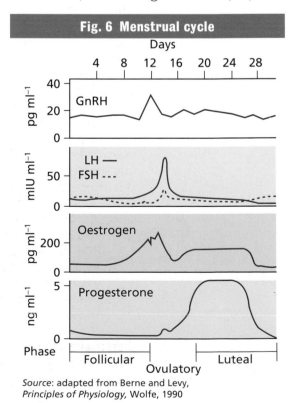

Fig. 6 Menstrual cycle

Days
4 8 12 16 20 24 28

GnRH (pg ml⁻¹): 40, 20, 0

LH — FSH --- (mIU ml⁻¹): 50, 0

Oestrogen (pg ml⁻¹): 200, 0

Progesterone (ng ml⁻¹): 5, 0

Phase: Follicular Ovulatory Luteal

Source: adapted from Berne and Levy, *Principles of Physiology*, Wolfe, 1990

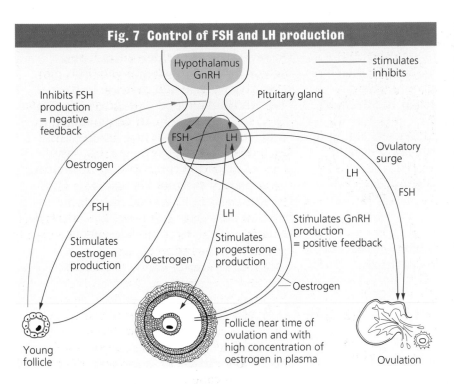

Fig. 7 Control of FSH and LH production

Hypothalamus GnRH

— stimulates
— inhibits

Pituitary gland

Inhibits FSH production = negative feedback

Oestrogen

FSH

LH

Ovulatory surge

LH

FSH

Oestrogen

FSH

Stimulates oestrogen production

LH

Stimulates progesterone production

Stimulates GnRH production = positive feedback

Oestrogen

Oestrogen

Young follicle

Follicle near time of ovulation and with high concentration of oestrogen in plasma

Ovulation

Most of this LH is stored in the pituitary gland rather than released into the blood plasma during this phase of the cycle. However, the slightly rising plasma concentration of LH stimulates the granulosar cells to produce small amounts of another hormone, called **progesterone**. This hormone becomes important in the luteal phase.

The inhibition of FSH production by rising levels of oestrogen illustrates a very important principle in control systems – **negative feedback** (Fig. 7). Negative feedback is a control system term that means that the output from a system tends to slow down or stop the system working. An example is the heater–thermostat system. An increase in temperature brought about by the heater results in the thermostat switching off the heater. Similarly, an increase in oestrogen levels brought about by FSH eventually switches off FSH production. FSH stimulates the production of oestrogen; oestrogen in turn inhibits the production of FSH.

Ovulatory phase

When the plasma concentration of oestrogen reaches the critical level of 200 pg cm^{-3}, it stimulates the production of GnRH by the hypothalamus. This effect is enhanced by the small rise in plasma progesterone concentration. The increased concentration of GnRH stimulates the release of the LH, built up in the pituitary gland, into the plasma. It also stimulates a temporary increase in FSH production and release into the plasma. The high plasma concentration of oestrogen actually enhances FSH production in this phase of the cycle. This is an example of **positive feedback** (Fig. 7). Positive feedback is the opposite of negative feedback – increased output results in further increases in output. You may have noticed this effect when a microphone is placed in front of a loudspeaker in the same amplification system. The microphone picks up sound from the speaker – this sound is again amplified. The result is usually a deafening whistle!

There is therefore a sudden surge in the concentrations of FSH and LH in the plasma on approximately day 14 of the cycle. This is called the 'ovulatory surge'. The high levels of FSH and LH in the plasma cause the enlarged follicle to burst and release the oocyte into the **fallopian tube**. The oocyte, or egg, then passes down the fallopian tube towards the **uterus**. If a sperm meets the oocyte during the next 12–24 hours fertilisation may occur and the woman will become pregnant.

A cause of infertility in some women is low FSH production – too low to stimulate a follicle to grow. This may be treated by FSH injections. If the FSH dose is miscalculated, several follicles may grow, each releasing an egg.

Q9 **What is the likely effect of several follicles growing? Why?**

Luteal phase

The ovulatory surge of LH stimulates the granulosar cells to form the corpus luteum. The LH also stimulates these cells to increase progesterone production greatly and to increase oestrogen production, although to a lesser extent. These high levels of oestrogen and progesterone inhibit FSH and LH production.

Q10 **What type of feedback is this? Explain the reason for your answer.**

The levels of FSH and LH fall and cannot maintain the activity of the corpus luteum cells, so these cells begin to wither. Progesterone and oestrogen secretion therefore declines. This removes the hormones that were inhibiting FSH production and the cycle begins all over again.

The oestrogen–progesterone cocktail pill that has been in use for the last 40 years works on the principle derived from the luteal phase – that high plasma levels of oestrogen and progesterone levels inhibit FSH and LH production.

Q 11 Explain how this inhibition prevents a woman becoming pregnant.

These pills have become almost 100% effective in preventing pregnancy. However, there are side-effects. These include nausea and weight gain but, more seriously, an eightfold increase in the risk of death from a blood clot lodging in the blood vessels of the heart or the lungs.

RU486 seems to act in a different way. A small dose – as little as 2 µg a day – can prevent ovulation, probably by preventing the ovulatory surge of LH and FSH. Thus the woman is not exposed to high plasma levels of oestrogen and progesterone, with their possible dangerous side-effects.

7.5 Effects of hormones on the uterus

So far we have only considered the interrelationships of the hormones. Oestrogens and progesterone have important effects on the uterus, both during the normal menstrual cycle and during pregnancy.

The menstrual cycle
The function of the uterus is to nourish and protect a developing fetus. The lining of the uterus, the **endometrium**, is specialised to do this. At the beginning of the menstrual cycle the rising plasma levels of oestrogens (Fig. 8) produced by the follicles in the ovary cause the endometrium to increase in thickness. Glands in the endometrium enlarge and blood vessels begin to elongate.

After ovulation the increasing plasma progesterone levels cause the endometrial glands to become twisted and to accumulate glycogen. The glands then begin to secrete a nutritive fluid, ready to receive a fertilised egg. If a fertilised egg is not received in the endometrium, the corpus luteum stops secreting progesterone and oestrogen. The endometrial glands then stop secreting nutrients. The lowering plasma levels of progesterone and oestrogen result in the contraction of the arteries in the endometrium. The loss of blood supply causes the tissue to die and the surface layers of tissue are shed, along with blood clots, as the menstrual flow (menstruation).

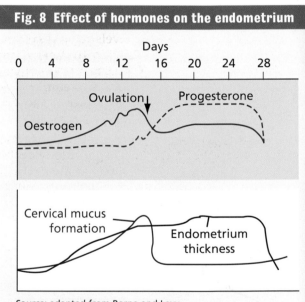

Fig. 8 Effect of hormones on the endometrium

Source: adapted from Berne and Levy, *Principles of Physiology*, Wolfe, 1990

Pregnancy
If fertilisation does occur, the fertilised oocyte divides continually to form a ball of cells called a **blastocyst**. Some of these cells will lead to the formation of the actual fetal tissues. Others form the membranes that surround the fetus. One of these membranes becomes specialised for exchanging materials between the blood of the fetus and the mother. This membrane is known as the **placenta**.

The early placental cells secrete a hormone called **human chorionic gonadotrophin** (HCG) (Fig. 9). This is the key hormone of pregnancy. It mimics the effect of LH: it causes the corpus luteum in the ovary to continue to secrete both oestrogen and progesterone, rather than wither.

Q 12 What effect will this have on the endometrium of the uterus?

Pregnancy test kits usually work by detecting the presence of HCG in the woman's urine – it can be detected within 8 days of conception.

Later in pregnancy, the placenta secretes its own progesterone to augment that produced by the corpus luteum. Eventually a fall in HCG levels leads to the corpus luteum wasting away, but by this time the placenta is producing sufficient progesterone on its own. High plasma levels of progesterone are essential to maintain the endometrium during pregnancy. Oestrogens secreted by the corpus luteum during pregnancy make the uterus grow to accommodate the developing fetus.

Parents-to-be attend antenatal clinics so that they can learn about the changes that have happened to the woman's body, and the changes that will happen, and how to respond to those changes.

Q 13 Explain in terms of hormones and 'feedback' why a woman cannot usually conceive a second child whilst she is pregnant.

An understanding of the mechanism of hormonal control enabled scientists to develop the birth control pill, which has had enormous social effects, mainly in the freedom of women. The pill gave them control over conception rather than relying on the man to use, for example, a condom. The pill is not without side-effects, but smaller doses have reduced the risks considerably. Artificial hormones such as RU486 might reduce these risks even further.

When women reach middle age, sex hormone production declines. This can have some deleterious effects on the body. One possible effect is osteoporosis – which can make the bones become brittle. This can be prevented by giving women oestrogens and progesterones when natural production declines. This treatment is known as **hormone replacement therapy** (HRT). Research in this area is leading to the conclusion that sex hormones are not just about controlling the menstrual cycle and pregnancy – they affect much wider areas of a woman's body. Perhaps all hormones do this. Each hormone has its own special target, but the hormones work together to maintain the smooth running of the body's internal environment.

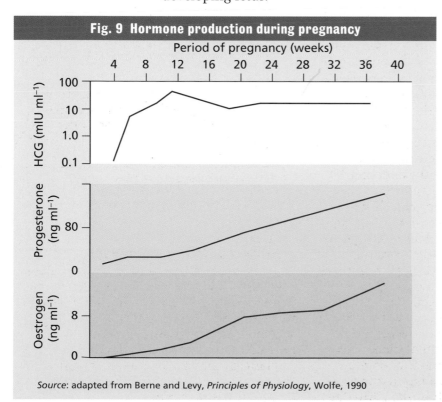

Fig. 9 Hormone production during pregnancy

Period of pregnancy (weeks)

Source: adapted from Berne and Levy, *Principles of Physiology*, Wolfe, 1990

Key ideas

- The oestrous cycle in human females is controlled by hormones.

- GnRH, secreted by the hypothalamus, stimulates the production of FSH by the pituitary gland.

- FSH stimulates the maturation of a follicle once a month in one of the ovaries.

- The maturing follicle secretes oestrogens, which cause the endometrium of the uterus to increase in thickness; they also stimulate the production of LH by the pituitary body.

- Due to negative feedback, increasing amounts of oestrogen inhibit the secretion of FSH.

- Due to positive feedback, high concentrations of oestrogen cause the ovulatory surge of FSH and LH, which in turn causes ovulation.

- LH causes the follicle to become the corpus luteum and stimulates the production of progesterone by the corpus luteum.

- Progesterone stimulates the endometrial glands to secrete a nutritive fluid for the fertilised oocyte.

- Falling levels of FSH and LH cause the corpus luteum to wither, resulting in menstruation.

- The placental cells of an early fetus secrete HCG to maintain the action of the corpus luteum in the early stages of pregnancy.

- The placenta secretes progesterone to maintain the endometrium during the remainder of the pregnancy.

8 Genetic engineers

'Tracey', a transgenic sheep, with two lambs.

A present-day beet sugar factory.

Scientists at Pharmaceutical Proteins in Edinburgh have a sheep called Tracey. In each litre of her milk – thanks to gene transfer – are 35 grams of a protein called human alpha-1-antitrypsin, which can save the lives of children who have cystic fibrosis.

Laboratories can extract the protein from human blood at enormous expense and in limited quantities, but Tracey and her fellows churn it out every day, just from grass. They have a golden future!

By the end of the decade farmers could also be sowing sugar beet and reaping granules of plastic. The plastic – known as PHB for short – is a feedstock for the chemical industry: the Germans, for instance, turn it into shampoo. Farmers could be doing this because it would be cheaper to convert carbon from sucrose or starch in a real plant than in a chemical plant. They will be able to do it because of a new understanding of DNA, the genetic code. Industry is already using a bacterium to make PHB in fermenters, in the way microbes make beer. American scientists have snipped two genes from the bacterium and inserted them into a weed and watched the plant grow PHB in its leaves. The next trick is to insert the genes into plants that make a lot of starch and sugar, such as sugar beet.

Today plastics are made from feedstocks of coal or petroleum, which are fossil plants, altered by time and pressure. All the genetic scientists are doing is finding a quicker route from field to factory: about 100 million years quicker.

The PHB gene did not have to be invented. Nature had already done that. Nobody had to invent the Tracey protein either. Most humans have it.

Source: adapted from an article by Tim Radford, *The Guardian*, 21 July 1993

Genetic engineering is a powerful technology. How does it work, and can it be controlled?

8.1 Learning objectives

After working through this chapter, you should be able to:

- **describe** the structure of DNA using simple diagrams;

- **explain** how DNA acts as a genetic code by determining the sequence of amino acids in proteins;

- **explain** how DNA replicates;

- **interpret** the experimental evidence for the semi-conservative replication of DNA;

- **explain** how new alleles can arise as a result of genetic mutations;

- **explain** how a change in the sequence of nucleotides in a gene may change the amino acid sequence in a protein and the way in which the protein functions;

- **explain** the roles of DNA, mRNA and tRNA in the transcription and translation stages of protein synthesis;

- **relate** the structures of DNA, mRNA and tRNA to their functions.

8.2 Genes and proteins

Each of us has many thousands of genes, which contain the instructions that control the way our bodies are built. These genes are sections of a molecule called **deoxyribonucleic acid** (DNA). DNA is a **nucleic acid** that makes up the chromosomes in the nuclei of our cells. We inherit one copy of every gene from each of our parents, and make a complete set of copies every time a cell divides. Every cell therefore has a full set of instructions. The genes control the production of proteins in the cells; most of these proteins are enzymes, which control all the other processes in the cell.

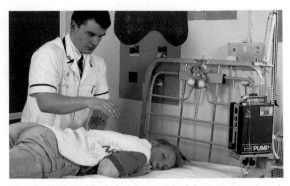

The physiotherapist is helping to clear excess mucus from Sally's lungs, a process that has to be carried out two or three times a day.

Cystic fibrosis

Most people have a gene which produces a protein consisting of 1480 amino acids linked together called cystic fibrosis transmembrane regulator (CFTR). CFTR is an essential component of the membranes of epithelial cells, and its job is to transport chloride ions across the membrane. This must work properly to maintain the ionic balance in cells.

Sally suffers from cystic fibrosis, and her CFTR gene has a mutation. This means that one of the 1480 amino acids is missing. This tiny defect prevents CFTR functioning normally, so the cells lining Sally's lungs cannot secrete chloride ions. As a result the cells retain too much water and the mucus in the lungs is much thicker and stickier than in people with normal CFTR molecules. This sticky mucus blocks the airways and traps bacteria which can act as a source of infection.

Techniques such as gene transfer, used in Tracey the sheep, are helping to overcome genetic disorders such as cystic fibrosis. To understand these techniques you first need to know about the structure and replication of DNA, and how genes produce proteins.

8.3 DNA – the double helix

The genetic revolution began in 1953 with Francis Crick and James Watson, at Cambridge University. They worked out the molecular structure of DNA, the key constituent in all animal and plant genes. By unravelling the code in DNA, Crick and Watson could claim to have unlocked the door to the understanding of life and living things. The applications of this could be of immense benefit to the whole world. Yet Crick and Watson's work was mainly driven by curiosity – a desire to know and understand.

DNA molecules can:
• record the sequence of amino acids in a protein;
• produce exact copies of themselves.

DNA is made up of monomers called **nucleotides.** Each nucleotide has three parts:
• a sugar;
• a phosphate group;
• a base.

The sugar in DNA is called **deoxyribose**, and there are four different bases. These four bases are called **adenine**, **thymine**, **cytosine** and **guanine**, and are often referred to by their initial letter. This means that there are four types of nucleotide in a DNA molecule. The nucleotide monomers link together to make long chains, or polymers, forming a **polynucleotide** (Fig. 1).

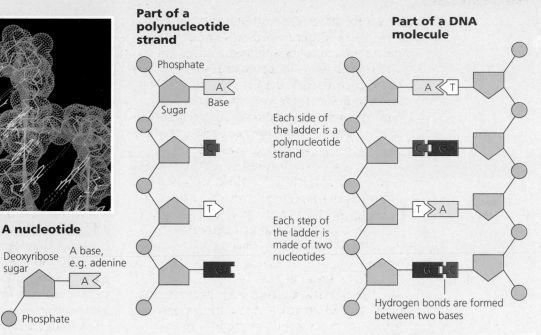

Fig. 1 A DNA molecule

Part of a polynucleotide strand

Phosphate
Base
Sugar
A

A nucleotide

Deoxyribose sugar
A base, e.g. adenine
A
Phosphate

Part of a DNA molecule

Each side of the ladder is a polynucleotide strand

Each step of the ladder is made of two nucleotides

Hydrogen bonds are formed between two bases

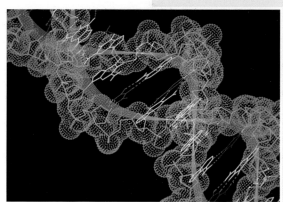

This computer representation of a small piece of DNA may look complicated, but its basic structure is very simple.

1 Draw a diagram of a polynucleotide strand with the bases in the following order: thymine, thymine, adenine, guanine, cytosine, adenine, using the shapes shown in Fig. 1.

The 'ladder' is completed when two polynucleotide strands link together. The bases of the nucleotides link together, forming weak hydrogen bonds. The hydrogen atoms on one base are attracted to oxygen and nitrogen atoms on another.

The shapes and sizes of the bases mean the nucleotides can only link together in certain ways. Cytosine always combines with guanine, and adenine always with thymine. As a result a regular and stable DNA molecule is produced, with two sugar/phosphate sides joined by pairs of bases (Fig. 1). The twisting of the two strands, like two long springs plaited together, earns DNA its famous nickname – the Double Helix. The twisting prevents the two strands coming apart at the weak hydrogen bonds.

On a molecular scale, DNA molecules are huge. Keeping the information in large molecules makes it easier to ensure that all the information is passed from generation to generation. Each of the 46 chromosomes in a fertilised human egg has only one molecule of DNA.

2 Complete the other strand of the DNA molecule that you drew for question 1.

Table 1 shows the proportions of the four bases in DNA from four organisms.

3 Use your understanding of the structure of DNA to explain the pattern in these proportions.

Table 1. Bases in DNA

Organism	Amount of each base (%)			
	Adenine	Cytosine	Guanine	Thymine
Human	31	19	19	31
Locust	29	21	21	29
Yeast	32	18	18	32
Tuberculosis bacterium	15	35	35	15

Source: Herskovitz, *Principles of Genetics,* Collier Macmillan, 1977

8.4 How do genes work?

The only difference between molecules of DNA is the number and order of the **base pairs**. This means genes must differ by having the bases in different sequences. In effect the instructions in genes are written in an alphabet with only four letters. By having long sequences DNA can code vast amounts of information, just as computers can store their information with a two-letter 'binary' code. A human fertilised egg has about 10^9 pairs of nucleotides – these carry all the coded instructions for the development of a complete adult body with billions of cells.

Every time a cell divides a complete copy of all the DNA in its nucleus, and hence all its genes, is made. The copy must be exactly the same as the original to preserve the information. The hydrogen bonds connecting the bases are weak, so the two strands can separate quite easily. An enzyme 'unzips' sections of the DNA molecule by breaking the hydrogen bonds, and exposes the bases (Fig. 2). The bonds between the sugar and phosphate in the polynucleotide strands are relatively strong, and help to keep the strands intact.

Another enzyme, called **DNA polymerase**, attaches free nucleotides to the exposed bases on each strand (Fig. 2). Only the complementary bases will fit together.

A new strand is built on each of the original strands, so that the two new DNA molecules are exact copies of the original (Fig. 2).

Q4 Draw diagrams to show how the section of DNA in Fig. 3 would be replicated.

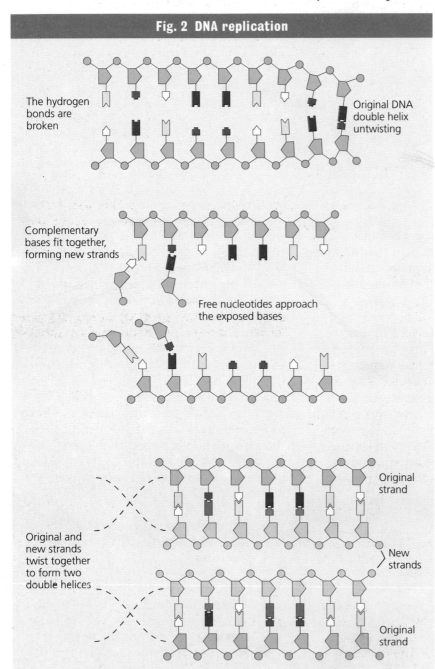

Fig. 2 DNA replication

The hydrogen bonds are broken

Original DNA double helix untwisting

Complementary bases fit together, forming new strands

Free nucleotides approach the exposed bases

Original and new strands twist together to form two double helices

Original strand

New strands

Original strand

Fig. 3 A section of DNA

The genetic technique behind the film Jurassic Park was yesterday awarded science's highest accolade, winning for its inventor the Nobel Prize for Chemistry. Dr Kary Mullis, 48, a Californian researcher, developed a way of 'photocopying' DNA, including that from ancient animals. The technique, known as the polymerase chain reaction (PCR), can amplify tiny amounts of DNA into quantities large enough for scientific analysis.

To make copies of DNA, Dr Mullis' technique uses the same polymerase enzyme that living cells use to replicate their DNA.

The use of genetic fingerprinting to identify criminals from a single hair or drop of blood relies on PCR to replicate a strand of DNA billions of times. PCR is now the most widely used technique for analysing DNA. People who may be at risk of passing on diseases such as cystic fibrosis can now be tested beforehand.

Most fantastic of all, researchers have used PCR to replicate DNA preserved in amber from animals extinct for more than 20 million years. Although this is the technology upon which the plot of Jurassic Park turns, the recreation of whole dinosaurs remains strictly for Hollywood!

Source: adapted from an article by Tom Wilkie, *The Independent*, 14 October 1993

A macrophotograph of a fossilised fly embedded in Baltic amber, approximately 30 million years old.

5 Why do you think it is unlikely that whole dinosaurs could be recreated?

8.5 DNA replication

Shortly after Watson and Crick published their theories, Matthew Meselson and Franklin Stahl set out to prove whether or not DNA did replicate in the way suggested.

From the original theory we can predict that each new molecule contains one strand from the original DNA molecule and one 'new' strand made from a supply of nucleotides in the cell. This is called the **semi-conservative mechanism**, because one strand in each molecule is conserved (Fig. 4).

Meselson and Stahl used bacteria grown in culture medium containing amino acids made with 'heavy nitrogen' (the isotope ^{15}N). All the nitrogen in the nucleotides of the bacterial DNA was therefore ^{15}N. The researchers extracted DNA from these bacteria and centrifuged them in caesium chloride solution. The DNA molecules settled at a point in the centrifuge tube depending on the mass of the molecule. You can read about centrifuging on pages 39 and 40.

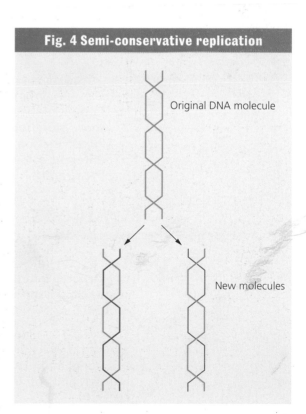

Fig. 4 Semi-conservative replication

Original DNA molecule

New molecules

After centrifuging the concentration of caesium chloride varies uniformly from the top to the bottom of the tube, with the highest concentration at the bottom. The density changes slowly from the top to the bottom and the DNA extract settles as a band at a particular level.

Meselson and Stahl then took bacteria from the ^{15}N medium and grew them on ^{14}N medium (Fig. 5).

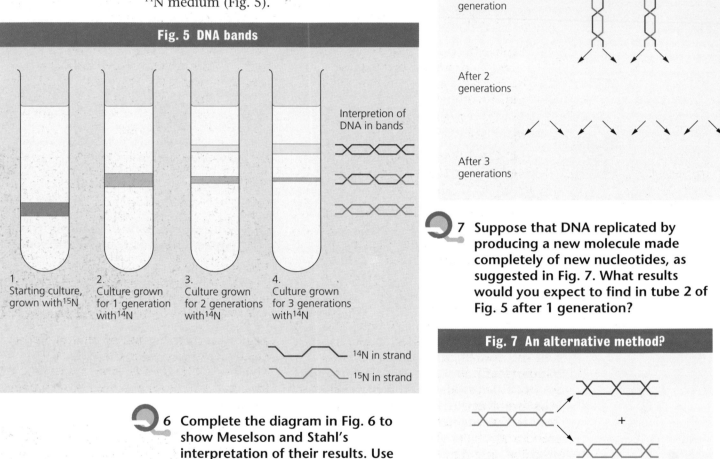

Fig. 5 DNA bands

Interpretion of DNA in bands

1.
Starting culture, grown with ^{15}N

2.
Culture grown for 1 generation with ^{14}N

3.
Culture grown for 2 generations with ^{14}N

4.
Culture grown for 3 generations with ^{14}N

^{14}N in strand

^{15}N in strand

Fig. 6 Interpreting the results

DNA from original culture

After 1 generation

After 2 generations

After 3 generations

Q6 Complete the diagram in Fig. 6 to show Meselson and Stahl's interpretation of their results. Use different colours for the ^{15}N and the ^{14}N strands.

Q7 Suppose that DNA replicated by producing a new molecule made completely of new nucleotides, as suggested in Fig. 7. What results would you expect to find in tube 2 of Fig. 5 after 1 generation?

Fig. 7 An alternative method?

+

Key ideas

- The bases in the nucleotides enable the DNA to store information about the sequencing of the amino acids used in proteins.

- The double-stranded structure of DNA and the way in which the bases pair up enable this stored information to be copied precisely and with a high degree of accuracy.

- The helical structure of the DNA makes the molecule chemically stable so the information does not become corrupted.

- The large size keeps the information together, making it easier to ensure that all is passed from generation to generation.

- DNA replicates by a semi-conservative mechanism.

8.6 Mistakes can happen

From time to time errors occur during DNA replication. For example, one nucleotide in a strand may be replaced by another, or extra nucleotides may be added in.

One strand of DNA has the following sequence of nucleotide bases:

C A T C A T A G A T G A G A

Q 8 Explain how each sequence below could be produced by mistakes during replication of the original sequence.
(i) C A T C A G A G A T G A G A
(ii) C A T C A T A A G A T G A G A
(iii) C A T C A T A G G T A A G A
(iv) C A T A T A G A T G A G A

These changes can alter the code, so that a different protein is produced by a gene. This protein may not have the same properties as the original, and often does not work in the same way. This sort of change is called a **gene mutation**; its effect is to produce a different form of the gene, a new **allele**. Gene mutations occur naturally at random. As we get older, more and more cells will contain gene mutations. When the mutated DNA replicates the new form is copied, so the mutation passes on to other cells. If a mutation occurs in an ovary or testis as the gametes are being produced, the new allele may be passed on to offspring, and may spread to many individuals. Often an allele cannot spread because its effects are too damaging, and the protein it codes for is completely absent. For example, the thrush in the photograph has a mutation in its genes which means it is unable to make the black pigment. It probably has a poor chance of survival because it is so conspicuous. Sometimes the absence of the correct protein may be either harmless or at least not too serious a problem. Occasionally mutations can increase survival chances, as we shall see in later chapters.

Mutations in body cells cannot be passed on to offspring. Mutations that occur during development may cause abnormal growth of the parts formed from the cell with the mutation, as you can see in the photograph of a horse chestnut with a patch of leaves without chlorophyll.

Cancers can develop when mutations occur in the genes that control cell division, with the result that unchecked irregular growth takes place and a tumour develops.

False colour scanning electron micrograph of lung cancer. The cancerous cells fill the air spaces, preventing the absorption of oxygen. Magnification × 180.

An albino thrush.

85

The frequency of mutations is increased by certain **mutagenic** agents. High energy radiation, including X-rays, gamma rays and ultraviolet light, causes mutations, as do high energy radioactive and ionised particles. Many chemicals, especially organic compounds such as those that occur in tobacco tar, are mutagens. New drugs and pesticides, etc., have to be tested to check whether they cause mutations.

Professor B. Bramma, at the University of Leicester, examining an electrophoresis gel to determine the base sequence of the DNA under examination.

Q 9 Explain why mutations in skin cells in a woman would not be passed on to her children.

Inherited disorders

Cystic fibrosis is one example of an inherited disorder in which the normal gene has at some time suffered from a mutation. People such as Sally have inherited these altered forms of the gene. As explained on page 80, Sally is unable to make CFTR. It may be possible to treat the victims of this disorder with the correct protein obtained from sheep like Tracey. However, it may also be possible to reduce the number of children born with such disorders by testing parents for the presence of particular abnormal genes.

" Photocopying DNA "

Research assistants in the DNA analysis laboratory at St Mary's Hospital Medical School search through human genes for mutations responsible for cystic fibrosis. They use a diagnostic test kit developed by Cellmark Diagnostics, an ICI subsidiary. The kit employs PCR to make hundreds of millions of copies of DNA. PCR takes a single strand of DNA as a template and rebuilds the double helix by stitching together the missing complementary strand. If this helix is then denatured, the two new single strands can act as templates for two new helixes.

The process takes about four hours and appears simple: add the appropriate biochemicals and put the mixture in a special machine. The chemical reagents cost a

couple of pounds, and the DNA-duplicating machine is about half the price of a commercial photocopier. The machine copies DNA obtained from cells, for example from a mouthwash sample, until there are hundreds of millions of copies of the cystic fibrosis genes. The DNA fragments are then sorted by electrophoresis to produce a pattern of the DNA fragments that can reveal the presence or absence of mutations in the genes. Twenty-four out of 25 people carry the intact gene and do not have the cystic fibrosis mutation.

Source: adapted from an article by Tim Wilkie, *The Independent*, 14 October 1993

Q 10 a Give the advantages and disadvantages of testing for faulty genes.
b Would you like to be tested? Explain your answer.

" The Human Genome Project "

The Human Genome Project has been described as biology's equivalent of the Apollo Moon programme, and it is estimated that the undertaking will cost 2 billion dollars to complete. Unlike other big science enterprises, however, there is no central laboratory or research block where the project is administered and implemented. Instead, individual nations have set up their own programmes for mapping and sequencing genes, and the project's different tasks are shared out on a largely informal basis between scientists working at these various centres.

These different activities are coordinated by an international group of scientists known as the Human Genome Organisation (Hugo) to ensure there is no duplication of effort between different countries. The scientists aim to trace every single member of our gene system (which is called the human genome) and assign each gene to its proper place on its appropriate chromosome. They intend to unravel the structure of each gene and determine the composition of its corresponding protein.

Researchers will gain unprecedented knowledge about human physiology and the multitude of proteins and hormones that constantly interact during our body's normal functioning. We will learn about individual susceptibilities to disease and be able to target these for early treatments. The information will also be applied to create new drugs and other medicines to counteract cancers, heart diseases, immune disorders and other illnesses.

Source: adapted from *Genes and Mankind*, Imperial Cancer Research Fund, 1994

Q 11 a Do you think that the Human Genome Project is a worthwhile use of research funds? Give your reasons.
b What possible disadvantages are there in having detailed knowledge of all human genes?

Key ideas

- Gene mutations occur naturally at random.
- During replication, one nucleotide may be replaced by another, or an extra one added in or deleted.
- A change in the sequence of nucleotides may change the amino acid sequence in a protein.
- The effect of a gene mutation on survival can vary, from beneficial to harmless to fatal.

8.7 Making proteins from genes

One of the first proteins to be analysed to find the order of amino acids was insulin (Fig. 8). How can the insulin gene make sure that the amino acids appear in the correct order? The DNA of the gene has only four different bases in its nucleotides. How can these bases have a code for each of the 20 naturally occurring amino acids? The bases are arranged in particular sequences which can code for a particular amino acid. A single-base code could identify up to four amino acids. A two-base code could code for more amino acids.

 12 a How many amino acids could a two-base code (e.g. AA, AC, AG...) identify?

b How many amino acids could a three-base code identify?

Fig. 8 Amino acids from insulin

These are the first seven amino acids in an insulin molecule

Phenylalanine — Phe
Valine — Val
Asparagine — Asn
Glutamine — Gln
Histidine — His
Leucine — Leu
Cysteine — Cys

Insulin has 51 amino acids in total

A sequence of three bases provides a code for a particular amino acid:

AAA = phenylalanine (Phe);
CTC = glutamine (Gln);
ACG = cysteine (Cys);
GTG = histidine (His);
ATT = asparagine (Asn);
TAG = leucine (Leu);
CAC = valine (Val);
TGA = threonine (Thr).

The first triplet of bases, AAA, in a gene for insulin is the code for phenylalanine, the next for valine (Fig. 9). This section of the DNA strand is therefore the code for the first four amino acids in an insulin molecule.

13 What will be the order of the next nine bases on this strand of the insulin gene?

Fig. 9 Genes for insulin

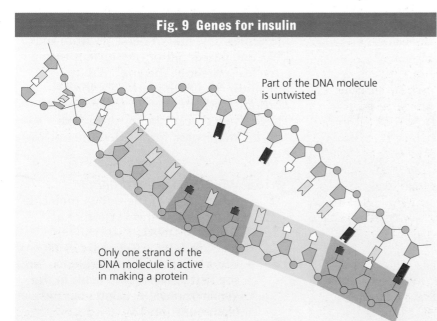

Part of the DNA molecule is untwisted

Only one strand of the DNA molecule is active in making a protein

The sequence of nucleotides in another strand of DNA is:

A C G A T T G T G C A C G T G

 14 What sequence of amino acids will this section of DNA add to a protein?

Suppose a mistake occurs while the DNA is replicating, and the sequence becomes:

(i) A C G A T T G T G C T C G T G

or:

(ii) A C G A T T G T G A C G T G A

 15 a What effect will each of these mistakes have on the protein being produced?
   b A mutation in which a base is missed out is more likely to produce a non-functional protein than a mutation in which one base is swapped for another. Explain why.

You can see how DNA carries the coded information to make a protein. But how can one small section of DNA on one chromosome in a cell nucleus make enough of the protein to supply the whole cell? Imagine trying to make enough copies of a best-selling compact disc from a single original master disc. Clearly it is much more efficient to make several copies of this master disc and then use these as moulds to produce the compact discs to sell (Fig. 10).

Cells operate in much the same way. Copies, or 'imprints', of the DNA code are produced, just as a garden gnome manufacturer might make plaster casts of a new gnome. The casts then pass from the nucleus into the cytoplasm, where the copy of the code is used to manufacture the protein.

Transcription

The copies of the DNA are strands of another nucleic acid, called **ribonucleic acid** (RNA). The structure of RNA is very similar to a single strand of DNA, except that the sugar **ribose** replaces deoxyribose, and the base thymine is replaced by another base called **uracil.** Uracil molecules are similar in size and shape to those of thymine, and uracil will link to adenine in the same way as thymine. The process of copying the code in the DNA is called **transcription** (Fig. 11).

An enzyme makes a section of the DNA of a gene untwist. Another enzyme, **RNA polymerase**, then assembles the RNA nucleotides along one strand. This copies the DNA code and produces a single-stranded molecule of **messenger RNA** (mRNA). mRNA molecules are similar to DNA in the way that they carry information, but are much smaller molecules. The mRNA detaches from the DNA and passes out of the nucleus through a nuclear pore into the endoplasmic reticulum. The mRNA attaches to the ribosomes, which are also made of RNA. They have a special shape, rather like enzyme molecules, into which the mRNA fits.

 16 a What will be the order of nucleotides in the mRNA molecule produced by this section of a strand of DNA?
A C G A T T G T G C A C G T G
   b Work out the mRNA sequence for the first seven amino acids in the insulin molecule, using your answer from question 13.

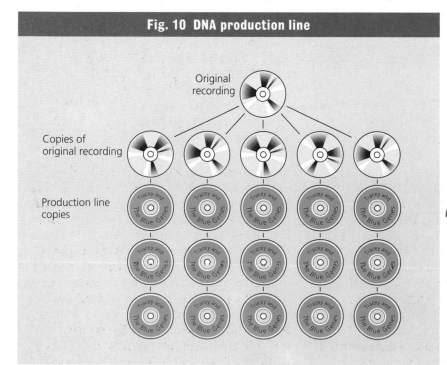

Fig. 10 DNA production line

Original recording

Copies of original recording

Production line copies

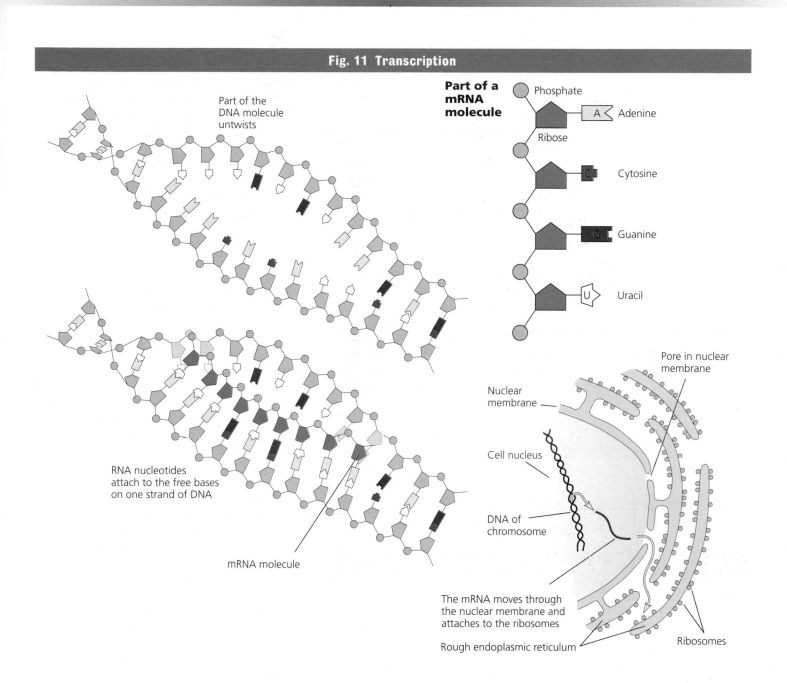

Fig. 11 Transcription

Part of the DNA molecule untwists

Part of a mRNA molecule

Phosphate

Ribose

Adenine

Cytosine

Guanine

Uracil

RNA nucleotides attach to the free bases on one strand of DNA

mRNA molecule

Pore in nuclear membrane

Nuclear membrane

Cell nucleus

DNA of chromosome

The mRNA moves through the nuclear membrane and attaches to the ribosomes

Rough endoplasmic reticulum

Ribosomes

Translation

Once the DNA code has been transcribed and the mRNA copies have passed out of the nucleus to the ribosomes, the code on the mRNA is used to assemble the amino acids of the protein in the correct order. This process is called **translation** (Fig. 12).

In the endoplasmic reticulum, around the ribosomes, are molecules of **transfer RNA** (tRNA). These are small molecules and they can form temporary bonds with both amino acids and mRNA. One end of the tRNA molecule can attach to an amino acid molecule. Energy from ATP is needed for

this process. There are different tRNA molecules for each of the 20 amino acids. Each type of tRNA has a specific sequence of bases in the **anticodon** at the opposite end to the amino acid.

The mRNA molecule passes through the ribosome, and as it does so the tRNA with the appropriate anticodon is attached to the **codon** on the mRNA. Since the tRNA is carrying the correct amino acid, the amino acids are brought together in the right sequence. Peptide links form between the amino acids to build the protein chain.

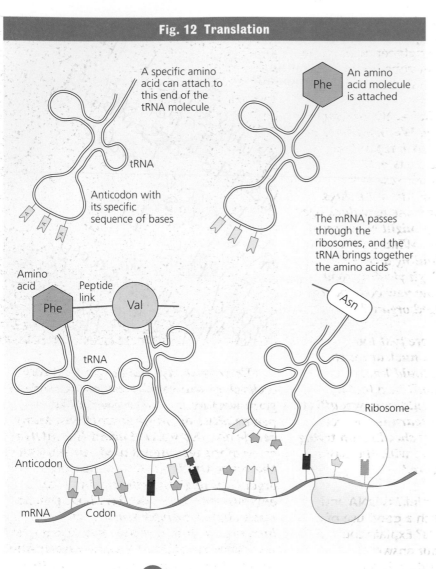

Fig. 12 Translation

A specific amino acid can attach to this end of the tRNA molecule

tRNA

Anticodon with its specific sequence of bases

An amino acid molecule is attached

Phe

The mRNA passes through the ribosomes, and the tRNA brings together the amino acids

Amino acid

Peptide link

Phe

Val

Asn

tRNA

Ribosome

Anticodon

mRNA   Codon

17 Copy and complete Table 2, showing the codes at each stage of the process in producing the first bases of the insulin molecule.

Making a protein from a gene therefore involves three sets of codes. The DNA of the gene has a code which is transcribed to mRNA. The mRNA code is then translated to assemble the tRNA in the correct order, using the codes on the tRNA molecules.

This is a highly effective process enabling cells to make the proteins they need.

DNA can store information about the sequencing of the 20 amino acids used in proteins in a very compact form. All the genetic information for the population of Britain could easily be stored in DNA occupying a volume smaller than that of a single silicon chip in a computer. The way in which the bases pair up means stored information can be copied quickly and accurately. The helical structure of the DNA makes the molecule chemically stable so that the information does not become corrupted.

Using genetic research

Understanding the processes by which genes make proteins like CFTR has suggested a range of ways in which conditions such as cystic fibrosis can be treated. Although the protein from Tracey is used as a drug to overcome the effects of cystic fibrosis, it is not a cure. A more effective treatment would be to get the missing protein produced by the normal gene, CFTR, into the lungs. One way of doing this is to insert CFTR-producing genes into a harmless virus and then spray the virus into the patient's lungs. Inside the lungs the virus will produce CFTR. Alternatively, it may be possible to get the gene into the patient's own cells, making an even more effective cure. We shall see in Chapter 10 more about how this sort of genetic engineering may be carried out.

Tracey's life-saving protein, and plastic-producing plants, are just two examples of useful developments that are derived from DNA research. Curing genetic diseases, such as haemophilia and muscular dystrophy, by replacing 'faulty' genes with 'healthy' ones has become a distinct possibility. Food crops may be improved, perhaps by developing potatoes with extra protein and tomatoes that ripen more slowly. Farm

Table 2. Coding of bases							
Amino acid in insulin	Phe	Val	Asn	Gln	His	Leu	Cys
DNA code in gene	AAA	CAC	ATT	CTC	GTG	TAG	ACG
Codon in mRNA	UUU	GUG	CAA				
Anticodon in tRNA	AAA	CAC	AUU				

animals may be genetically 'designed' to produce more or better quality meat. Techniques of genetic engineering open up the prospect of using microbes to make a huge range of useful products.

'We don't have a choice. We cannot "un-invent" technology. We should not be frightened of what might happen but instead encourage scientists and technologists so that their research produces benefits for all human beings. It's no good hoping for some new dark age just because something might go wrong if we take a step forward. What's so terrible about the chance of finding a cure for cancer, or a range of high yielding food plants, or a way to grow new body parts for people with damaged organs?'

'Some technologies are just too dangerous. A fault in a nuclear reactor or a biotechnology plant could have worldwide effects. A fault in a factory making plastic cups would not even affect the next city. Until we learn to control ourselves human beings should stop trying to play god and interfere with the basic building blocks of nature.'

'There is always the danger that this technology will be misused, for example in germ warfare or even to control the personalities of future generations. Many people are also worried about the safety of some of the techniques used, for example that uncontrollable disease-causing organisms might be released into the environment. How you feel about genetic research, for example transferring a human gene into a sheep, may depend on whether you suffer, or know someone who suffers, from cystic fibrosis, or any other condition caused by a 'faulty' gene, that could be cured or prevented by using the knowledge we have of DNA.'

 18 a What do you think? Is DNA and genetic research a good use of research grants? Explain the reasons for your answer.

b Would you produce legal guidelines to control genetic research? What would they be and why?

Key ideas

- Nucleic acids store and communicate genetic information.

- Messenger RNA molecules have similar properties to DNA in the way that they carry information, but are much smaller and therefore can readily transfer the relevant section of stored information in the DNA to the part of the cell where it is needed.

- Transfer RNA molecules are also small and have the ability to form temporary bonds with both amino acids and mRNA.

- The shape of tRNA molecules makes them able to attach to the mRNA according to the specific anticodon, and align the amino acids in the right position for the formation of peptide bonds.

Sex and reproduction

At the ancient Olympics in Greece, sex testing was a simple procedure. Athletes walked naked through the gates. No penis, no admittance.

Sex tests were first introduced to the modern Olympic games in 1966. They were invasive and controversial gynaecological examinations.

For the Mexico Games in 1968 a less invasive sex chromatin test was introduced. A sample of cells is taken from inside a woman's cheek. This 'buccal smear' is then stained and examined under a microscope. If a cell has two X chromosomes, one will be inactivated, and will show up as a dark blob in the cell's nucleus, a so-called Barr body. A woman fails the test if no Barr body is detected.

For the Barcelona Olympics in 1992 the sex chromatin test was replaced by a more modern, and more expensive, genetic test. The new procedure tests for the so-called male-determining gene, *SRY*. It uses the technique of the polymerase chain reaction, PCR, to make copies of a targeted stretch of DNA from the Y chromosome, so producing enough DNA to detect the presence of the *SRY* gene.

Source: adapted from articles by Alison Turnbull, *New Scientist*, 15 September 1988; Gail Vines, *New Scientist*, 4 July 1992

Sally Gunnell will have been tested for the *SRY* gene before she could compete at the 1992 Olympic games.

Is it important to determine if a person taking part in the Olympic games is male or female? Trying to decide if a person is male or female has had unexpected implications, because there is so much variety. Is the difference between the two sexes a rigid, biological one, or is it, for humans, a result of social and cultural differences? Why do organisms need males and females at all?

9.1 Learning objectives

After working through this chapter, you should be able to:

- **appreciate** the biological variety between maleness and femaleness;

- **explain** the genetic basis of sex determination and testing;

- **explain** how genetic abnormalities can arise;

- **explain** that sexual reproduction involves gamete production and fertilisation;

- **recall** how pairs of homologous chromosomes are separated by the process of meiosis during gamete production;

- **explain** how meiosis contributes to producing genetic variation;

- **explain** how ova and sperm are adapted for their functions;

- **explain** the importance of males and females in genetic variation;

- **recognise** each stage in the process of cell division by mitosis;

- **explain** how cell cloning procedures work.

9.2 Male or female?

The distinction between male and female is not always as evident as you might think. Biologists need to look clearly into our cells to decide – and even then it is not always obvious. Within the nucleus of every cell in our body are **chromosomes**. Chromosomes are made from DNA and protein. You will remember from Chapter 8 that the DNA consists of a long chain of genes. Chromosomes are therefore packages of genes.

Sex chromosomes determine the maleness and femaleness of individuals. They are called X and Y chromosomes. Normally a female human has a pair of X chromosomes, whereas a male human has one X chromosome and one much smaller Y chromosome. One of the X chromosomes in a female usually becomes inactive at an early stage in development of the embryo and forms the dark Barr body (Fig. 1). The presence of a Barr body in a nucleus is used in the sex chromatin test as evidence that an individual is female.

Fig. 1 A Barr body

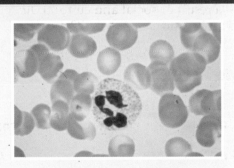

A light micrograph of a white blood cell, surrounded by red blood cells. The white blood cell has a large nucleus with five lobes. On the right of the top lobe, you can see a drumstick-shape sticking out. This is the condensed X chromosome, or Barr body. Magnification × 700.

The Y chromosome is much smaller than the X, and many of the genes that are present on the X chromosome are missing from the Y. However, the *SRY* gene that causes the developing reproductive organs to become testes rather than ovaries is situated on the Y chromosome and is not present on the X chromosome. The hormones that the testes produce probably stimulate other male features to develop. So the *SRY* gene is thought to be the key to maleness. However, there is still considerable uncertainty over this and there may well be other genes involved.

 1 a Some individuals have unusual sex chromosomes. People with Turner's syndrome have XO sex chromosomes; people with Klinefelter's syndrome have XXY sex chromosomes.
(i) In what way are these sex chromosomes unusual?
(ii) Would you expect an individual with either syndrome to be male or female? Explain your answers.
  b Use the information above to suggest how the development of females is controlled.

Genetic abnormalities can confuse the difference between male and female in complex ways. It is possible to have females with XX chromosomes who have abnormally masculine bodies and muscle strength, because their adrenal gland does not respond to female hormones normally. It is also possible to have females, with female body shape and muscle strength, who have XY chromosomes because their cells do not respond to male hormones in the usual way. Sex testing at athletic games is meant to protect women from unfair competition, but it can be very difficult to say if an individual is not female.

Alison Carlson, a retired American athlete and biologist, says: '*The majority of women athletes still feel that there has to be some kind of guarantee, some sort of protection. They fear that there are "abnormal women" who have an unfair advantage in women's sport. In fact male and female are really a biological continuum. We're so much more alike than different. It's culture that makes us see sex as black and white. Physical differences relevant to sport are not clear cut and are much more plastic than we realised.*'

2 Explain why sex testing may be unfair to some individuals.

Studying the sex chromosomes has shown how much variety there is between individuals. The next sections show why this variety exists.

9.3 Passing on the packages

Chromosomes are packages of genes. The information in these genes has to be passed on from one generation to the next. The simplest method of reproduction is for an organism to split in two, or to separate off cells or small parts that can grow into new individuals. This produces offspring identical to each other and their parents. This kind of reproduction is called **asexual reproduction**. Most organisms have developed some form of **sexual reproduction**. Sexual reproduction introduces variety by mixing together genes from two individuals. You can find out more about the need for genetic variety in Chapter 11.

Normally, when chromosomes are working, they are long and thin so that transcription and protein synthesis can occur. During cell division, the chromosomes shorten and thicken, and the DNA in the chromosome forms very tightly packed supercoils (coils of coils) that are shorter and thicker than usual. By staining them at this stage, it is much easier to see differences and similarities between chromosomes. The **karyotype** of a cell describes the number, appearance and arrangement of chromosomes (Fig. 2).

Humans usually have 46 chromosomes. The chromosomes occur in pairs, so there are only 23 different types. Each chromosome consists of a very long molecule of DNA with smaller protein molecules attached at various points. When the nucleus is in the process of cell division, each chromosome has two strands, called **chromatids**, joined together at a point called the **centromere**.

You will have noticed that the chromosomes in a body cell nucleus occur in pairs. The chromosomes in a pair are called **homologous** because both chromosomes have genes for the same features in the same positions. One of the chromosomes of a homologous pair will be a copy of one that originally came from the female parent, and the other will be a copy of the original from the male parent (Fig. 3). Chapter 8 explained how new versions of genes, alleles, can arise as a result of mutations which produce changes in the DNA. So individuals may have different forms of the gene for a particular feature, but the alleles of a gene still occupy equivalent positions on the chromosome.

Fig. 3 Homologous chromosomes

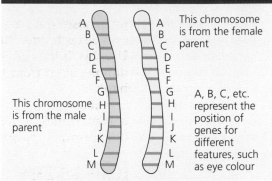

This chromosome is from the female parent

This chromosome is from the male parent

A, B, C, etc. represent the position of genes for different features, such as eye colour

Cell division by **meiosis** reduces the **diploid** number (2n) of homologous chromosomes to the **haploid** number (n) in **gametes** (Fig. 4). Gametes are the sex cells. Each gamete must get one chromosome from each homologous pair. When the gametes fuse in **fertilisation**, homologous pairs reform in the fertilised ovum, the **zygote**. Meiosis ensures that the number of chromosomes stays constant from generation to generation. If fertilisation took place without first halving the number

Fig. 2 Sorting chromosomes

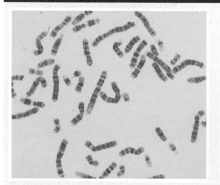

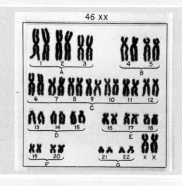

46 XX

A false colour light micrograph of the full complement of normal human male chromosomes. The banding is due to the way the chromosomes have been stained. Magnification × 2700.

The karyotype of a normal adult female human. These chromosomes have been sorted into pairs and numbered according to shape and banding pattern.

Fig. 4 Meiosis and fertilisation in humans

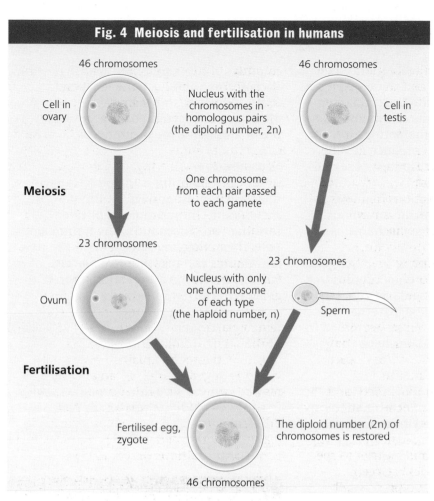

46 chromosomes

Cell in ovary

Nucleus with the chromosomes in homologous pairs (the diploid number, 2n)

46 chromosomes

Cell in testis

Meiosis

One chromosome from each pair passed to each gamete

23 chromosomes

Ovum

Nucleus with only one chromosome of each type (the haploid number, n)

23 chromosomes

Sperm

Fertilisation

Fertilised egg, zygote

The diploid number (2n) of chromosomes is restored

46 chromosomes

Table 1. Numbers of chromosomes

Organism	Diploid number of chromosomes	Organism	Diploid number of chromosomes
Human	46	Cat	38
Pea	14	Barley	14
Mouse	40	Onion	16
Maize	20	Horse	64
Fruit fly	8		

3 a What is the haploid number of chromosomes in:
(i) a cat;
(ii) an onion?

b How many chromosomes would you find in:
(i) a human sperm;
(ii) a leaf cell of a pea;
(iii) a mouse ovum;
(iv) a fertilised ovum (zygote) from a horse;
(v) a pollen grain nucleus (gamete) from maize?

It is essential that a copy of each gene from each parent's homologous chromosomes is passed on, otherwise there would be incomplete or no instructions at all for some features, such as for the synthesis of haemoglobin or for the pigment in the eyes. Most organisms have between ten and 50 pairs of chromosomes. Packaging large numbers of genes into a small number of chromosomes, and reducing the size of the chromosomes before cell division, help prevent any genes being lost as they are passed on.

by meiosis, the chromosome number would double each time that fertilisation occurred. Usually all the cells of an organism are diploid, apart from the gametes which are haploid.

Table 1 shows the number of chromosomes in the body cells of certain organisms, i.e. the diploid number, 2n.

Key ideas

- In humans the Y chromosome is small and does not have all the genes that are present on the larger X chromosome.

- In humans, female cells normally contain two X chromosomes, whereas male cells have one X and one Y chromosome.

- Plants and animals have large numbers of genes that are grouped together in a small number of chromosomes.

- In most cells the chromosomes occur in homologous pairs. Each chromosome in a pair has genes for the same characteristics as its partner.

- During meiosis the chromosomes of a homologous pair are separated. As a result the gametes have only one chromosome from each pair.

- Fertilisation restores homologous pairs in the zygote.

9.4 Sexual reproduction and variation

Meiosis and fertilisation will produce new combinations of alleles and these may give rise to individuals that are better adapted for survival. The survivors can then pass on their successful gene combinations to their offspring. This ability to produce genetic variation is the major advantage of sexual reproduction.

The possible combinations of alleles from sexual reproduction are enormous, and they depend on three mechanisms.

Independent assortment

In each homologous pair one chromosome comes from the female, and one from the male. During meiosis these maternal and paternal chromosomes can be reshuffled in any combination, that is, they are 'independently assorted'.

 **4 Using the pattern shown in Fig. 5, how many different combinations would be produced if there were:
(i) four pairs;
(ii) 23 pairs of homologous chromosomes?**

Fig. 5 Combinations of chromosomes

A cell from an organism with two pairs of homologous chromosomes

The pink chromosomes are originally from the female parent

The purple chromosomes are originally from the male parent

There are four possible ways the chromosomes could be reshuffled in the gametes

If the organism had three pairs of homologous chromosomes, there are eight ways the chromosomes could be reshuffled in the gametes

Random fertilisation

Fertilisation is the joining together of male and female gametes. During fertilisation any female gamete can join with any male gamete. Since the gametes will normally come from different individuals, vast numbers of new combinations are possible. Each chromosome may have several thousand genes and there may be several alleles for each gene. The number of possible variants is astronomical.

Crossing-over

Additional variation is introduced during meiosis by crossing-over. At the start of meiosis the chromosomes replicate, forming two chromatids. The homologous pairs then come together. Two of the new chromatids coil together like mating snakes. When the chromatids separate again parts are swapped over (Fig. 6).

Fig. 6 Crossing-over

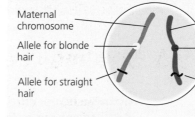

A homologous pair of chromosomes has a gene for hair colour and a gene for hair structure. The maternal and paternal chromosomes carry different alleles for these genes.

Maternal chromosome

Paternal chromosome

Allele for blonde hair

Allele for dark hair (hair colour gene)

Allele for straight hair

Allele for curly hair (hair structure gene)

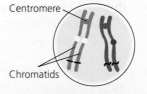

The chromosomes replicate, forming two chromatids joined at the centromere

Centromere

Chromatids

The chromosomes come together as a pair, and two of the chromatids cross-over

Point where chromatids cross-over

Four possible gametes can be produced by meiosis

This gamete has the same alleles as the maternal chromosome

These two gametes have new combinations of alleles – one for blonde and curly hair, the other for dark and straight hair

This gamete has the same alleles as the paternal chromosome

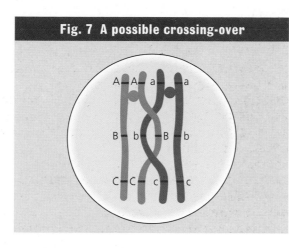

Fig. 7 A possible crossing-over

Q 5 A chromosome has three genes on it. Each gene has two alleles, that is A and a, B and b, C and c. Crossing-over occurs at two points, as shown in Fig. 7. Draw diagrams to show the chromosomes in the gametes that would be produced.

There is enormous variation between males and females, and between individuals of the same sex. Genetic 'abnormalities' like XXY and XO are a natural part of this variation. Is it fair to exclude people with these variations from sporting events?

Key ideas

- Sexual reproduction produces variation in the offspring because meiosis and fertilisation mix together alleles for different characteristics in new combinations.

- As a result of independent assortment during meiosis, gametes have new combinations of maternal and paternal chromosomes.

- Random fertilisation brings together alleles from different parents in new ways.

- Crossing-over in chromosomes links alleles of different genes in new ways.

9.5 Are men really necessary?

Reproduction is much easier without fertilisation, and many organisms, such as some bacteria, reproduce asexually. There are many methods of asexual reproduction, but they all share two characteristics: no gametes or fertilisation are needed, and offspring are identical to each other and the parent. Asexual reproduction is much quicker and more certain, and so helps the species to spread more rapidly than sexual reproduction.

Q 6 How can genetic variation occur in a species when it only reproduces asexually?

Some organisms, such as many fungi and plants, use both asexual and sexual reproduction. Sexual reproduction needs two cells to meet and fuse. In some organisms there is no apparent difference between the cells that fuse together. An example is the common bread mould (Fig. 8).

In most species the male and female gametes are clearly different. The gamete produced by the female is usually a relatively large cell and often contains food reserves. It is frequently retained in the parent body before fertilisation. The male gamete is much smaller, without significant food reserves, and produced in much larger numbers. It is usually able to move itself with a swimming motion and seems to be able to find the female gamete using some form of chemical sense. In most animals there are separate male and female organisms. Each is adapted to ensure that the gametes they produce successfully undertake fertilisation with the minimum of wastage of food reserves. In humans sexual reproduction means passing on one set of genes in the female sex cell, the **ovum**, and one set in the male sex cell, the **sperm** (Fig. 9).

Fig. 8 Sexual reproduction in the common bread mould

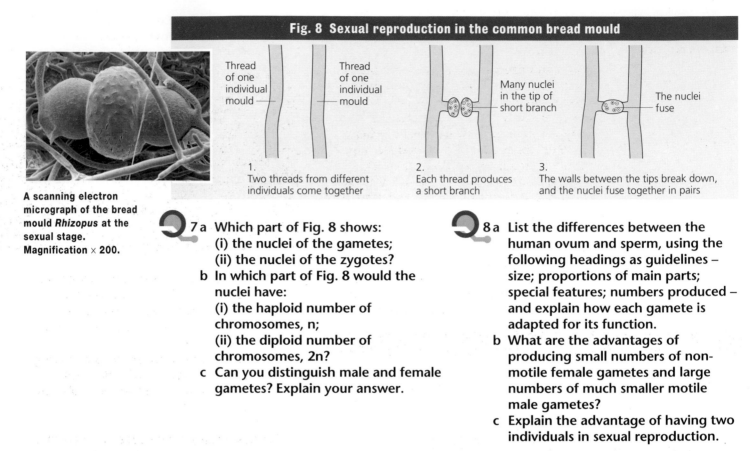

A scanning electron micrograph of the bread mould *Rhizopus* at the sexual stage. Magnification × 200.

1. Two threads from different individuals come together

2. Each thread produces a short branch

3. The walls between the tips break down, and the nuclei fuse together in pairs

7 a Which part of Fig. 8 shows:
(i) the nuclei of the gametes;
(ii) the nuclei of the zygotes?
b In which part of Fig. 8 would the nuclei have:
(i) the haploid number of chromosomes, n;
(ii) the diploid number of chromosomes, 2n?
c Can you distinguish male and female gametes? Explain your answer.

8 a List the differences between the human ovum and sperm, using the following headings as guidelines – size; proportions of main parts; special features; numbers produced – and explain how each gamete is adapted for its function.
b What are the advantages of producing small numbers of non-motile female gametes and large numbers of much smaller motile male gametes?
c Explain the advantage of having two individuals in sexual reproduction.

Fig. 9 A human ovum and a human sperm

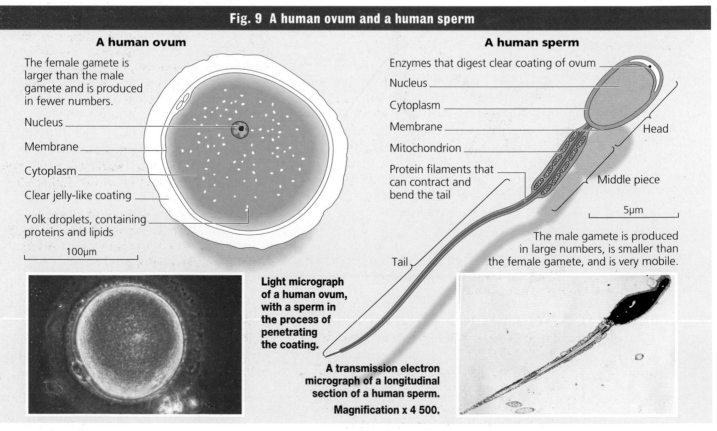

A human ovum

The female gamete is larger than the male gamete and is produced in fewer numbers.

Nucleus

Membrane

Cytoplasm

Clear jelly-like coating

Yolk droplets, containing proteins and lipids

100µm

A human sperm

Enzymes that digest clear coating of ovum

Nucleus

Cytoplasm

Membrane

Mitochondrion

Protein filaments that can contract and bend the tail

Head

Middle piece

5µm

The male gamete is produced in large numbers, is smaller than the female gamete, and is very mobile.

Tail

Light micrograph of a human ovum, with a sperm in the process of penetrating the coating.

A transmission electron micrograph of a longitudinal section of a human sperm. Magnification x 4 500.

9.6 Maintaining the balance

Males and females are equally important in promoting genetic variation, and most species have to make sure there is a balance between the sexes. In mammals the proportion of males and females is kept more or less even. Meiosis produces equal numbers of male and female gametes (Fig. 10). The *SRY* gene, which determines the development of testes, occurs only in Y chromosomes.

Not every male and female of a species will necessarily reproduce. Some mammals, such as lions, live in harems, where one male breeds with several females.

 9 a Why do human ova contain only X chromosomes?
   b Which determines whether a child is a boy or a girl – the ovum or the sperm? Explain your answer.

10 a Some farmers want all their calves to be cows, for milk production. How, in principle, would it be possible to ensure that only cows are produced?
   b What are the advantages of having an equal balance of males and females, when not all the males will breed?

Understanding how the sex of a child is determined makes it possible to develop techniques to choose whether to have a boy or a girl. One technique depends on the fact that a Y chromosome is smaller than an X chromosome. Sperm with a Y chromosome therefore have a slightly smaller mass and can be separated by centrifuging.

11 a What do you think are the problems that would arise if people could choose what sex their child would be?
   b Do you think it would ever be possible to choose to have a child that would definitely be a good female athlete?

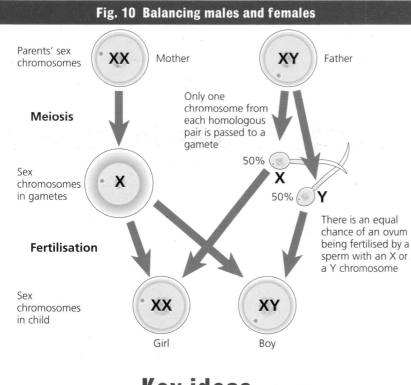

Fig. 10 Balancing males and females

Parents' sex chromosomes — XX Mother — XY Father

Only one chromosome from each homologous pair is passed to a gamete

Meiosis

Sex chromosomes in gametes — X — 50% X — 50% Y

Fertilisation

There is an equal chance of an ovum being fertilised by a sperm with an X or a Y chromosome

Sex chromosomes in child — XX Girl — XY Boy

Key ideas

- Most species produce large numbers of male gametes and much smaller numbers of female gametes.

- Female gametes have food reserves that are used in the early stages of development of the embryo. Male gametes are small and able to swim to the female gamete.

- Two individuals are usually necessary for sexual reproduction.

9.7 Copying the instructions

A fertilised ovum has a diploid set of chromosomes with all the instructions in its DNA for the growth and development of the new individual. Every time cell division takes place during growth the chromosomes have to be copied so that every cell nucleus has a full set of instructions and can make all the proteins that it needs.

This time there is no need to separate the chromosomes of a homologous pair as in meiosis. Instead, a complete copy of each chromosome is made. This type of cell division is called **mitosis** (Fig. 11).

Fig. 11 Mitosis

These light micrographs show the stages of mitosis in cells of the hyacinth root. The nuclei are yellow and the cell contents are blue.

Interphase

For most of the time the chromosomes in a nucleus cannot be seen. The DNA molecules are stretched out and busy synthesising proteins. At the onset of mitosis the DNA replicates. This happens during interphase, before any sign of cell division can be seen. The two smaller cells in the centre of this micrograph are smaller, with comparatively larger nuclei, because cell division has occurred and they are in interphase before cell division happens again.

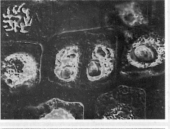

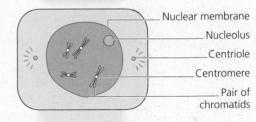

Chromatin threads
Nuclear membrane
Nucleolus
Cytoplasm
Cell surface membrane
Centrioles

Prophase

After the chromosomes have replicated, they coil up and contract. They then become visible. The replicated chromosomes appear as double strands. In fact they consist of the two new chromosomes, at this stage called chromatids, still firmly joined together at the centromere.

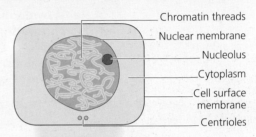

Nuclear membrane
Nucleolus
Centriole
Centromere
Pair of chromatids

Metaphase

The membrane of the nucleus breaks down and a web of protein fibres called the **spindle** forms from one end of the cell to the other. The centromeres attach to the spindle in the middle of the cell.

Spindle fibres (microtubules)
Centromeres on 'equator' of spindle

Anaphase

The centromeres now split and the chromatids separate. The spindle fibres contract, pulling one chromatid of each pair to one end of the cell and the other chromatid to the opposite end.

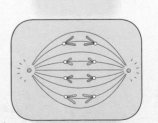

Daughter chromosomes move apart led by their centromeres

Telophase

The separated chromatids, which are exact copies of the original chromosomes, group together at opposite ends of the cell. New nuclear membranes develop and the chromosomes uncoil. Mitosis is complete when new cell membranes form. Plants also form new cell walls.

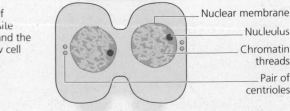

Nuclear membrane
Nucleolus
Chromatin threads
Pair of centrioles

Q 12 a How will the amount of DNA in a nucleus differ between the start and the end of interphase?

b Estimate how many chromosomes the hyacinth cell has.

c Using your estimate, predict how many chromatids there are in prophase.

d Why do you think the chromatids contract separately from each other during prophase?

e How does the process ensure that each new nucleus gets only one copy of each chromosome?

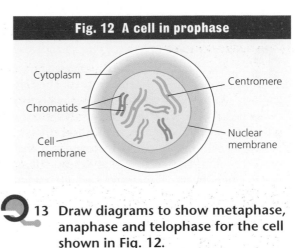

Fig. 12 A cell in prophase

Cytoplasm

Centromere

Chromatids

Cell membrane

Nuclear membrane

Q 13 Draw diagrams to show metaphase, anaphase and telophase for the cell shown in Fig. 12.

9.8 Cloning

Since every cell has the same genes it is in theory possible to grow a complete new organism from any cell or group of cells. The genetic information would be passed on by mitosis, without the need for meiosis and fertilisation. Organisms such as strawberries that use asexual methods of reproduction do just this. The offspring are called **clones**. Since all the new plants will be of the same variety as the parent plant, growers can be sure that they will get fruit with the same characteristics and of the same quality.

This strawberry plant has grown several runners with a small plant at the end. The plantlets will take root and grow into new plants. Each will have exactly the same genes as the parent.

Q 14 Many plants use asexual reproduction as well as sexual reproduction. What are the advantages for the plant of reproducing asexually?

Not all plants and very few animals can reproduce asexually. Scientists have tried to use artificial cloning to grow exact copies of particularly valuable organisms. This is not

Errol Flynn in the Adventures of Robin Hood.

always easy, especially in animals, because, although the genes are present in a cell, they cannot easily be 'switched on' in order to go through the whole process of development. The extracts from articles illustrate some aspects of research into cloning.

❝ Oak clones destined for greatness ❞

Scientists have produced hundreds of tiny clones of the Major Oak in Sherwood Forest and hope to grow an exact copy of Robin Hood's favourite tree. The famous oak is reputed to mark the site where Robin Hood and his merry men set up camp. It is at least 500 years old, making it one of Britain's oldest living trees It stands about 80 feet high, with a 36 ft circumference, and a span of 240 ft.

. Researchers at a small Leicestershire-based company, Micropropagation Services, are growing miniature versions of the tree in racks of glass honey jars. The work is being carried out with help from the local council, which has allowed the scientists to remove small branches from the tree close to its main trunk. These then bud and are grown in a culture; the shoots sprout clusters of miniature buds, each genetically identical to the next, and to the Major Oak itself. Each cluster can then be divided many times over. The cloned trees, although genetically identical, will differ in appearance according to the climate and environment in which they grow.

Source: adapted from an article by Susan Watts, *The Independent*, 21 May 1992

Cloning is achieved by a process called nuclear transfer. Using microscopic surgical tools, a scientist removes the nucleus from a single-cell sheep or cattle embryo. The empty cell is then fused with another, complete cell taken from a second embryo which has already developed to a 16-cell stage. This newly formed, fused cell will itself grow into an embryo and survive into adulthood. And as there are 16 individual cells in the original sheep embryo, that means 16 clones can be created from it. The technique has almost endless potential. From each of the 16 clones by nuclear transfer, scientists can make 16 copies – thus creating a second generation of clones. And from this generation, there is no theoretical reason why others – a third, a fourth and so on – could not be created. One embryo could therefore be multiplied one thousandfold. Such technology will have a profound impact on British farmstock. Cloning top-quality embryos, freezing them, and then transferring them as requested by farmers into poor-quality cattle, will effect a giant leap in the quality of the country's cattle and sheep. 'Care will be needed', says Professor Cross. 'If you produce beef that has exactly the same flavour and texture, you might end up creating the meat equivalent of the Golden Delicious apple – something that is universally boring. On the other hand, cloning could make top-quality meat more easily available – if we are careful about what we clone.'

Source: adapted from an article by Robin McKie, *Observer Magazine*

Q 15 a What are the possible advantages in agriculture and horticulture of using cloning techniques?
b What dangers can you foresee if it becomes possible to clone human beings, such as successful athletes? What steps would you suggest that a government should take to combat these dangers?

An American scientist has cloned a human embryo by splitting it in a test-tube to create identical twin or triplet embryos, in what is believed to be the first reported such experiment. Dr Jerry Hall of George Washington University Medical Center, Washington DC, was attempting to devise a method of creating extra embryos for couples undergoing *in vitro* fertilisation (IVF) treatment. He adopted techniques common in livestock breeding to produce identical offspring, and used genetically abnormal human embryos in the experiment. None was viable and all have been discarded. However, the work raises important ethical questions if such a technique was perfected using normal embryos. Embryos can be frozen for many years and it would, in theory, be possible for identical people – twins or triplets – to be born years apart to the same woman or to others implanted with the cloned embryos. American ethicists have also raised the possibility of parents keeping a 'back-up' embryo in case their child died or needed an organ donation.

Source: adapted from an article by Liz Hunt, *The Independent*, 1 November 1993

Key ideas

- Except when producing gametes, cells divide by mitosis.

- In mitosis each chromosomes replicates, and one copy is passed on to each daughter cell.

- All the cells produced by mitosis have identical sets of chromosomes and hence of genes (unless mutations have occurred during the process of replication).

- Organisms produced by asexual reproduction are identical to their parents because only mitotic cell divisions are involved (unless mutations have occurred during the process of replication).

"   Hunting the Huntington gene   "

In 1968 the young Nancy Wexler's mother, who was a geneticist, was diagnosed as having Huntington's disease. Nancy's three uncles, all brothers of her mother, had already died of the distressing condition, the symptoms of which only appear in middle age and include relentless loss of coordination and mental deterioration. Nancy realised that she had a 50:50 chance of developing the disease in later life. However, the Wexler family was not prone to giving in easily.

Nancy's father, Milton, resolved to set up a research foundation to find a cure, if possible in time to save his wife. Sadly, the search was to take much longer than their optimistic hopes. Nancy's mother died ten years later, but Nancy remained as a driving force in the hunt for the elusive gene that causes the disease.

The first breakthrough in the search for the gene came when a Venezuelan doctor reported a family in a remote part of his country with large numbers of cases of the disease. Nancy Wexler immediately organised a research team to collect blood samples and eventually traced 11 000 descendants of one nineteenth century woman who had carried the fatal gene. Back in the USA, the team analysed the blood samples and discovered that the gene was found on the homologous chromosome pair number 4.

The gene was much more tricky to find than those of several other genetic disorders, but in 1993, after searching through some 5 million nucleotide bases on chromosome 4, it was found.

The mutant form of the gene responsible for the disease is nicknamed the 'stuttering gene' because one DNA triplet was found to be repeated up to 100 times in people suffering from the disease.

Identifying the gene makes it much easier to test, before any symptoms appear, whether individuals in affected families have actually inherited the disease, and to identify affected children before birth. The next stage is to understand how the mutant form of the gene actually affects the brain and wreaks its terrible havoc. Then treatment and a cure become a real possibility.

Source: adapted from an article by Susan Katz Miller, *New Scientist*, 24 April 1993

Huntington's disease is a genetic disorder. Once we understand how the genes are inherited, genetic counsellors are able to offer advice to families at risk from this and other disorders. However, human genetics is highly complex, and breeding experiments cannot be carried out on people to test the genetic principles. Can we use the same principles that apply to the breeding of other organisms, such as cats, to humans?

In the future we will probably be able to map the inheritance of a range of genetic disorders. Might people need a genetic licence to breed so that we can reduce the incidence of genetic disease?

10.1   Learning objectives

After working through this chapter, you should be able to:

- **recall** that genes are sections of DNA that control specific characteristics in an organism;

- **recall** that there may be two or more versions of a gene, called alleles;

- **explain** the meanings of the terms genotype and phenotype;

- **use** the terms dominant, recessive and codominant correctly;

- **predict** the results of monohybrid and dihybrid crosses;

- **explain** how the way in which genes are inherited is related to the process of meiosis;

- **explain** and use the term linkage related to genes;

- **explain** how the inheritance of genes carried on the sex chromosomes will be linked to the sex of the offspring;

- **evaluate** issues involved in genetic counselling;

- **explain** how genetic engineering may be used to overcome genetic disorders.

10.2 Dominant and recessive

In eukaryotic cells, the chromosomes in the cell nucleus contain the DNA. A gene is a small section of the giant DNA molecule that forms each chromosome. In every cell nucleus in the body, therefore, there are two copies of the gene that controls whether or not Huntington's disease develops. These two genes are found on the fourth pair of homologous chromosomes. Each gene is found in exactly the same position, called the **locus**, on each chromosome of the pair. There are two slightly different versions of the gene found at that locus. Each version is called an **allele**. Only one allele can occupy the locus on one chromosome.

Even if only one of the two copies of the gene on the homologous pair is the abnormal allele, the disease will develop. This allele is therefore said to be **dominant**. The normal allele is called **recessive**, because its effect is 'hidden in a recess' by the dominant allele when a person has both alleles. A dominant allele usually produces a functional protein, e.g. an enzyme, whereas the recessive gene does not. We do not yet know how the dominant allele causes Huntington's disease, but it may be that it produces a protein that interferes with normal brain functioning.

The composition of the alleles of a person is known as the **genotype**. The **phenotype** is the actual effect of the alleles on the person (Fig. 1).

Fig. 1 Huntington's disease

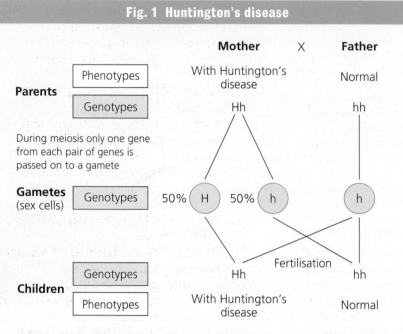

Parents

	Mother	X	Father
Phenotypes	With Huntington's disease		Normal
Genotypes	Hh		hh

During meiosis only one gene from each pair of genes is passed on to a gamete

Gametes (sex cells) — Genotypes: 50% (H) 50% (h) (h)

Fertilisation

Children

Genotypes	Hh	hh
Phenotypes	With Huntington's disease	Normal

Ratio of phenotypes   50:50   With Huntington's disease : Normal

In this genetic diagram, the allele that causes Huntington's disease is H. A capital letter indicates the allele is dominant. The normal recessive allele is h.

Fig. 2 Passing on a deadly allele

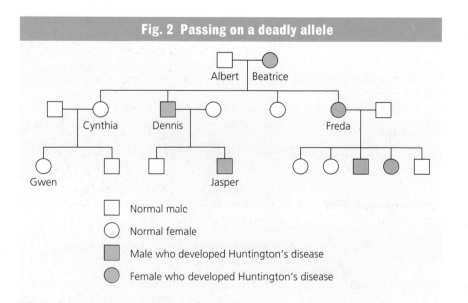

Albert   Beatrice

Cynthia   Dennis   Freda

Gwen   Jasper

☐ Normal male
○ Normal female
■ Male who developed Huntington's disease
● Female who developed Huntington's disease

1 a How can you tell from the family tree in Fig. 2 that only one of Beatrice's genes was the Huntington's disease allele?

b Gwen has three children. She is worried that they might develop Huntington's disease. What advice would you give her? Explain your answer with a genetic diagram.

c What are the chances that a child of Jasper will develop the disease?

d It would be possible to test Jasper's children when they are young, or even before birth, to find out whether they have the allele for the disease. Do you think that this would be a good thing to do? What problems might result from such a test?

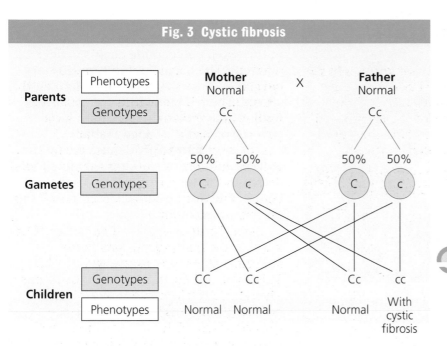

Fig. 3 Cystic fibrosis

		Mother	X	Father
Parents	Phenotypes	Normal		Normal
	Genotypes	Cc		Cc

Gametes Genotypes — 50% C, 50% c (Mother); 50% C, 50% c (Father)

Children	Genotypes	CC	Cc	Cc	cc
	Phenotypes	Normal	Normal	Normal	With cystic fibrosis

Cystic fibrosis

Huntington's disease is unusual in that it is a disease caused by a dominant allele. Cystic fibrosis is an example of a disorder that only appears if both the alleles on each chromosome are the mutated allele (Fig. 3).

Chapter 8 explained that the normal allele of the cystic fibrosis gene makes an important membrane protein, CFTR (page 80). As long as one normal allele is present the cells are able to make CFTR. The recessive allele has a mutation that makes the DNA code incorrect, and CFTR is not made. People who have one normal and one mutant allele are **heterozygous** for that pair of genes. For cystic fibrosis the phenotype of a heterozygous individual is the same as that of people whose alleles of the gene are both normal. These people do not suffer from cystic fibrosis. Children only suffer from the condition if they inherit the recessive allele from both parents. People who have two identical alleles of a gene are called **homozygous**.

Q 2 a What is the ratio of the phenotypes of the children in Fig. 3?
  b What percentage of the children in Fig. 3 would suffer from cystic fibrosis?
  c What percentage of the children would be carriers of the cystic fibrosis allele?
  d About 1 in 25 people carry the cystic fibrosis allele:
  (i) what are the chances of a carrier marrying another carrier;
  (ii) what are the chances of the children having cystic fibrosis if both parents are carriers;
  (iii) in the population as a whole, what proportion of children would you expect to be born with cystic fibrosis?

10.3 Codominance

Different alleles of a gene are not always either dominant or recessive. If two alleles both produce a protein that can function, the phenotype of the heterozygote may be different from that of either homozygote. The alleles are then said to be **codominant**.

Sickle-cell anaemia
Red blood cells depend on the presence of the complex protein haemoglobin to transport oxygen (Fig. 4).

Fig. 4 Haemoglobin

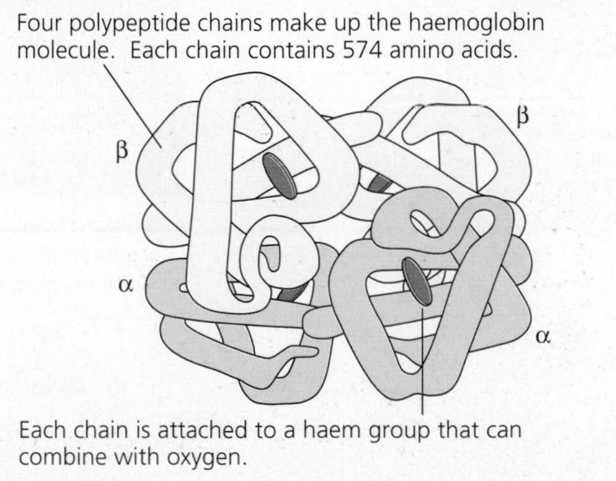

Four polypeptide chains make up the haemoglobin molecule. Each chain contains 574 amino acids.

β

β

α

α

Each chain is attached to a haem group that can combine with oxygen.

The sickle-cell trait is common in the black population in many parts of Central Africa. Malaria is a major killer in these areas. The trait has also been common in the USA among the black population whose ancestors came from Central Africa. The frequency is now declining in this population. The trait is rare in the white population of the USA.

A mutant allele of the normal haemoglobin gene causes one amino acid in the two β polypeptide chains to be different. The haemoglobin can still carry oxygen, but the shape of the molecule is altered. The red blood cells formed as a result of the mutant allele tend to be crescent or 'sickle' shaped (Table 1).

Sickle cells are easily damaged, and the reduced number of working red blood cells decreases the supply of oxygen to the tissues. The heart pumps harder in order to get more blood to the tissues and so

Table 1. Sickle-cell anaemia

Genotype	Phenotype		Effect	
$Hb^A Hb^A$	Normal Red blood cells are normal	A coloured scanning electron micrograph of normal red blood cells.	Efficient oxygen transport. The malarial parasite can grow in the red blood cells, so there is no resistance to malaria.	A light micrograph of malarial parasites growing in human red blood cells.
$Hb^S Hb^S$	Sickle-cell anaemia Red blood cells are sickle-shaped	A coloured scanning electron micrograph of sickled and normal red blood cells. Magnification × 1700.	The red blood cells break up easily, resulting in severe shortage of red blood cells. The extra demand for oxygen supply to the tissues puts excessive strain on the heart. Most victims die in early childhood.	
$Hb^A Hb^S$	Sickle-cell trait About one-third of the red blood cells are sickle-shaped; the others are normal		Sufficient oxygen transport. The malarial parasite cannot grow well in the red blood cells, so there is a high resistance to malaria.	

Hb stands for the gene for haemoglobin. The alleles are represented by superscripts; A is the normal allele; S is the sickle allele.

maintain the oxygen supply. However, the damaged cells tend to clump together, making the blood more sticky and harder to pump. This has numerous side-effects, including increased likelihood of kidney failure, strokes and heart attack. The spleen is over-burdened with breaking down the damaged red cells and loses its ability to remove bacteria from the blood, so the victim suffers from frequent infections.

On the other hand, red blood cells with some sickle-cell haemoglobin molecules prevent malarial parasites from developing. Thus one minor change in the DNA code in a gene can have far-reaching effects that, although often harmful, may be beneficial in certain circumstances.

3 a How do people who are heterozygous differ from those who are homozygous for the normal haemoglobin allele?

b What would the ratio of the phenotypes of the offspring of two heterozygotes be? Use a genetic diagram to explain your answer.

c Using the information opposite explain the declining frequency of sickle-cell anaemia in the USA.

Factors like codominance make it very difficult to explain the precise action of genes. To make things even worse, most human characteristics are determined by several, or many, pairs of genes.

10.4 Good breeding

A Scottish wild cat.

The study of genetics has helped us to understand human genetic disorders like Huntington's disease and cystic fibrosis. It is also extremely useful when it comes to breeding domestic animals and improving the quality of crop plants. Most of the animals that we commonly have as pets or use for food are very different from their wild ancestors.

4 List the similarities and differences between the cats in the photographs.

A long-haired domestic cat.

A short-haired domestic cat.

A Siamese-Burmese cross domestic cat.

Siamese and Burmese cats both have particular alleles of a gene, C. The normal allele, C^C, makes the cat's coat blackish and is dominant. Siamese cats have a recessive allele, C^s, and must be homozygous for this allele. This allele codes for an enzyme which synthesises black pigment, but only below body temperature. This is because the mutant allele produces an enzyme with a tertiary structure that is slightly different from that of the normal enzyme, and which happens to unfold (denature) at about 37°C. The Siamese cat therefore is only black in the cooler parts of the body, such as the tail, ears and lower legs. The rest of the coat is pale cream coloured. This shows how the phenotype is affected by both the genotype and the environment.

The Burmese cats have a different allele of the gene, C^b, which makes the coat colour dark brown instead of pale cream. The extremities are black as in the Siamese.

5 a What are the genotypes of:
   (i) a Siamese cat;
   (ii) a Burmese cat?
   b Most cats have the 'normal' allele, C^C. What will the kittens be like if a Siamese mates with an ordinary homozygous black cat? Explain your answer with a genetic diagram.

6 a What is the genotype of the breeder's pale brown kittens?
   b Are the alleles codominant? Explain your answer.
   c What results would you expect if two of these pale brown cats interbreed?
   d If the breeder wants to sell kittens with this pale brown coat colour, how should she obtain litters that are entirely pale brown?

Crosses involving one gene are called **monohybrid** crosses. There are patterns in the ratios of the phenotypes of offspring that will be produced in monohybrid crosses. For example, if two alleles of a gene are dominant and recessive, respectively, crossing heterozygotes will give a 3:1 ratio of phenotypes, whereas if the alleles are codominant the ratio will be 1:2:1.

Manx cats are tailless. When bred together they produce an apparently odd ratio of 2 tailless:1 normal tailed. This was explained when it was realised that embryos that are homozygous for the Manx allele fail to develop in the womb and are therefore never born (Fig. 5).

7 What proportion of the kittens will have tails if a Manx cat mates with a tailed cat?

'In order to preserve the pedigree of my cats, I have to be careful that my different varieties do not interbreed. However, when one of my Siamese did breed with a Burmese, the kittens had pale brown coats, which some people thought was very nice.

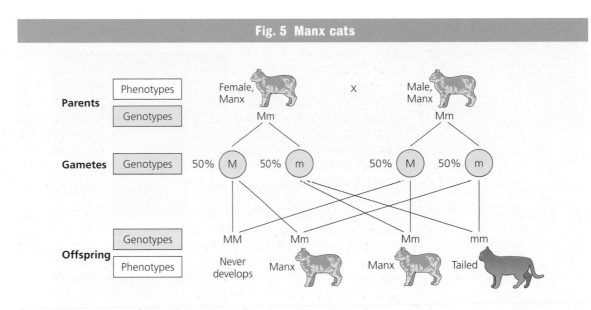

Fig. 5 Manx cats

Parents	Phenotypes	Female, Manx	X Male, Manx
	Genotypes	Mm	Mm
Gametes	Genotypes	50% M 50% m	50% M 50% m
Offspring	Genotypes	MM Mm	Mm mm
	Phenotypes	Never develops Manx	Manx Tailed

Key ideas

- The DNA of a gene usually codes for the production of a protein that determines or influences a particular characteristic.

- A body cell has a pair of genes at the same locus on homologous chromosomes that controls the production of a particular protein.

- One allele can be dominant over another, recessive, allele.

- Only the dominant gene is expressed in the phenotype of a heterozygous individual.

- Codominance is when two different alleles are both expressed in the phenotype of a heterozygous individual.

- The phenotype of an individual depends not only on the individual's genotype, but also on the environment in which it develops.

10.5 Dihybrid inheritance

The inheritance of coat colour in cats is complex. Several pairs of genes are involved. Crosses involving two pairs of genes are **dihybrid** crosses.

When Mrs Smith wants to breed particular combinations of colour in her Siamese cats, she has to take more than one pair of genes into account. As well as the coat colour genes, $C^s C^s$, two other pairs of genes control the colour of the tail, face, legs and ears (the 'points' as cat breeders call them). One pair of genes makes the hair on the points either black or brown.

The other pair affects the spread of pigment in the points. This makes the hair either dark or lighter.

These two pairs of genes affect each other. For example, if a cat with genes for black hair also has genes for evenly spread pigment, it will have dark black points which the breeders call seal. If instead the cat is homozygous for patchy pigment the points will look pale black (called blue by breeders). Similarly, brown hair may be either dark brown (chocolate) or pale brown (lilac).

Table 2. Siamese cats

Gene	Allele	Genotype	Phenotype
Colour of hair in points	B	BB Bb	Black hair
	b	bb	Brown hair
Density of hair colour in points	D	DD Dd	Pigment in hair evenly spread and therefore dark
	d	dd	Pigment in hair patchy and therefore lighter

This seal-point cat could have the genotype BBDD.

This blue-point cat could have the genotype Bbdd.

This chocolate-point cat could have the genotype bbDD.

This lilac-point cat must have the genotype bbdd.

8 **Using Table 2, what colour would the genotypes BBDd, bbDd, BBdd, BbDd produce?**

When working out the possible results of a particular breeding programme, a breeder needs to draw charts that show the various combinations of the alleles of the two pairs of genes.

Suppose Mrs Smith starts with a Siamese cat with seal points, whose pedigree was entirely seal, i.e. all its known ancestors also had seal points. Such a cat will be pure-bred for the two genes and will have the genotype BBDD. She mates this cat with one with lilac points, whose genotype must be bbdd.

Remember that as a result of meiosis the gametes will receive one of each pair of genes. Therefore each gamete must get one gene for hair colour and one for colour density (Fig. 6).

All the kittens must be seal because they have the dominant alleles for both black and dense colour. This example is quite straightforward because the gametes of a pure-breeding organism are all the same.

Fig. 6 BBDD x bbdd cross

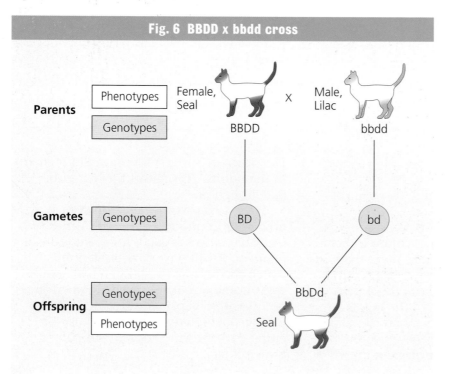

Parents	Phenotypes	Female, Seal X Male, Lilac	
	Genotypes	BBDD bbdd	
Gametes	Genotypes	BD bd	
Offspring	Genotypes	BbDd	
	Phenotypes	Seal	

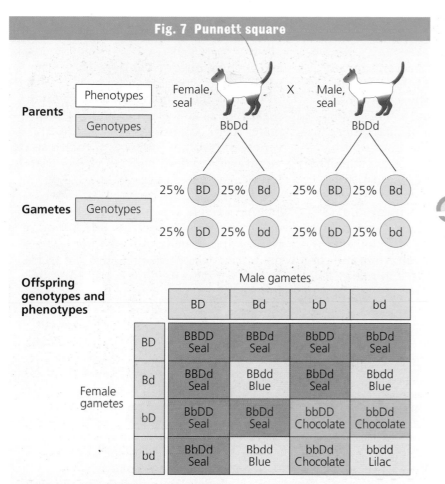

Fig. 7 Punnett square

Parents		Female, seal	X	Male, seal
Phenotypes				
Genotypes		BbDd		BbDd

Gametes Genotypes: 25% BD, 25% Bd, 25% BD, 25% Bd, 25% bD, 25% bd, 25% bD, 25% bd

Offspring genotypes and phenotypes

Female gametes		Male gametes			
		BD	Bd	bD	bd
	BD	BBDD Seal	BBDd Seal	BbDD Seal	BbDd Seal
	Bd	BBDd Seal	BBdd Blue	BbDd Seal	Bbdd Blue
	bD	BbDD Seal	BbDd Seal	bbDD Chocolate	bbDd Chocolate
	bd	BbDd Seal	Bbdd Blue	bbDd Chocolate	bbdd Lilac

Ratio of phenotypes   9 Seal: 3 Blue: 3 Chocolate: 1 Lilac

What would happen if two cats like those from the last cross mated, i.e. cats which were heterozygous for both genes? Four different gamete genotypes are produced by heterozygotes, and the possible crosses are best shown in a chart. A **Punnett square** is one sort of chart that can be used (Fig. 7).

Notice that the ratio of the four phenotypes is 9:3:3:1. This is the mathematical effect of the 3:1 ratio applied to each of the two pairs of genes.

9 a What are the phenotypes and their ratio for the cross shown in Fig. 8?

b In order to get particular varieties, a breeder has to keep careful records of the results of all matings. Mrs Smith wants to get pure-breeding blue-point cats. She has some blue-point males and females obtained from crosses between seal-point cats.

(i) What are the possible genotypes of these blue-point cats?

(ii) Explain how she can use these blue-point cats to obtain blue-point cats which are definitely true-breeding. You can assume that each mating will produce between four and seven kittens. Draw genetic diagrams to show the results of the crosses that you describe.

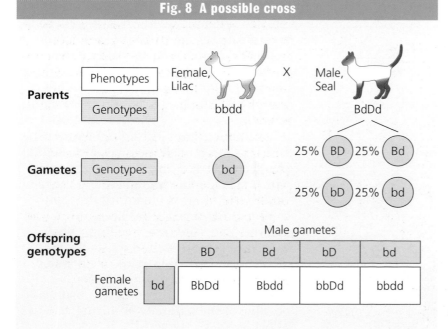

Fig. 8 A possible cross

Parents		Female, Lilac	X	Male, Seal
Phenotypes				
Genotypes		bbdd		BdDd

Gametes Genotypes: bd ; 25% BD, 25% Bd, 25% bD, 25% bd

Offspring genotypes

Female gametes		Male gametes			
		BD	Bd	bD	bd
	bd	BbDd	Bbdd	bbDd	bbdd

10.6 Independent genes

Genes do not always interact in the same way as the two that affect the colour of the points in Siamese cats. The effects of two different pairs of genes are usually completely independent of each other.

One pair of genes determines whether the stem of pea plants is long or short. The allele for tallness, T, is dominant to the allele for dwarfness, t.

Another pair of genes controls the production of an enzyme involved in starch synthesis in the pea seeds. Normally peas have the allele, R, for this enzyme, and the dried pea seeds are smooth and round. The mutant allele, r, has an extra section of DNA which prevents the enzyme working. As a result the seeds contain more sugar and become distorted as they dry, so the seeds appear wrinkled.

Because the wrinkled seeds have more sugar they taste sweeter, and many people prefer them. A grower who has a dwarf variety of pea that produces wrinkled seeds might want to develop a tall variety that has wrinkled seeds (Fig. 9).

On average only three out of 16 seeds will have a genotype that will give a tall plant with wrinkled seeds. Only a third of these will be **true-breeding**. In order to obtain a stock of true-breeding plants, the grower will have to grow wrinkled seeds from the F_2 plants. The tall plants will be allowed to self-fertilise. All the seeds in this next F_3 generation will be wrinkled, but some will grow into dwarf plants. These come from F_2 plants that are not true-breeding; only seeds from F_2 plants whose offspring are all tall should be used by the grower as the basis of his stock.

10 a What is the genotype of tall F_2 plants with wrinkled seeds which produce dwarf plants?
  b Draw a genetic diagram to show how dwarf plants are produced when these F_2 plants self-fertilise.

Plant and animal breeders often need to manipulate several pairs of genes in order to get the desired characteristics into a particular variety of organism. For example, a new strain of rice produces 25% more grain by having seed heads on every shoot. Before this variety can be of commercial use it has to have other features bred into it. Resistance to fungal disease is one essential characteristic. Fortunately there are genes which provide this resistance, and the new variety will be cross-bred until the right combination of genes has been introduced and the plants are true-breeding. Often genes for features such as resistance to disease occur in wild strains of cultivated plants, and it is for this reason that geneticists are concerned that as many as possible of the naturally occurring varieties of plants are conserved.

Fig. 9 Pea crosses

Pollen is transferred with a brush from the anthers of a tall plant grown from round seeds to the stigma of a dwarf plant, grown from wrinkled seeds.

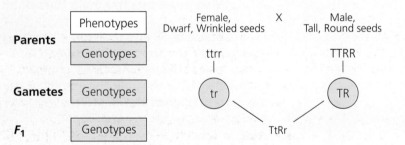

Parents

| Phenotypes | Female, Dwarf, Wrinkled seeds | X | Male, Tall, Round seeds |

| Genotypes | ttrr | | TTRR |

Gametes Genotypes — tr — TR

F_1 Genotypes — TtRr

All the seeds of the first generation, called the F_1, will be round and will grow into tall plants. The flowers of the F_1 plants are allowed to self-fertilise, i.e. the pollen transfers to the stigma of the same flower. This generation is called the F_2.

Pollen (male gametes)

F_2 genotypes and phenotypes		TR	Tr	tR	tr
Egg cells (female gametes)	TR	TTRR Tall Round seeds	TTRr Tall Round seeds	TtRR Tall Round seeds	TtRr Tall Round seeds
	Tr	TTRr Tall Round seeds	TTrr Tall Wrinkled seeds	TtRr Tall Round seeds	Ttrr Tall Wrinkled seeds
	tR	TtRR Tall Round seeds	TtRr Tall Round seeds	ttRR Dwarf Round seeds	ttRr Dwarf Round seeds
	tr	TtRr Tall Round seeds	Ttrr Tall Wrinkled seeds	ttRr Dwarf Round seeds	ttrr Dwarf Wrinkled seeds

Ratio of phenotypes 9 Tall, Round seeds : 3 Dwarf, Round seeds : 3 Tall, Wrinkled seeds : 1 Dwarf, Wrinkled seed

The Baudet du Poitou ass is a rare, unusually large breed.

11 a **11 a** Cultivated varieties of crop plants tend to be homozygous for a large proportion of genes. Explain how artificial breeding causes this.

b A number of societies maintain stocks of old-fashioned breeds of animals, which often have poorer yields or qualities than more modern varieties. What is the possible benefit of keeping these breeds?

Of course the process of combining alleles in different ways also occurs naturally. Chapter 9 showed how meiosis and fertilisation bring together new combinations of alleles, and it is this which maintains a range of genetic variation in each species. Breeders simply control this process in order to obtain particular combinations of characteristics.

10.7 Linkage

In the previous examples of dihybrid inheritance we have assumed that the two genes are on different chromosomes. If, however, the two genes are both on the same chromosome, the alleles will not separate randomly. Indeed the genes on the same chromosome will be linked together, and different alleles will only separate if crossing over occurs in meiosis.

Sex linkage

Chapter 9 explained how the sex of an animal is determined by a special pair of chromosomes. Human females have two X chromosomes, whereas males have an X and a Y. These chromosomes also have genes for other characteristics on them.

However, as the X chromosome is much larger than the Y, many of these genes occur on the X chromosome but not on the Y.

One gene on the X chromosome affects a pigment in the retina of the eye. A mutant allele of this gene causes red/green colour blindness. This means the sufferer cannot distinguish between red and green. Since males only carry this gene on their one X chromosome, they will be red/green colour blind if this gene is the mutant allele. Females will only be red/green colour blind if they inherit the allele on both chromosomes. Males have a one in two chance of inheriting the condition if their mother carries the mutant allele (Fig. 10).

Fig. 10 Colour blindness

In genetic diagrams, a sex-linked gene is shown alongside the sex chromosome. In red/green colour blindness, the allele for normal colour vision is C, and the mutant is c. A chromosome with the normal allele is written X^C, and with a mutant allele, X^c. The Y chromosome has no gene for this characteristic.

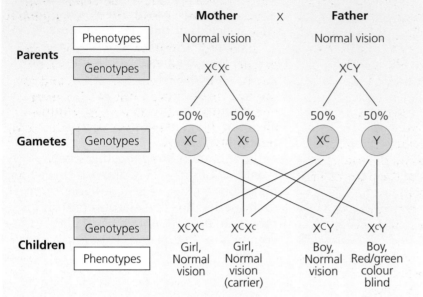

12 a What proportion of boys from the cross in Fig. 10 is red/green colour blind?

b What parental genotypes could produce a red/green colour blind girl?

c Why does a boy never inherit red/green colour blindness from his father?

Key ideas

- Genes that are on different chromosomes are separated independently, and all combinations of two pairs of genes are possible.

- A ratio of 9:3:3:1 is common when two factors are controlled by two independently sorted genes.

- If two pairs of genes are linked together on the same pair of chromosomes, the genes will remain linked during meiosis, unless crossing over takes place between them.

- Some genes are present on the sex chromosomes, and their effects are therefore linked to the sex of the individual.

- In males a recessive allele on some parts of the X chromosome can show its phenotype because it has no partner on the Y chromosome.

10.8 Looking forward

Knowing the history of a disorder in a family, a genetic counsellor can advise parents about the chances of their children having that particular disorder. For example, when her mother was diagnosed as having Huntington's disease, Nancy Wexler knew that she had a 50:50 chance of developing the same illness.

13 a Explain with a genetic diagram how Nancy knew her chances of developing Huntington's disease.

b A couple's first child has cystic fibrosis. What advice could a genetic counsellor give them about the chance of their next child also having cystic fibrosis?

Haemophilia

Haemophilia is an inherited disorder in which the blood fails to clot easily. Haemophiliacs suffer from internal bleeding, especially in the joints, due to shortage of a blood clotting protein known as Factor VIII. The gene for Factor VIII synthesis is found on the X chromosome and so is sex-linked. It is written as X^H. A recessive allele causes the failure in Factor VIII production. It is written as X^h.

Counselling can help people to decide whether or not to have children. Couples whose babies are at risk from a serious genetic disorder may choose to have tests during the early stages of pregnancy and perhaps opt for an abortion if the embryo is affected.

Such understanding does not offer any prospects of a cure for genetic disorders. The more recent research on DNA and the ways in which genes work has, however, opened up a whole range of possibilities, including the potential for finding cures for inherited disorders.

14 a What is the genotype of a haemophiliac male?

b Haemophiliac females are very rare. What would be the most likely genotypes of the parents of a haemophiliac girl?

c A haemophiliac man marries a woman who does not have haemophilia.
(i) What advice would you give this couple about the likelihood of any of their children having haemophilia?
(ii) The couple has a family which includes both boys and girls. What advice would you give to the boys and to the girls about the chances of passing on haemophilia to their children?

Queen Victoria was a carrier of haemophilia.

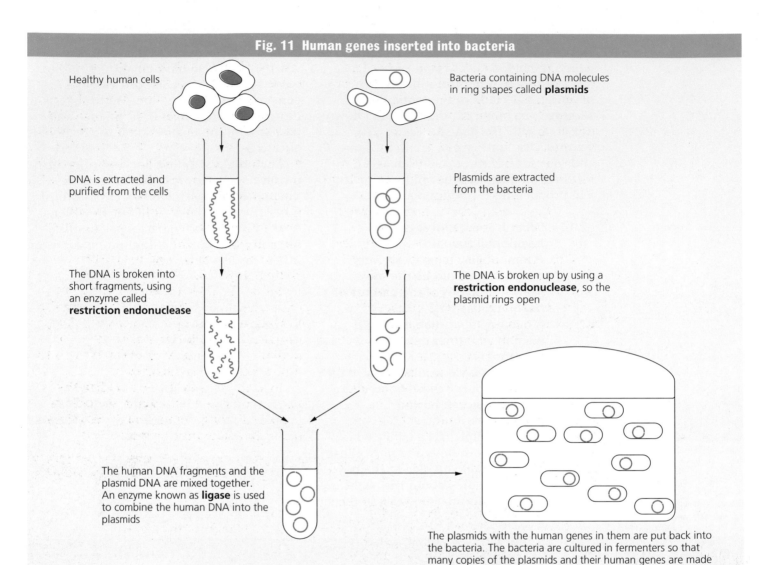

Fig. 11 Human genes inserted into bacteria

Healthy human cells

Bacteria containing DNA molecules in ring shapes called **plasmids**

DNA is extracted and purified from the cells

Plasmids are extracted from the bacteria

The DNA is broken into short fragments, using an enzyme called **restriction endonuclease**

The DNA is broken up by using a **restriction endonuclease**, so the plasmid rings open

The human DNA fragments and the plasmid DNA are mixed together. An enzyme known as **ligase** is used to combine the human DNA into the plasmids

The plasmids with the human genes in them are put back into the bacteria. The bacteria are cultured in fermenters so that many copies of the plasmids and their human genes are made

Genetic engineering

Chapter 8 mentioned that scientists have found ways of taking genes from one organism and inserting them into another. The collection of techniques that make this possible is known as **genetic engineering**.

Genes for useful products can be put into other animals so that they make quantities of the substance. This was the technique used to produce alpha-1-antitrypsin in Tracey's milk, described on page 79. The protein extracted from the sheep's milk can be used to treat cystic fibrosis sufferers.

Genes can also be inserted into crop plants to improve their qualities. Genes have been added to tomatoes to slow down the ripening process so that the fruit will stay fresh longer.

Genes for useful products can be put into bacteria. The bacteria can then be cultured so that they make large quantities of the useful substance. Human growth hormone and insulin have been made in this way.

Using the technique of inserting human DNA fragments into bacteria means that substances that are identical to those produced by human genes can be made in large quantities by culturing the bacteria in fermenters (Fig. 11). The substances are more effective, much cheaper and less likely to cause allergic reactions than equivalent products obtained from animal sources. For example, insulin can be obtained from the pancreases of cattle killed for meat, but about 5% of diabetics are allergic to this cow's insulin. Human growth hormone is extracted from pituitary glands taken from human corpses. As only small amounts are present in each gland, it is very expensive, and there is also the risk of the extract being contaminated by disease. The genetically engineered hormone can safely be used to treat children who have stunted growth.

However, it is not easy to isolate the required gene from the DNA extracted from human cells. The way that was used to obtain the human growth hormone gene was to collect mRNA from an active pituitary gland. An enzyme was then used to make the complementary strand of DNA from this mRNA, putting the normal process of transcription into reverse. This ensured that only growth hormone DNA was used to insert into the plasmids.

A different technique was used to make insulin. Insulin is an exceptionally small protein, with only 51 amino acids. It was therefore possible to synthesise the DNA artificially with the correct sequence of bases to code for the amino acids in the right order.

In some cases the problems have been overcome by the careful selection of a restriction endonuclease. Restriction endonucleases are enzymes that occur naturally in bacteria. They protect the bacteria from viruses by chopping up the viral DNA. There are many different forms of the enzyme, and they break the DNA molecules at particular places according to the base sequence. The most useful ones cut the parallel strands of DNA unevenly, leaving 'sticky ends' which are readily inserted into plasmids by another enzyme called ligase (Fig. 12).

Viruses are often used in genetic engineering. This is because viruses reproduce by injecting their genes into other cells, which then make copies of the genes and hence copies of the virus. By using strains of virus that are not potentially harmful, viruses can be used to insert useful genes into cells.

By using viruses, genes from healthy people could be inserted into the cells of people suffering from a genetic disorder in order to replace missing genes. This

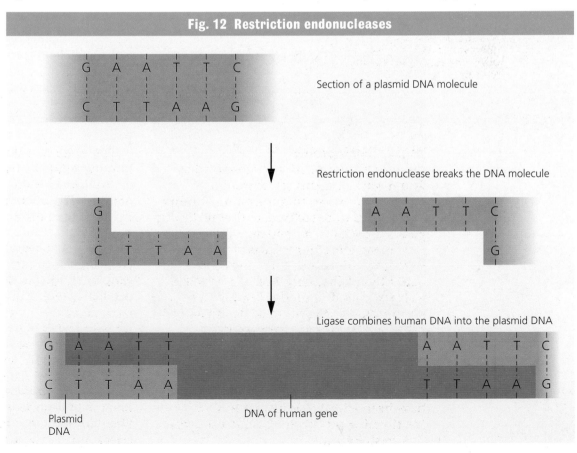

Fig. 12 Restriction endonucleases

Section of a plasmid DNA molecule

Restriction endonuclease breaks the DNA molecule

Ligase combines human DNA into the plasmid DNA

Plasmid DNA

DNA of human gene

Fig. 13 Using viruses

A restriction endonuclease is used to isolate the normal ADA gene from the DNA of healthy cells

The normal gene is inserted into a virus

The virus is incubated with a cell culture. The virus injects its genetic material into the cell, which makes many copies of the virus with the ADA gene

The viruses with the ADA gene are mixed with the patient's white blood cells. The viruses inject their genetic material into the nucleus of the white blood cells

Developing white cells are removed from the bone marrow of the patient with ADA deficiency

Nucleus

The white blood cells are cloned in the laboratory

White blood cells, which now contain normal ADA genes, are transfused back into the patient. In the body of the patient these young cells will divide to produce a supply of cells with ADA genes

This child is playing inside a biological isolation garment. It is a type of space suit that has been customised for patients who are highly vulnerable to infection, e.g. after a bone marrow transplant or if suffering from ADA.

technique could provide a cure for diabetes if insulin genes could be put into pancreatic cells. It has been used to help the victims of one rare immune deficiency disease, ADA.

ADA deficiency is a genetic disorder in which a child is unable to make an enzyme (called adenosine deaminase) that the immune system needs to function properly. If the allele of the gene that normally makes ADA is missing, the child is susceptible to many infections, and often has to be protected in an isolation 'bubble' to prevent exposure to germs. A carefully chosen virus can be used to replace this gene in children suffering from ADA deficiency (Fig. 13).

15 a The ADA gene inserted by the virus would not be passed on to any child of the patient that was treated. Explain why not.

b If the patient has children, they are unlikely to suffer from ADA deficiency. Explain why.

Genetic engineering is opening up many possibilities. It may be that members of Nancy Wexler's family could be cured of Huntington's disease by inserting normal genes into them. It may even be possible to replace the faulty genes in their reproductive cells so that the disease cannot be passed on to their children.

Many people, however, are worried about some aspects of the developments in this field. Consider, for example, the following issues.

- Is it right to transfer genes from one species to another?
- Is it safe to release organisms with altered genes into the environment, as in the case of crops with genes added to make them resistant to weedkillers?
- Is it ethical to use animals with extra genes to supply substances to satisfy human needs, as with Tracey and her milk?
- Is there a danger of producing bacteria or viruses with new genetic combinations that might cause diseases which cannot be controlled by existing drugs?

- Who should own potentially life-saving genes or genetically engineered organisms? Is it right for researchers or companies to patent them?
- Is it right to alter the genes in sperms or eggs and so to affect future generations?
- Should parents be able to choose genes to introduce into their baby in order to determine its characteristics and personality?

These and other similar problems have to be faced by scientists and politicians in order to make sure that genetic engineering is controlled responsibly. You should think about the arguments for and against these difficult questions and decide how you stand on these issues.

16 **Prepare a short speech, about 2 minutes, for a radio broadcast about genetic engineering. Summarise the argument on either side of one of the issues listed above.**

Key ideas

- Genetic counselling uses understanding of inheritance to explain to people the chances of suffering from genetic disorders and to help families manage the consequences of these.

- In genetic engineering genes are taken from one organism and inserted into another. Restriction endonuclease enzymes can be used to extract the relevant section of DNA. Ligase enzyme is used to join this DNA into the DNA of the other organism.

- Genetic engineering makes it possible to introduce new genes into organisms to improve their qualities, and to replace genes that cause genetic disorders. However, the techniques involved raise concerns about safety and ethics.

Introducing variation

Amnesty concerts raise awareness of human rights for people all over the world, whatever their race, creed or colour.

People vary and we all take it for granted that we can recognise each other on the basis of certain distinctive features. Some of the more obvious characteristics are used to group people into races, but closer analysis shows patterns of differences that do not match with generally accepted racial groups. Our genes suggest that we share many more similarities than differences.

A human being has about one hundred thousand functional genes. Of these, approximately two-thirds seem to be identical in all individuals. The other third have two or more alleles. These alleles combine in a vast number of different ways, so no two fertilised ova are exactly the same. It is rather like doing the pools with 30 thousand teams!

Two randomly chosen people of the same race will have from 85% to 88% of their genes in common. If the two people happen to be from different races, the proportion changes by less than 2%.

11.1 Learning objectives

After working through this chapter, you should be able to:

- **explain** the difference between continuous and discontinuous variation;

- **explain** how both genetic and environmental factors contribute to variation;

- **summarise** the possible causes of variation in living organisms;

- **explain** how particular variations may give some individuals a selective advantage, so that they are more likely to survive and pass on their genes to following generations;

- **explain** how the process of natural selection may result in a species changing over a period of time;

- **describe** examples of natural selection producing changes within a population.

11.2 A world of differences

Discontinuous variation

In Europe there are some distinctive differences between peoples living close together. The Basques who inhabit the Pyrenees on either side of the French/Spanish border have blood groups that are markedly different from those of their neighbours. This, as well as their distinctive language, suggests that they came to the area quite separately from the peoples around them.

All humans belong to one of four major blood groups: A, B, AB or O. Your blood group is controlled by a gene at one locus. There are three alleles, A, B and o. The alleles A and B are codominant and each codes for production of an **antigen.** Antigens are molecules on the membrane of red blood cells that are involved in the body's immune system. The allele o codes for no antigen, and is in effect recessive to A and B (Fig. 1). Individuals can have one of the four possible phenotypes. Such variation is called **discontinuous** because each of the phenotypes is quite distinct. You could not be halfway between A and O groups.

The phenotype blood group B occurs in different proportions in different populations of people (Fig. 2).

1 a In which populations are the proportions of people with blood group B similar to each other?
  b Does the occurrence of blood group B tie up with the characteristic of skin colour?
  c How might the different proportions in black and white people in the USA be explained?

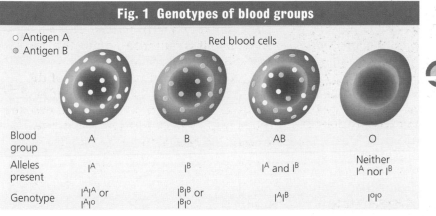

Fig. 1 Genotypes of blood groups

○ Antigen A
● Antigen B

Red blood cells

Blood group	A	B	AB	O
Alleles present	I^A	I^B	I^A and I^B	Neither I^A nor I^B
Genotype	$I^A I^A$ or $I^A I^o$	$I^B I^B$ or $I^B I^o$	$I^A I^B$	$I^o I^o$

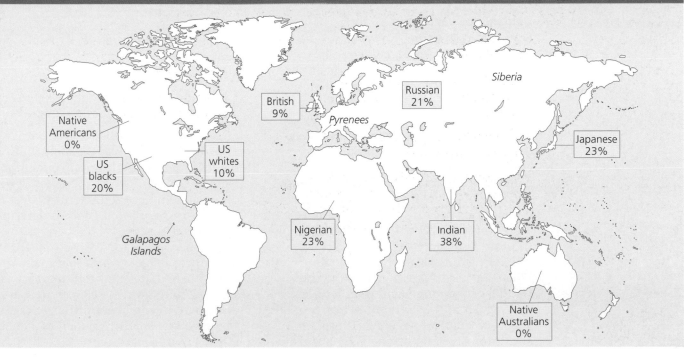

Fig. 2 Percentage of blood group B in peoples from different parts of the world

Native Americans 0%
US blacks 20%
US whites 10%
British 9%
Russian 21%
Siberia
Japanese 23%
Pyrenees
Nigerian 23%
Indian 38%
Galapagos Islands
Native Australians 0%

Blood groups A and B are well known because of the problems they can cause in blood transfusions. However, there are many other antigens on cell membranes that can cause transplanted tissue to be rejected. Two particular loci on human chromosomes are genes that are responsible for antigens on white blood cell membranes. They are known to have at least 23 and 47 alleles, respectively. Each allele produces a slightly different antigen molecule, which can be detected by a technique called human leucocyte antigen (HLA) typing. Even the HLA genes with their numerous alleles produce discontinuous variation because each antigen is distinctly different.

By studying the distribution of blood group, HLA and other genes it is possible to build up a picture of the complex patterns of migration that have taken place in human history.

It seems that the first humans originated in Africa and then spread around the world. Study of the genes of the **native** (original) inhabitants of North and South America suggests that a small group of people, with a limited range of alleles of some genes, reached North America from Siberia and then gradually populated the continent. This original population happened not to have the blood group B allele.

Continuous variation

Some characteristics, however, are affected by several genes in such a complex way that it is not possible to distinguish separate phenotypes. A person's height depends on many different factors, including the growth rate of several different bones, hormone production and metabolic rate. Each factor may be controlled directly or indirectly by several genes, so that a wide range of phenotypes occurs. This type of variation is called **continuous** because it is difficult to sort out all the possible types into distinct groups. In most cases the interactions of the different genes mean that the majority of individuals is somewhere close to the middle of the range, with many fewer individuals at the extremes. Thus very tall and very small adults are rare. A graph of a continuously variable characteristic usually

A man as tall as this is not a common sight! In 1972, Chris Greener was the tallest man in Britain, at 7 feet 4¾ inches.

Fig. 3 Normal distribution curve for height

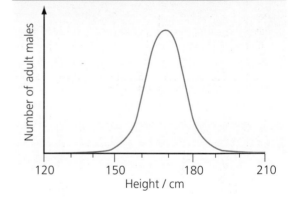

gives a normal distribution curve (Fig. 3).

Characteristics may also be affected by environmental factors. A person's adult height may well be affected by diet or disease during childhood. Often it is very difficult to distinguish the contributions made by genes and by environmental factors. For many years there has been disagreement between scientists over the extent to which intelligence is determined by a person's genes.

It is becoming increasingly clear that many people have genes that make them more likely to develop certain diseases, such as some forms of cancer. However, the disease may only occur if the genes are triggered by something, such as a chemical, in the environment.

In some organisms the way in which a gene is expressed depends on some environmental factor. The effect of temperature on the pigment gene in Siamese cats, described in Chapter 10, is a good example of this.

In alligators temperature even affects the genes that determine sex. Eggs incubated at 30°C all develop into females; eggs incubated at 33°C become males. The position and depth of a nest can therefore affect whether male or female young are produced. One effect of this is that the alligator can produce more females than males, and in practice there may be as many as eight females for every male.

An alligator on its nest of eggs in Florida.

Fig. 4 Graphs of variation

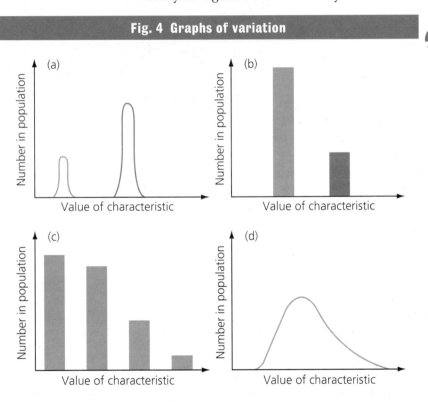

(a) Number in population / Value of characteristic

(b) Number in population / Value of characteristic

(c) Number in population / Value of characteristic

(d) Number in population / Value of characteristic

2a What might the advantage of the ratio of males to females described above be for the alligator population?

b What environmental factors might affect how tall a plant grows?

c Which of the graphs/bar charts in Fig. 4 shows the number of individuals in a population for each of the following characteristics? In each case give the reason for your answer:

(i) human ABO blood groups;

(ii) human earwax type, which is either wet or dry and is determined by one pair of alleles and is unaffected by the environment;

(iii) human mass, which is determined by several genes and by environmental factors;

(iv) tall and dwarf peas, determined by one pair of alleles, each being affected by the environment.

Key ideas

- Individual members of a species show many differences from each other.

- Where only one or a small number of genes causes the variation, there are clear-cut differences. This is discontinuous variation.

- Where many genes and environmental factors are involved, a range of variation, without distinct types, occurs. This is continuous variation.

- Variation depends on both genetic and environmental influences.

11.3 Why is a child different from its parents?

Table 1. Main causes of variation	
Cause of variation	**How variation is produced**
Gene mutation	Error occurs during replication of DNA in a gene. A change in the order of bases alters the amino acid sequence in the protein for which the gene codes (Chap. 8, page 85).
Independent assortment	During meiosis the maternal and paternal chromosomes are reshuffled. The chromosomes, and thus the genes, of each parent combine in new ways (Chap. 9, page 96).
Crossing-over	During the first stage of meiosis chromatids of homologous pairs exchange parts. Linked alleles may separate and rejoin in new combinations (Chap. 9, page 96).
Chromosome mutation	One or more chromosomes may also break during meiosis. Part of the chromosome with its genes may be deleted, or moved to another position.
Random fertilisation	Each parent produces huge numbers of different gametes. Which pair fuses is a matter of chance (Chap. 9, page 96).
Environmental factors	The effect of genes may be changed by factors such as diet, disease or temperature during development; other factors, like radiation and chemicals, may cause gene mutations in some tissues which then grow abnormally (Chap. 8, page 86; Chap. 10, page 108; Chap. 11, page 123).

3 a Using Table 1, explain what could cause the offspring of asexually reproducing organisms to differ from their parents.

  b What could cause identical twins to differ from each other?

  c Why do the two unfertilised ova which give rise to non-identical twins differ from each other?

Only their mother can tell them apart.

These two girls are identical twins.

Arnold Schwarzenegger and Danny DeVito are unidentical twins!

Despite the broad range of variation, people of all nationalities are quite clearly human beings. Human beings always produce human beings; cats always produce cats; earthworms produce earthworms; and so on. Why, then, do so many species reproduce sexually and therefore boost the amount of variation? What are the advantages of individuals being different? Why do members of a species not become more and more varied until they are no longer recognisably similar to each other?

Table 2. Percentages of genotype hh			
Generation	% of genotype hh failing to breed		
	2%	10%	50%
0	50	50	50
5	48	40	11
10	46	31	4
15	44	24	2
20	42	18	1

Q4 a In the model in Fig. 5, what factors could limit the size of the population that can live on the island?

b Suppose that each pair of rodents produces about 20 young in a year. What would happen to the population if all of these young survived to breed?

c If the adults live on average for only a year, how many of these young must survive if the size of the population is to stay roughly constant?

d Show the data in Table 2 graphically.

e Assuming that the population stayed constant at 10 000, how many individuals would show the phenotype of the recessive allele after 20 generations at each selection pressure?

f What would happen to the frequency of the h allele in the population in each case?

Fig. 5 Change over time

❸ Some might die from sheer bad luck, such as a rock falling on them. Some may inherit a pair of recessive genes that cause a fatal disorder. As a result of continuous variation some will be smaller than others, some will have thicker layers of fat under the skin, some will have longer fur, some may be better at finding seeds, some may be able to stretch higher to reach seeds on the shrubs, some may produce enzymes that help them to digest other parts of the plants, and so on. **Which of these features will help them to compete more successfully for food? Which will help the rodents survive the colder climate?**

❶ Imagine a small island on which just shrubs and grasses grow. A group of small rodents reaches the island, perhaps floating to it on tree trunks blown out to sea by a storm. The rodents feed on the seeds of the grasses and shrubs. The climate of the island is somewhat colder than the mainland from which the rodents came. **What would you expect to happen to the size of the population of rodents during the first few years?**

❹ The rodents have two alleles for a hair length gene: long, H, and short, h. On the mainland, from where the rodents originally came, the two phenotypes happened to be present in exactly equal numbers. The longer hair length gives better insulation against the cold, so on the island the short phenotype becomes less favourable (Table 2). **What will happen to the rodents with genes for features that favour survival? What will happen in the population to the frequency of the alleles that favour survival?**

❷ With no predators and plenty of food the rodents do very well. There is, however, a limit to the number of rodents that can survive on the island. Many of the young rodents will die before they can breed. **What might cause the rodents to die?**

❺ It seems a reasonable prediction that the rodents with genes that help them to survive are more likely to be successful. They are therefore more likely to breed and pass on these genes to their offspring. Alleles of genes for unfavourable features can be expected to disappear from the population as fewer and fewer rodents with these alleles are successful in breeding.

The rodent model is very simple compared with what happens in a real ecosystem. However, you can see that even quite a small selective advantage or disadvantage can, over relatively few generations, have a significant effect on a particular phenotype. You might predict that in time all the unfavourable alleles will disappear from the population and that the rodents will all be homozygous for the favourable alleles.

In practice, however, things change. In the example of the rodents, the climate of the island might become even colder or warm up. Some predators might reach the island. As a result of the rodents feeding on them, the plants would be likely to change; it might be that only very prickly shrubs or shrubs that produced fruits with a very hard shell, or poisonous flesh, were able to survive.

5 Suggest features that might show genetic variation and might make some rodents more likely to survive from predators.

Key ideas

- Sexual reproduction, and occasional mutations, means that populations of organisms have a considerable amount of variation of alleles.

- This variation allows organisms to adapt to changes in the environment.

- Alleles of genes that produce more favourable features are more likely to survive.

- More favourable alleles will be selected for and will become more common in a population.

- Unfavourable alleles may disappear altogether, and so reduce the range of variation in a population.

11.4 The theory of natural selection

The ideas that you have just worked through form the basis of Charles Darwin's theory of **natural selection**. Alfred Russel Wallace independently came up with much the same hypothesis (Fig. 6), and it was his pressure that persuaded Darwin to publish his ideas in 1858.

Darwin was ridiculed by many for the suggestion that humans had evolved by natural selection from ape-like ancestors, and the lack of direct evidence was often used to dismiss Darwin's ideas.

Having developed a model, a scientist must supply supporting evidence. Darwin pointed out that artificial selection of particular features when breeding animals can produce very considerable change within a few generations. He could not, however, go back in time and show that natural selection had produced change in a particular species.

Since Darwin's time evidence has been accumulated in support of the theory of natural selection. One well-documented example of change involves the peppered moth, *Biston betularia*.

The typical form of peppered moth has white wings that are speckled with black scales in an irregular pattern. Collections of moths from about 1850 show that at this time almost all peppered moths in Britain were this speckled form.

The melanic form of peppered moth has

Fig. 6 Natural selection

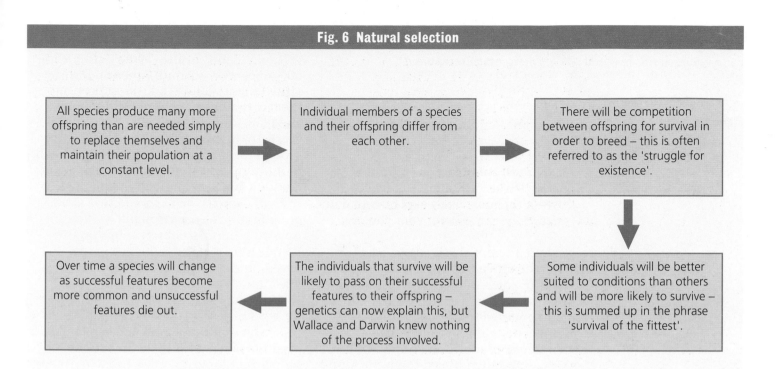

All species produce many more offspring than are needed simply to replace themselves and maintain their population at a constant level.	Individual members of a species and their offspring differ from each other.	There will be competition between offspring for survival in order to breed – this is often referred to as the 'struggle for existence'.
Over time a species will change as successful features become more common and unsuccessful features die out.	The individuals that survive will be likely to pass on their successful features to their offspring – genetics can now explain this, but Wallace and Darwin knew nothing of the process involved.	Some individuals will be better suited to conditions than others and will be more likely to survive – this is summed up in the phrase 'survival of the fittest'.

Peppered moths, *Biston betularia*, resting on a birch trunk.

wings that are almost entirely black. A small number of specimens appear in moth collections from 1850 when the industrial revolution had begun. However, by the end of the century nearly all the peppered moths in some areas, such as Manchester, were melanic. Over the same period of time, sulphur dioxide killed most of the lichens (compound organisms consisting of fungi and algae) living on tree trunks in industrial areas, and deposits of soot particles blackened the bark.

The wing colour is controlled by a single gene locus, the melanic allele being dominant to the speckled allele. Intermediate forms also occur in which the blackness is modified by genes at other loci.

Studies of the distribution of the typical and melanic forms showed that by the 1950s in the heavily polluted parts of Britain the melanic form was by far the more common, whereas in western areas with very little pollution almost 100% of moths were still the typical form.

Q 6 Suggest a reason for the differences in survival in different areas.

Although the increase in the number of melanics correlated with the increase in pollution, this did not prove that natural selection had occurred. The first step was to check that the melanics really did have a selective advantage in polluted areas. A biologist called Henry Kettlewell released marked moths of each type in an unpolluted wood in Dorset and a polluted wood near Birmingham. He then compared the proportions of each recaptured after a few days (Table 3).

127

Table 3. Recaptured moths		
Site where moths released	Percentage recaptured	
	Speckled	Melanic
Dorset (unpolluted)	12.5	6.3
Birmingham	15.9	34.1

Q 7a Suggest some interpretations of Kettlewell's results.
  b Pick the most likely explanation and give the reasons for your choice.

Next an attempt was made to establish whether the difference in survival rates was due to differences in predation levels. The fact that we see the speckled form more easily on polluted trunks does not prove that birds find the moth more easily. Kettlewell placed moths of each type on tree trunks and then filmed them. He found that birds did indeed catch more of the speckled form on blackened trunks, and vice versa. More recent researchers have criticised this experiment because the moths rarely rest on exposed trunks. Usually the moths select sites such as the underside of smaller branches. Increasingly detailed knowledge of the behaviour and habits of the moth have shown that the story is more complex than first thought. Nevertheless, the evidence strongly suggests that the melanic form has been selected in industrial areas mainly because it survives predation better than the speckled form.

Q 8 As acid gas and soot pollution levels are reduced in many areas the lichens are returning and tree trunks are becoming less blackened. If the theory of natural selection is correct, what would you predict will happen to the moth populations in these areas?

Darwin's finches

Scientists use theories to make predictions. One prediction that follows from the theory of natural selection is that as conditions change a species will adapt, within the limits of its range of variation. Is there any evidence to support this prediction?

The medium ground finch lives in the Galapagos Islands, an isolated group of volcanic islands in the Pacific Ocean, about 600 miles west of South America. Darwin visited these islands and was impressed by the fact that on each island the animals and plants were slightly different. Thirteen species of finch inhabit the islands, even though there are few other species of small birds. It was this that made Darwin question the idea of Creation and the literal truth of Genesis. Why should God create a different finch on each island in such an isolated group? His observations on the islands were a major influence in the development of the idea of natural selection.

The finches on the Galapagos Islands have been closely studied for many years. In 1983 a significant climate change occurred when a warm ocean current brought prolonged rainfall to the normally dry islands. Many of the cacti died in the wet conditions, which reduced the supply of large, hard seeds. On the other hand, plants which produced small, soft seeds flourished. So, the range of food available to the seed-eating finches changed considerably. There was a remarkably rapid response in the population. Whereas birds with large heavy beaks had been particularly successful in dealing with the cactus seeds, they could not pick up the smaller seeds of other plants very easily.

Medium ground finches on Isla Santa Cruz, Galapagos.

The medium ground finches with small beaks prospered; within a few generations the mean size of beak in the population had reduced appreciably. Mathematicians predicted the change in beak size on the basis of the estimated selective advantage. The actual results closely matched their predictions. Moreover, as the climate became drier again in the following years, the trend was reversed in precisely the expected way. This adaptation to changing conditions was only possible because there was continuous variation in beak size in the population, and this variation could be inherited. Interestingly, another species of finch that specialised on cactus seeds entirely was unable to adapt, and its numbers fell steeply.

" The tail of the peacock "

Critics of the theory of natural selection often suggest that it is difficult to explain how the more complex and specialised features of organisms could develop by a process of gradual change. Take for, example, the extraordinary tail of the peacock. Since it makes it quite difficult for the male to fly, what advantage could it have?

The most obvious possibility is that the tail is a means of attracting a female mate, and that the more splendid the tail the more chance the male has of breeding and passing on the relevant genes. However, if the large tail was a disadvantage in other ways, you would expect females that avoid males with large tails to be more successful. Perhaps the tail acts as a signal to the female that the male carries other beneficial genes?

To test this hypothesis a researcher randomly bred males and females in separate pens. She measured the number and size of the eyespots on the males' tails. After 12 weeks she weighed the chicks. She found that on average the more and larger the eyespots on the male's tail, the heavier the chicks produced by the female. Two years later more of the heavier chicks had survived.

Source: data from *Nature*, Vol. 371, p.598, quoted in *New Scientist*, 22 October 1994

A male peacock displays his tail.

9 **What does this information indicate about the advantage to the female of choosing a male with an impressive tail?**

Racial differences

Large numbers of observations and experiments like these have shown that species can change under natural conditions, and that the changes do result from the selection of genes that increase the chances of survival. Does the same happen in humans?

Skin pigment is produced by cells in the lower part of the **epidermis** – the outer protective layer of the skin. People with dark skin do not have any more of the cells than pale-skinned people; the cells simply produce more of the black pigment, **melanin**. The production of melanin is controlled by an enzyme, and several genes at different loci seem to be involved in determining the amount produced. This means that there is a wide range of possible skin colours. Environmental factors are also involved, and many pale-skinned people look forward to getting a sun-tan every summer.

Nobody can be sure how the skin colour of different peoples arose. It is likely that the dark pigment provided protection from intense sunlight in tropical areas. Chapter 8 explained that ultraviolet light can cause mutations; in pale-skinned people exposure to high levels of ultraviolet light in tropical sun considerably increases the chances of developing skin cancer. On the other hand, ultraviolet rays stimulate vitamin D production in the skin below the pigmented layer. It is possible that people moving into the duller climates of the north would not obtain enough vitamin D, and that having little pigment in the skin was a selective advantage because more vitamin could be made in the weaker sunlight.

Other hypotheses have suggested that skin colour might be related to temperature regulation or camouflage, or even to selection of a mate, rather like the peacock's tail. There is no simple answer,

since the depth of pigment does not correlate across the world in any straightforward way with ultraviolet levels, temperature or any other obvious factor. It is quite probable that a number of different factors have been involved at different times and in different places in the selection of skin colour.

Some variations are easier to explain. Chapter 10 showed how the sickle-cell allele is common in people that live in malarial regions. It is virtually unknown in, for instance, Northern Europe where malaria does not occur. People who are heterozygous for the sickle-cell allele are clearly at an advantage in the malarial regions because they are more resistant to the parasite. Therefore they are more likely to survive and have children. The allele would have no advantage in areas with no malaria, so there would be no selection in favour of heterozygotes.

10 a Quechua Indians have over 20% more red blood cells than people living near sea level. What is likely to be the selective advantage of this?
b These Indians also have particularly large lungs. Suggest how this feature may have been selected.

People from the same **race** share the same ancestors and therefore have the same culture and many genes in common. However, as we have seen, people from all races share the vast majority of genes and people of all races belong to the same species.

Under certain conditions individuals with some variants of a phenotype have a selective advantage and are more successful at producing offspring and passing on the relevant alleles. As conditions differ in different parts of the world, people in different and sometimes isolated places have developed different features. The more obvious characteristics tend to be the ones which we use to distinguish races, but there are also differences that are not visible. Overall only a relatively small number of genes may be involved in any differences, and all people have a huge number of genes in common.

The oxygen available for respiration in the atmosphere at high altitudes can be half that available at sea level. Quechua Indians in Ecuador have adapted to the high altitude environment.

Skin colour is an obvious characteristic and has been used in the past to separate people into races. However, skin colour is an example of continuous variation and many intermediate shades exist. The same is true of many of the other characteristics people have used to divide human beings into groups. Modern genetics shows that, although the balance of a small number of genes may be different between people, these genes are to do with making sure humans are best suited to their local environment. Cultural and social conditions may reinforce these differences as the people who conform to the accepted idea of normality may stand more chance of breeding. In the cooler temperate regions of Europe and America a sun-tan is regarded as a desirable fashion accessory. Over years, unless this attitude changes, we may see a gradual darkening of skin pigmentation.

11 a Sometimes people say that the world would be a much better place if everyone had the same colour skin and hair. How might a biologist respond to this idea?

b Why do you think the idea that human beings belong to definite and distinct races is so common?

Key ideas

- The theory of natural selection is that offspring struggle for existence, resulting in the survival of the fittest, which go on to breed.

- Species, including humans, are continuously changing in order to adapt to the changing environment.

- The frequency of certain alleles in the population of one race may be different from the frequency in another race.

- This difference has arisen because the populations are experiencing different conditions.

Family trees

A baboon, which is a species of monkey, has been given the heart of a genetically engineered pig in an operation that opens up a controversial phase in efforts to produce 'designer organs' for humans. Although the baboon died, it lived longer than expected. With shortages of human organs for transplants growing worse, the quest to engineer pigs with organs that are compatible with the human immune system is turning into a scientific race.

Normally, when organs are transferred from one species to another, rejection is too fast and violent to be curbed by drugs. In a response known as 'hyperacute' rejection, inflammatory proteins in the recipient's blood attack cells on the surface of the transplanted organ. Scientists aim to block this response by giving pigs human genes which produce molecules that can counteract the inflammatory proteins.

One way to measure the success of this is to remove hearts from pigs and transplant them into a close relative of humans, such as a baboon. In theory, the genes designed to prevent hyperacute rejection should work in a monkey as well as in humans. 'The inserted genes did help to delay the start of the rejection process', said John Logan, the chief scientist in charge of the experiment.

Source: adapted from an article by David Concar, *New Scientist*, 9 July 1994

An olive baboon in its natural habitat in Kenya. Apes and monkeys are genetically pretty similar to us. This genetic similarity makes them very useful in experiments designed to test the likely effects of new treatments in humans.

Thousands of people die each year from heart disease. They could be treated by means of a heart transplant. Unfortunately, there can never be enough human hearts available to meet these needs. Is it acceptable to exploit other animal species by using them as a source of replacement organs? If so, which species should be used? Pigs grow more quickly than apes and monkeys and have hearts of similar size to human hearts. Should we use pigs to grow genetically modified hearts for humans? Or should we use apes? Just how close, in genetic terms, are we to animals?

12.1 Learning objectives

After working through this chapter, you should be able to:

- **explain** what is meant by the term species;

- **explain** how natural selection may give rise to new species;

- **explain** the importance of genetic isolation in the development of new species;

- **explain** how evolution over a long period of time has resulted in a great diversity of types of living organism;

- **explain** how evolutionary history is used as the basis for classification of living organisms;

- **recall** the main categories used in classification;

- **classify** an organism according to these principles.

12.2 What is a species?

We can recognise a baboon, a pig and a human as being different **species** because they look different. However, do the two dogs below belong to the same species? People breed dogs for particular purposes. The distinctive features of each **breed** are the result of artificial selection of particular traits from the range of available variation.

A willow warbler.

A chiffchaff.

A Great Dane and a Yorkshire terrier.

The Great Dane was bred for herding and selected for its size and strength; the terrier was selected for its ability to follow small prey into underground burrows. Despite the great difference in size, the two dogs are quite prepared to mate with each other, and can produce fertile eggs which develop into mongrels with a mixture of the features of the two breeds. Because they can **interbreed** the dogs do belong to the same species.

In some instances, different species can look very similar, e.g. the chiffchaff and willow warbler. These are difficult to tell apart, even for experienced birdwatchers. They do, however, have quite different songs. Although they may live together in the same wood, they do not interbreed.

The mule is the result of a mating between a male donkey and a female horse. Donkeys and horses are different species and do not naturally mate together. Genetically, donkeys and horses are quite distinct, e.g. horses have 66 chromosomes but donkeys have only 62. Mules are unable to breed. They are an example of a **hybrid**, the offspring of closely related species or breeds.

1 Use your understanding of meiosis and fertilisation from Chapter 9 to suggest why hybrids are usually sterile.

A donkey.

A mule.

Some species of, for example, insects and roundworms can only be distinguished by careful microscopic examination, and some microorganisms only by biochemical tests. Visible features are often not a satisfactory way of defining a species.

Chapter 11 explained how species change due to natural selection. This also makes it difficult to define a species with precision. A good working definition is that a species is a group of organisms that:

- have similar physical, behavioural and biochemical features;
- can interbreed to produce fertile offspring;
- do not normally interbreed with any other group of organisms.

12.3 How can new species develop?

Imagine that you are able to observe a species of animal over many thousands or even millions of years. As discussed in Chapter 11 for imaginary rodents (Fig. 5, page 125), you would almost certainly notice significant changes. The animals may have increased in size, altered their diet, improved their camouflage and so on. As a result of random variation and natural selection, they will have adapted to the conditions in which they live. The unsuitable, or unfit, individuals will have been weeded out, and with them the less successful alleles. In effect the species will have moved with the times.

It is important to realise that this process is random and not necessarily progress. It is possible for changes to be reversed. An increase in size might well be an advantage when food is plentiful, but if the food supply decreases, perhaps if the climate became drier, smaller individuals would become more successful again. There is no destination, no perfect form, towards which a species is moving.

If, instead of being able to observe the changes, you obtained fossil remains from stages many years apart, the animals at each stage might seem so different that you would consider them different species. In fact each fossil would just represent a particular stage in a continuous process. There is no justification for taking any point in time as the point at which a new species had been produced (Fig. 1).

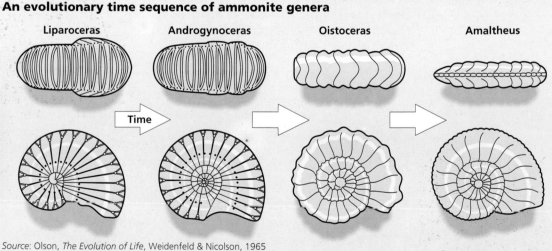

Fig. 1 Ammonites

An evolutionary time sequence of ammonite genera

Liparoceras   Androgynoceras   Oistoceras   Amaltheus

Time

Source: Olson, *The Evolution of Life*, Weidenfeld & Nicolson, 1965

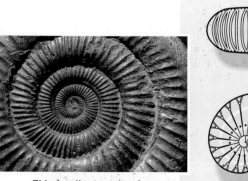

This fossil ammonite shows the appearance of the species at one point in time.

If you could go back in time, you may find that the animal you are going to observe has populations spread over a large area. Some populations may be separated from others by rivers, mountain ranges and even by unfavourable habitats such as desert. Over the millions of years that you keep watch, major geological upheavals could cause areas of land to split away, and volcanic activity to produce new islands. The separated populations would therefore experience quite different conditions in different locations. The climate, the food supply, the competition, the physical environment all may be significantly different.

2 What would you expect to have happened to the populations in the separate locations after a few million years?

Darwin worked out that a process of separated populations changing in different ways had occurred on the Galapagos

Islands (Fig. 2). He suggested that, following their volcanic origin, the islands had been colonised by a small selection of plants and animals reaching them by chance from the mainland. Perhaps a small group of finches, all of the same species, had arrived from South America. The finches were successful and gradually spread to all of the islands. But on each island conditions were different. On each island the finches developed a particular way of feeding and living, as a result of natural selection. In each population the frequency of certain alleles changed in a particular way. Birds from different islands rarely interbred, so alleles were not introduced from other populations. Gradually the finches on different islands became so different that they were, in effect, different species.

3 How would you decide whether finches from two different islands were separate species?

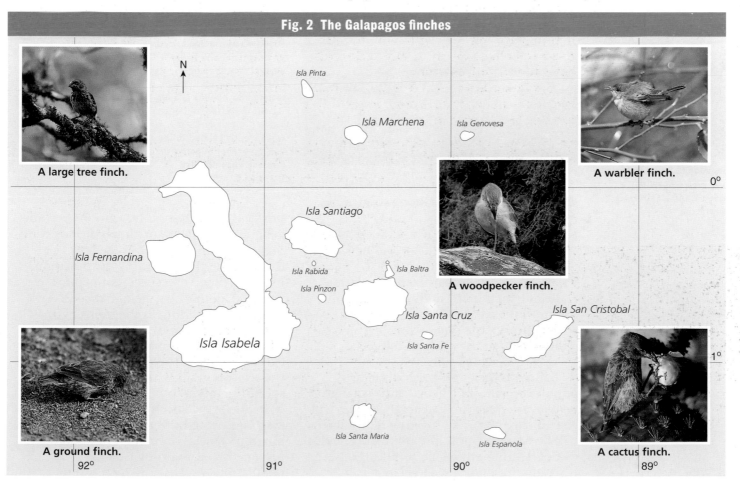

Fig. 2 The Galapagos finches

A large tree finch.

A warbler finch.

A woodpecker finch.

A ground finch.

A cactus finch.

Isla Pinta

Isla Marchena

Isla Genovesa

Isla Santiago

Isla Fernandina

Isla Rabida

Isla Baltra

Isla Pinzon

Isla Santa Cruz

Isla San Cristobal

Isla Isabela

Isla Santa Fe

Isla Santa Maria

Isla Espanola

N

0°

1°

92°

91°

90°

89°

We now recognise 13 distinct species of Galapagos finch. Some of these can breed together, others cannot. Even those that can and sometimes do interbreed are considered to be separate species because they do not normally do so. Nevertheless there are no hard and fast rules as to when two varieties or breeds should be classified as distinct species, and scientists often disagree.

If Darwin was right, islands in other parts of the world should have distinct species of plants and animals that are different from, yet recognisably similar to, species found on the nearest continental land masses. This is exactly what we do find.

Q 4 Explain what sort of environmental conditions could have enabled Komodo Dragons to become so big.

On the Indonesian island of Komodo lives a giant relative, the Komodo Dragon, which is a fierce predator of deer, pigs, goats and even humans.

Monitor lizards are common in Southern Asia, and feed on carrion, insects and small mammals.

The massive 'double-yolked coconut', the coco-de-mer (above), was sometimes mysteriously washed up on Asian shores. Its suggestive shape made it much prized as a 'love potion'. It was several centuries before its origin was traced to the isolated Seychelles islands far out in the Indian Ocean. There it grows on palm trees clearly related to the common coconut palms that produce coconuts like those on the right.

So, new species arise as a result of:
- **isolation** – two populations of a species are separated;
- **genetic variation** – each population contains a range of alleles, and new ones occur by mutation;
- **natural selection** – in each population alleles which help survival in the local conditions are selected;
- **speciation** – the populations become so different that they can no longer interbreed successfully.

For new species to develop the two populations must be genetically isolated. If regular interbreeding occurs the alleles will continually be mixed together, and there will be no separation into populations with distinctly different allelic compositions. Isolation does not have to be due to physical separation. If two groups become genetically isolated, or largely so, selection may quite rapidly result in **genetic divergence**, the beginning of speciation. Imagine a field of a species of plant that flowered all day. An allele that caused the plant to flower only in the morning may attract a particular insect to pollinate it. Another mutation may cause an allele to exist that meant the plant only flowered in the afternoon. This attracted another species of insect to pollinate it. Therefore both alleles are successful, and the plants becomes two groups that are pollinated by different species of insect. They could become two genetically isolated populations because the insects only

A predatory cichlid lies in wait for its prey, other cichlids.

This species of cichlid has lips specially adapted for sucking small fish and other organisms from rock crevices.

These cichlids are feeding on algae growing on rocks at a depth of 2 m.

pollinate one group of flowers. Each population could continue to develop quite independently and eventually produce two new species.

Many different species of cichlid fish live in Lake Malawi in central Africa. They have remarkably different feeding habits, as different as those of the lions, anteaters and antelopes of the surrounding bush. Yet they have probably all evolved from a single ancestral species in less than a quarter of a million years. Each species has taken advantage of the wide range of possible feeding opportunities in the lake. Groups of fish which happened to have features that enabled them to exploit a particular food source must have remained together, bred and become more and more specialised. By using different food sources, the different populations will not have been in competition with each other.

Surprisingly the difference in DNA composition between all these species is very small, generally less than half of one per cent, which suggests that relatively few genes are involved in controlling the distinctive features.

5 What is the disadvantage to a species of being specialised to feed on one food source?

Key ideas

- Members of the same species generally look similar and only interbreed with each other.

- Species change over time as a result of natural selection.

- Populations of a species may become isolated from each other, either geographically or genetically.

- Eventually isolated populations may be so different that they become separate species and can no longer interbreed.

- New species arise as a result of isolation.

12.4 Classifying species

Scientists have so far given a name to something approaching two million species of living organism. Over half of these are insects. In Britain alone there are over 3500 different species of beetle. In the rainforests of the world there may well be millions of still unnamed species; one estimate is that there could be over 30 million species in the world today, although human activities may be rapidly reducing this total.

According to the theory of natural selection this immense diversity results from diverging pathways of adaptation in genetically isolated populations occurring over millions of years. Many species, however, will have arisen quite recently from a common ancestor. They will share many features and genes. They can therefore be considered as close relatives.

The common ancestor will itself have originated by a similar process. You can represent this process as a branching tree, with its main boughs and trunk going far back into geological time (Fig. 3).

In general the more recently species have separated, the more closely related they are. This is the basis of the system used to classify living organisms. Those that have very similar features, and are therefore genetically similar, are grouped together into the same **genus**. Similar genera are considered to belong to the same **family**, and similar families belong to the same **order**.

This system of classification was devised before ideas of **evolution** by natural selection and speciation were developed. Organisms were classified according to a common sense view of similarity in features. It is interesting, however, to find how well modern methods based on comparing DNA and proteins agree with this common sense classification. This provides additional evidence for the accuracy of the evolutionary history derived from study of fossils and comparative anatomy. New research, including DNA studies, means that detailed classification of some species is being revised to bring it into line with evolutionary relationships. However, it is never possible to be certain about the actual pathway of evolution, and scientists often disagree about how a particular species should be classified.

Classifying organisms is therefore a great deal more than producing a catalogue. It enables scientists to understand the relationships between organisms, and to keep track of the changes that are occurring as a result of human pressures on habitats. When, for example, a species appears in a new habitat, perhaps brought there on ships or in exported crops, it can quickly be identified, and its possible effect, maybe as a pest, may be predicted. There is also a wealth of species and genetic diversity that has yet to be researched for possible uses as sources of food, drugs or other useful products.

Fig. 3 Branching speciation tree

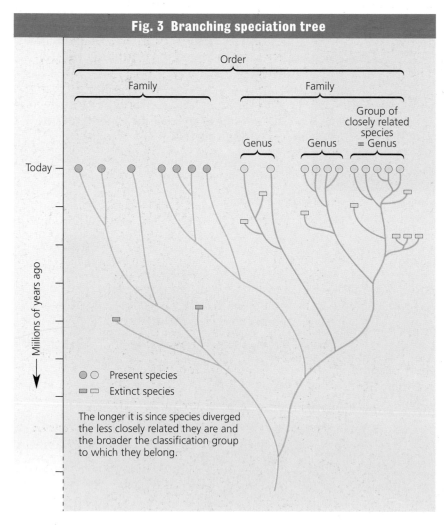

Present species
Extinct species

The longer it is since species diverged the less closely related they are and the broader the classification group to which they belong.

6 Draw a simple tree diagram to show the following information. Groups of a species of bird reached three separate isolated islands a million years ago. A distinct species evolved on each island. The species living near the coast on the mainland did not change. This species had evolved 5 million years ago when a mountain range was formed, separating the coastal population from another in lowland forest. The lowland forest species died out 2 million years ago when the climate became much drier and the forest disappeared.

Humans, like all other species, are classified on the basis of assigning them to smaller and smaller groups according to the closeness of the relationships (Fig. 4). The grouping is called **phylogenetic**, meaning 'origin of race', because it tries to trace the evolutionary history of a particular species.

7 Suggest a group that could be represented by each of the boxes A to D in Fig. 4.

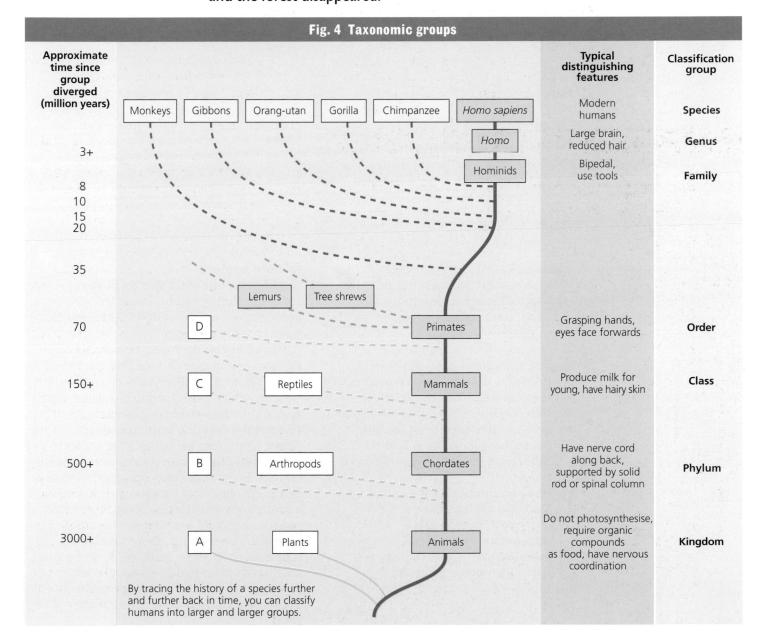

Fig. 4 Taxonomic groups

By tracing the history of a species further and further back in time, you can classify humans into larger and larger groups.

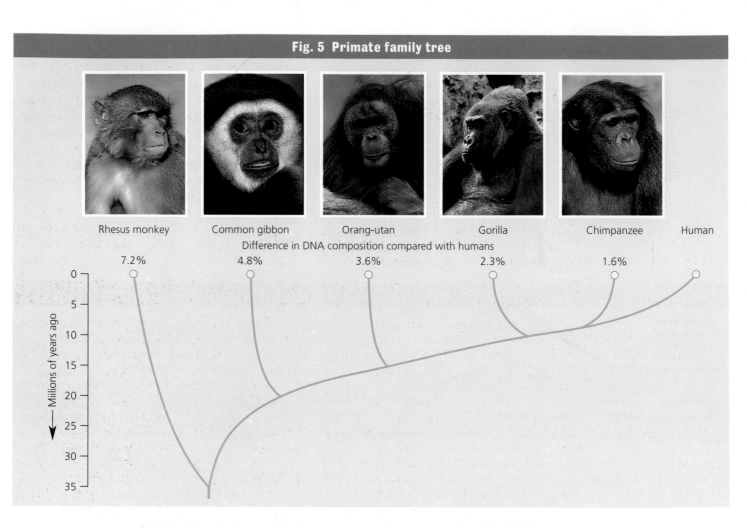

Fig. 5 Primate family tree

Rhesus monkey   Common gibbon   Orang-utan   Gorilla   Chimpanzee   Human

Difference in DNA composition compared with humans

7.2%   4.8%   3.6%   2.3%   1.6%

Millions of years ago

A more detailed family tree can show how humans relate to the other primates, and the approximate time when each species is thought to have diverged from a common ancestor (Fig. 5).

8 a The time since each of these primates shared a common ancestry is calculated from the relative difference in DNA composition, as given under each photograph. About how long did it take for a 1% difference in DNA composition to develop?

b The common gibbon and the Siamang gibbon have a 2.2% difference in their DNA. Approximately how many million years ago did these two species share a common ancestor?

Modern humans

Humans are the only species in the Hominid family today. There is fossil evidence of closely related species which have become extinct.

Homo habilis and *Australopithecus robustus* are species of hominid that lived in Africa about 2 million years ago, although they may not have lived in the same places (Fig. 6). *Australopithecus robustus*, nicknamed 'Nutcracker man' because of the heavy jawbones, probably lived on a vegetarian diet of fruits, roots and grasses. Nutcracker man walked upright, but was relatively short (about 130 cm tall) and had a brain volume only about one-third that of modern humans. *Homo habilis* was taller and less heavily built, more similar in structure to modern humans. Judging from their teeth they had a less tough diet, probably of meat. They also had larger brains and there is evidence that they used tools.

Fig. 6 Extinct ancestors

Source: based on Leakey, *The Making of Mankind*, Michael Joseph, 1981

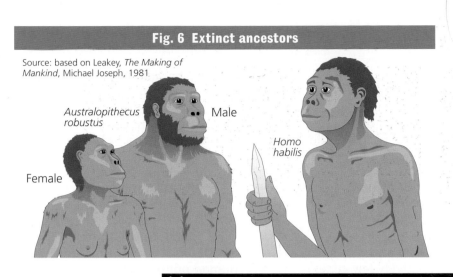

Australopithecus robustus

Female

Male

Homo habilis

The *Australopithecus* genus died out, but we have no way of knowing whether or not this was a result of competition with *Homo*. The genus *Homo* spread across the world, and several species arose. One of these was *Homo sapiens*, modern humans.

It is impossible to know what factors drove the early evolutionary history of hominids. Scientists have, however, been speculating for many years. How did the human brain develop its size and superiority? Why did *Homo* adopt a two-legged posture? Why did *Homo* lose most of its fur and become 'the naked ape'?

" The naked ape "

Men and women walk tall to stay cool. Researchers have shown that a two-legged gait allowed early humans to screen out most of the searing heat of our equatorial African homeland.

Instead of beating down on our backs, the sun's rays would have fallen vertically on our heads – a far smaller area. We would have kept cooler and have needed less precious water, giving us a kickstart to biological supremacy.

In addition, cool humans would no longer have needed the thick pelts that shield other animals on the grassland plains from the sun. So we became naked apes. Also, 'by walking on two feet, humans developed the animal world's most powerful cooling system, and that allowed us to acquire large brains', said Professor Peter Wheeler of John Moores University in Liverpool.

To demonstrate this theory, Professor Wheeler made a model of *Australopithecus*, which he named Boris. This model could be bent to either an upright or four-legged position while the movements of the sun overhead were simulated. A camera recorded the area exposed to the rays of the sun. 'We discovered that there was a 60% reduction in the heat received by Boris in his two-legged position compared with his quadruped posture', reported the Professor. He also calculated that far more of the body is raised away from the heat radiating from the hot ground, and that only just over half as much water would be lost in sweat.

Source: adapted from article by Robin McKie, *The Observer*, 14 November 1993

This sort of environment, of intense heat, may have been where *Homo* first evolved.

9 a **If Professor Wheeler's theory is correct, how might natural selection have resulted in hominids losing most of their body hair and becoming 'naked'?**

b **Suggest why a larger brain would require a more powerful cooling system.**

c **Suggest another hypothesis that might explain the loss of hair in the hominids.**

Homo sapiens emerged very recently in geological terms, probably less than 100 000 years ago. One hypothesis is that somewhere in Africa an isolated population evolved the large complex brain and skilled coordination typical of modern humans. This population spread from its area of origin and successfully replaced its hominid relatives as it expanded throughout the world. Selection of some features as adaptations to local conditions in certain areas would account for the racial differences found today. However, the time scale has been far too short for separate species to become established and, as we saw in the last chapter, relatively few genes are involved. Increased mobility and intermixing will enhance genetic variety.

As we find out more and more about our genetic make-up, and our links with other species, we can use that knowledge to help individuals with genetic disorders. Modern medicine has reduced the ruthlessness of natural selection in human populations. Far fewer people die because of unfavourable genetic combinations. We are now close to being able to make significant alterations to the genes of an individual. We may even be able to use organs grown in other animals for transplants. It is a strange irony that some of the most modern biotechnology draws on our understanding of the early evolution of our species.

10 a What effect do you think these developments might have on the human population over the next few million years?

b Suggest how knowing the evolutionary relationships between species could help conservation programmes for endangered species.

Key ideas

- Evolutionary change over millions of years has resulted in huge numbers of different species.

- The classification of organisms is based on their presumed evolutionary history.

- Closely related species, which diverged relatively recently in evolution, are grouped together in one genus.

- Increasingly large groupings comprise a hierarchy consisting of genus, family, order, class, phylum and kingdom.

Food, farming and tigers

The devastation caused by rabbits in Australia covered large areas. The wild rabbit above is suffering from myxomatosis. Pet rabbits could also catch the disease.

Rabbits are timid grazers, living entirely on vegetation. In the wild they are constantly threatened by foxes, weasels, buzzards and many other predators. On farmland, however, they may devastate crops, menace the livelihood of farmers, and even endanger their own food supply. How can one species display the characteristics of both Jekyll and Hyde? And is it right to use myxomatosis to control the rabbit's potential for destruction? Are there acceptable and practicable alternatives?

> ## A rabbit killer
>
> On the night of 11 August 1953, as a strong south-easterly wind was blowing from France to England, a 'temperature inversion' occurred over the Channel, the air becoming warmer from sea level up to 500 metres. It was almost certainly this meteorological combination that brought myxomatosis, the horrendous and lethal rabbit disease, to Britain for the first time.
>
> Within a few months, the infection was spreading quickly and causing widespread consternation over the ugly and agonising way in which rabbits were dying, with swollen eyes and faces, and grotesque, glutinous skin tumours.
>
> *Source*: adapted from article by Bernard Dixon, *The Independent*, 9 August 1993

13.1 Learning objectives

After working through this chapter, you should be able to:

- **explain** the factors that can affect the size of a population;

- **recall** the difference between interspecific and intraspecific competition;

- **explain** the principles of biological control;

- **describe** one example of biological control;

- **appreciate** the effects of the expanding human population on natural resources and the demand for increased food production;

- **explain** how farmers maintain land for food production;

- **explain** how land may be colonised by a succession of types of vegetation until a climax community develops;

- **make** balanced judgements in relation to conflicts between the demands for increased food production and environmental protection and conservation.

13.2 Populations

Our knowledge of myxomatosis dates from just before the turn of the century. Rabbits imported into Uruguay in South America, for the preparation of antibodies in a public health laboratory, died of a ghastly and extremely infectious disease. The infection, then unknown in Europe, was myxomatosis.

In 1950, Australian agriculturists released infected rabbits in the Murray Valley in an attempt to cull the European wild rabbit that had become a major pest. The splendid weather that summer and over the following two years provided excellent conditions for mosquitoes to breed and travel. They carried the myxomatosis virus from warren to warren and the virus spread rapidly. Millions of rabbits – about four-fifths of those in south-eastern Australia – perished.

The myxomatosis virus was introduced in France in 1952 to kill wild rabbits that were damaging crops. The weather conditions in August 1953 meant the mosquitoes were able to travel across the Channel carrying the virus with them.

Source: adapted from article by Bernard Dixon, *The Independent*, 9 August 1993

A female rabbit can produce up to ten young in a litter and within 24 hours she may be pregnant again. A month later another litter is born. At this reproductive rate a rabbit **population** could quickly rise to a phenomenal level. A population of a species is made up of all the individuals of that particular species in a given area or **habitat**. A habitat is the particular **environment** in which a species lives. An environment is made up of all the conditions that affect the life of an organism.

When introduced to Australia, an exceptional rise took place in the rabbit population. There were few native predators, so a high proportion of the young rabbits was able to survive to adulthood and become parents themselves.

The native grazing animals that were present in Australia were marsupials, such as kangaroos and wallabies. Marsupials are mammals that carry their young in an external pouch. Their reproductive rate is much slower than that of a rabbit, and they do not graze as close to the ground as the rabbit. The rabbits therefore had little competition for food or space, and their population growth was not seriously restricted by predators or, until myxomatosis, disease.

It is rare in natural conditions for a population of an organism to be able to grow without being limited by some factor(s).

1 a Suppose that ten bacteria, which reproduce asexually, are put into a culture broth. Assuming that the bacteria keep dividing at regular intervals and that all survive, work out how many bacteria there would be in the culture after each of the first ten generations.

b Draw a graph of the growth of this bacterial population, and describe its shape.

c In what way is the graph in Fig. 1 similar in shape to the one you drew for the bacteria?

d Explain what happened to the algal population in Fig. 1 after 15 days.

Fig. 1 Growth of an algal population

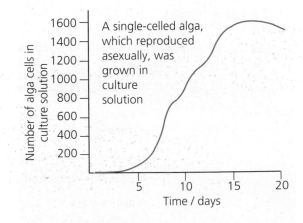

A single-celled alga, which reproduced asexually, was grown in culture solution

In a culture in a container, a population expands rapidly until the organisms start to run out of food and space. In these circumstances the individual organisms have to compete with each other for limited resources. Because they are all the same species, this is called **intraspecific competition**. Intra means 'within'. In a natural habitat the food supply is usually replaced regularly, as new plants grow or prey animals reproduce. It is vital for the success of a species that it does not exhaust its food supply as the species would not then survive.

One way in which some animals reduce the likelihood of using up all the available food in a habitat is by **territorial behaviour**. A robin will aggressively chase off any other robin that invades its territory. In this way it preserves an area for feeding itself and its young. Other robins normally recognise the rights of the territory owner and retreat without a challenge. The red breast and song act as powerful signals. In one experiment a caged robin in its own territory was still able to deter intruders. When the same bird, still in the cage, was moved into a rival's territory, it lost its bravado and crouched in the bottom of the cage.

The robin stakes its claim to a territory by singing loudly from conspicuous perches.

In Australia, with few checks on their population growth, rabbits almost destroyed the environment on which they depended for survival. The low rainfall in Australia means that native plants are slower growing and less quick to recover than plants in the rabbit's native habitats in Europe.

In Europe rabbits seem to have evolved a system of regulating their own numbers. Although capable of breeding throughout the year, rabbits restrict breeding to the spring months. They may mate at other times, but the female does not become pregnant. The embryos of at least 60% of the litters that are conceived are never born. The way in which this process is controlled is not clear. Natural selection has favoured those individuals that do not overproduce, because their young are more likely to survive to breed themselves. Such mechanisms may seem surprising but they are quite common, e.g. several species of birds vary the number of eggs they lay according to food availability.

2 What would you expect to happen to the population of an organism that does overproduce?

13.3 Population cycles

A few species have a cycle in which the population expands rapidly and then crashes to a low level. One of the most famous is the lemming (Fig. 2). The lemming is a small herbivorous rodent that lives on the Arctic tundra.

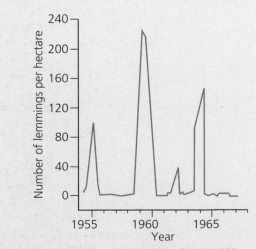

Fig. 2 Lemming population cycle

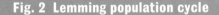

Source:adapted from Begon et al., Ecology, Blackwell Science, 1986

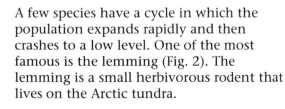

The spring thaw in the tundra can reveal the lemmings to their predators.

In years when the population explodes, rapid breeding occurs while the land is still snow-covered. The young lemmings consume large quantities of grass and other plants and are protected from predators by the blanket of snow. Once the snow melts predators move in to take advantage of the large supply of prey. Various factors may be involved in the subsequent population crash, e.g. food shortage, predation, disease and hormonal changes. One hypothesis is that:

- the rising population consumes the most nutritious plant material first;
- this means that when the lemming population is at its peak, the diet is short of key nutrients;
- this may weaken the lemmings and make them much more susceptible to predators and disease;
- the high density of animals may also lead to frequent aggressive encounters between individuals, which reduce their reproductive capacity and cause hormonal imbalances;
- the population then drops to a low level that is sustainable until the plants recover sufficiently for a new cycle to begin.

3 The Arctic fox preys on lemmings. What pattern would you expect to find in the Arctic fox population over the same period as that shown in Fig. 2?

One possible advantage to the lemmings of this population cycling is that it avoids a build up of predators because for much of the time there is an inadequate food supply for them. Most organisms in less severe climates do not have such 'boom and bust' cycles. In most habitats the numbers of each species remain fairly constant, and a relatively stable **community** exists. A community contains populations of different organisms within a particular habitat, which interact with each other and the non-living environment.

There is competition for resources between all the organisms in a community. This is both intraspecific, and **interspecific**. Interspecific competition is between members of different species. Both contribute to natural selection (Fig. 3). Over time the organisms with features that favour survival will be more successful.

Plants and animals in any community have a range of defences that enables them to survive. Plants may have obvious defences such as spines or stings, or less obvious ones like an unpleasant taste or poisons.

Grass can survive the effects of grazing animals like rabbits because the growing point of its stem is tucked away at the base of the leaves, very close to the ground. New leaves can grow if old ones are bitten off. Tree seedlings and many other plants will die if the top of the plant is grazed.

Fig. 3 A possible sequence of changes as a result of competition and selection

Plants

Soft-leaved; tasty

Hairy, tougher leaves

Hairs developed into sharp prickles

Leaves contain poisons as well as hairy prickles

Grazers

Small in size; small cutting teeth

Teeth larger, with grinding surfaces

Larger in size; thicker 'rubbery' lips and tough tongue

Thicker protective coats; only animals resistant to poisons survive

The grazing animals themselves are in constant danger from predators. One of the ways in which rabbits are protected is by living in underground burrows. They also have acute hearing and 'all-round' eyesight, so that they can sense danger and escape quickly when feeding above ground. However, narrow-bodied predators such as the weasel and polecat can follow them into their burrows, and many rabbits are killed by these predators.

4 a What would you expect to happen to the rabbit population in Table 1 if this level of predation continued? Explain your answer.

b How might the colony's numbers be restored by natural means?

Rabbits choose to feed close to their network of burrows so that they can make a quick escape when threatened. Their grazing has a marked effect on the vegetation. Grass and any young plants that grow upwards, such as tree seedlings,

are regularly grazed. Plants that have leaves very close to the ground, like daisies, may escape being grazed. The rabbits will also ignore plants such as ground ivy and forget-me-not which are hairy, and the poisonous ragwort and prickly creeping thistle. These plants may therefore be particularly successful around the burrows. So, there may be a greater variety of species in a grazed area than where rabbits are absent.

5 a Explain what happens to the vegetation when grazing is prevented.

b What effect will this have on the small plants that are present when the area was grazed?

c From Fig. 4 explain what happens to the number of species in the plot when grazing stops.

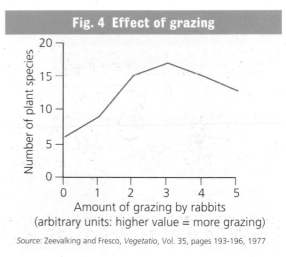

Fig. 4 Effect of grazing

Amount of grazing by rabbits (arbitrary units: higher value = more grazing)

Source: Zeevalking and Fresco, *Vegetatio*, Vol. 35, pages 193-196, 1977

Table 1. A study of a colony of rabbits	
Number of adult rabbits at start of observations	70
Number of breeding females	36
Total number of young emerging to feed	280
Number of young in colony at end of first season*	28
Number of adults in colony at end of first season	11

*A few of the young may have moved away to another colony, but the great majority were killed by predators in their first week above ground

Key ideas

- The total number of individuals of a species in a particular habitat or area makes up the local population.

- The size of the population depends on how much food, space and other resources are available and the level of predation.

- In the absence of competition from other organisms, the population will grow rapidly until limited by the availability of food, space or other resources.

- Individuals of the same species will compete with each other for any resource that is in limited supply. This is called intraspecific competition.

- Members of different species may compete for the same resources. This is called interspecific competition.

- Competition between individuals and species results in the continuous process of natural selection. Individuals with more favourable adaptations are more likely to survive and breed.

13.4 Biological control

In natural conditions the competing interactions between species normally maintain a fairly stable community. Human activities, however, can have a major disruptive effect. By growing crops people create large areas with one type of plant, usually a particularly attractive one for herbivores. As a result there is a continuous battle to prevent a corresponding expansion of populations of primary consumers. These organisms are pests in these circumstances.

Large areas of just one species are particularly susceptible to disease, as the organism causing the disease can be transmitted from one individual to another very easily.

Animals too, when maintained by farmers, have to compete with other species for food and other resources. Rabbits became major pests in Australia because they were competing with the sheep for grass, and were destroying pasture land by shaving the vegetation to a level that made it useless for the sheep. It was a deliberate decision to introduce the virus that causes myxomatosis into Australia, and it was effective in killing a high proportion of the rabbits. Using a living organism to kill a pest is called **biological control** (Fig. 5).

Fig. 5 Biological control of whitefly

These tomato plants have been severely damaged by the growth of sooty mould caused by whitefly and aphid infestation in greenhouse plants.

Whiteflies are small insects, about 1 mm long, that damage greenhouse crop plants such as tomatoes by sucking sap from them and laying their eggs on the leaves. The eggs hatch into larvae that look like flat semi-transparent scales attached to the leaf.

They also excrete a sugary deposit that can block the leaf stomata and provide an excellent growth medium for the fungal disease 'sooty mould'.

The parasitic wasp *Encarsia formosa* lays an egg in each larval scale. The developing wasp eats away the body of its host before emerging through a hole bored in its surface. Scales infected with the parasite turn black. Greenhouse owners can buy supplies of these infected scales. As soon as the wasps emerge they are attracted by the smell of their prey. As each wasp can lay about 50 eggs they can soon bring a whitefly infestation under control.

An *Encarsia* wasp emerging from a whitefly host.

Whitefly scales on a leaf. The black scales have been infected with *Encarsia* wasp larvae.

Q 6 a Explain how each of the effects of whitefly will reduce the crop yield.
  b Explain the features of *Encarsia* that make it particularly useful as an agent of biological control.

Advantages of biological control

Provided that the killer is carefully selected, it is possible to target the pest alone in biological control systems. Chemical pesticides and weedkillers are much more likely to kill other organisms as well, including beneficial ones. Therefore chemical controls can have unwanted effects on the environment. Once introduced into a population, a biological control organism can spread by natural contacts between the pests. Biological control is also generally cheaper than repeated applications of chemicals.

Disadvantages of biological control

Releasing a predator or disease organism into a natural community may have unpredictable results. For example, the cane toad, originally released into Australian sugar cane plantations to control a beetle pest, has become so common that it is now a pest itself.

The control organism rarely eliminates a pest altogether, because once the number of pests falls to a low level, the agent is unable to find enough of its prey. It is therefore often necessary to reintroduce the control organism at regular intervals.

The way in which the pest is killed, e.g. by a disease, may be unacceptable.

Many people felt that the effects of myxomatosis were too unpleasant to justify the use of the virus as a control method.

The pest may also become resistant to the control organism. Not all rabbits were killed by the myxomatosis virus. In Britain the population of rabbits has risen again quite rapidly in many areas, and most of the rabbits are now resistant to the virus. However, the same resistance problem can arise with chemical methods of control.

7 Use the principle of natural selection to explain how rabbit populations have become resistant to myxomatosis.

Key ideas

- Large numbers of one species used for agriculture and horticulture offer ideal opportunities for certain pests to thrive.

- Pests can be controlled by means of chemicals, but these tend to be expensive and some have a damaging effect on the environment.

- Biological control uses another organism as a predator or parasite of the pest to control the pest population.

- One example is the use of the parasitic wasp, *Encarsia formosa*, to control the whitefly pest in greenhouses.

- Care is needed in using biological control to ensure that the control agent does not have other effects which make it a pest in itself.

13.5 The human impact

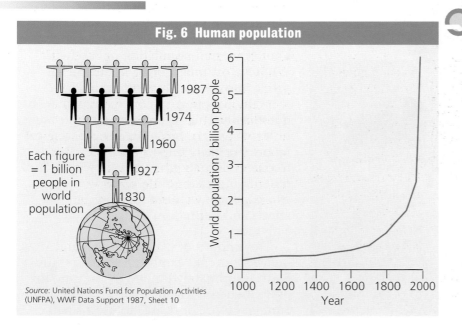

Fig. 6 Human population

Each figure = 1 billion people in world population

1987
1974
1960
1927
1830

Source: United Nations Fund for Population Activities (UNFPA), WWF Data Support 1987, Sheet 10

8 a The world population is now close to 6 billion. It took about one million years for the population to reach one billion. From Fig. 6, how long has it taken to add each further billion?

b When would you estimate that it might reach 10 billion?

Table 2. World food production (thousands of metric tonnes)					
Year	1965	1970	1975	1980	1985
Cereals					
Developing	470 248	587 418	683 263	770 799	928 135
Developed	535 678	617 710	689 463	796 673	919 301
Root crops					
Developing	246 432	302 483	330 014	353 652	370 625
Developed	242 851	259 290	223 216	184 563	216 712
Meat, milk and fish					
Developing	114 547	136 140	152 288	183 957	224 422
Developed	387 200	421 362	453 988	489 421	523 591
Oil crops, pulses, vegetables and fruits					
Developing	284 179	322 986	373 709	435 070	505 428
Developed	229 982	261 313	279 903	303 713	316 231
Total	2 511 117	2 908 702	3 185 844	3 517 848	4 004 445

Source: adapted from UN/FAO reports

These vast wheat fields in Montana, USA, have replaced the original community and have to be maintained by hard work. The crops are susceptible to widespread disease, and the soil is susceptible to erosion.

This terraced vegetable farmland in Cameron Highlands, Malaysia also has to be maintained by hard work, but it maintains a more natural interrelated community and a variety of products. Widespread outbreaks of disease and pests are far less likely, and the soil is protected by the way the land is used.

Ecosystems are made up of one or more communities. Humans can have a huge impact on different ecosystems. This is often due to humans using the land to produce food (Table 2).

Can the human population go on increasing at the present rate? The world is a finite size so there must be a limit to the amount of food that can be grown. It is estimated that over 40% of plant growth is already used for human consumption. That leaves less than 60% for all the other species. If the human population were to double again would the world's ecosystems be able to cope? At what stage would the limit of human population be reached? What factors might bring to an end the accelerating expansion of humankind?

Many people are trying to grapple with questions such as these. Clearly there are no easy answers, but some people seem to ignore the likely impact on the Earth's resources of such gross over-crowding. In order to understand the possible consequences we need to appreciate the effects and limitations of agricultural activities.

The amount of plant material, and hence food, that can be produced on the Earth is ultimately limited by the amount of light energy reaching the Earth from the Sun. Plants are only able to use a small proportion of this energy in photosynthesis, less than 5%. An even lower proportion is eventually available to humans as food (Table 3).

Table 3. Energy available from food	
Food	% of Sun's energy available for human use
Sugar beet	0.21
Rice	0.17
Wheat	0.16
Milk	0.05
Meat	0.03

9 a Use your knowledge of food chains to explain the difference between the amounts of energy provided by the plants and by meat and milk.
b Suggest why different plants provide different proportions of useful energy.

Chapter 6 showed that the productivity of different ecosystems varies. The amount of energy fixed by rainforest is over twice as much as that fixed by grassland. Cultivated crops such as wheat have an even lower mean net primary productivity than grassland, about 650 g m^{-2} year^{-1} for wheat compared with 900 g m^{-2} year^{-1} for grass. Most of the plant material in rainforests is unsuitable as human food. However, the effect of converting forest to cultivated land is to reduce substantially the overall amount of plant growth on the Earth's surface. One incidental effect of this is that less carbon is stored in plants, and therefore the carbon dioxide concentration in the atmosphere is increased. This may lead to global warming.

Humans have to work hard to maintain food production. The rapidly expanding human population places ever greater demands on the food producers. Production has been improved by:
- breeding varieties of plants and animals with greater yields;
- increasing the use of fertilisers;
- bringing more land into agricultural use;
- using herbicides and pesticides to reduce losses;
- making more efficient use of land.

However, there are limits to the extent to which production can be increased further.

Although in many parts of Europe there is at present overproduction of certain crops, in other parts of the world land is continually being lost to agriculture. Soil is being lost by erosion at a rate far greater than it is being formed. This erosion can be the result of human activity. Shortage of organic fertiliser results in soils losing their **humus** content and texture. Humus is decomposed, organic material in the soil. Soils without humus are unable to retain nutrients or water and are liable to turn into desert. This process is know as desertification.

Many farmers are unable to afford the fertilisers, herbicides and pesticides needed to provide the best yields. Continued use of particular herbicides and pesticides results in the development of weeds and pests that are resistant.

10 Several weeds have become resistant to the widely used herbicide, 2,4-D. Use the theory of natural selection to explain how this resistance may have arisen.

These cattle in the Sahel in Niger are looking for grazing, but the pastures are gradually turning into desert. Until recently this was productive agricultural land, but overgrazing and lowered rainfall is rapidly reducing it to unproductive desert.

Farming

With few exceptions, food production for human purposes involves the destruction of the natural community. Farmers then have to maintain their land so that it does not revert to the original community (Fig. 7). Of the many thousands of plant species that exist, a remarkably small proportion is exploited as sources of human food. If you think of the plants that you commonly consume, you will probably find that it is no more than a couple of dozen or so. The ones grown on the largest scale are the cereals, plus one or two staple crops such as potatoes.

11 a How does aeration help in the recycling of materials?

b It is important not to spray herbicides in windy conditions. Explain why.

c Which of the farming practices shown below help to maintain the fertility of the soil, and hence the productivity of the land? Explain your answers.

d Which practices help to reduce competition from plants that are not useful as sources of human food? Explain your answers.

e From what you learned in Chapter 6, explain how growing clover in a field after harvesting a cereal crop would help to restore soil fertility. Why would the farmer still need to add some fertilisers in order to grow more cereals?

Fig. 7 Cultivating the land

◄ Ploughing removes plants that would compete with the crop, and so gives the crop seedlings the opportunity to establish themselves quickly and evenly. Weeds and the remains of previous crops are buried and their materials recycled. Ploughing also helps to aerate the soil.

◄ Harrowing breaks up lumps of soil and makes the surface smooth. This allows the farmer to sow the seeds at a consistent depth and also removes competitor weed seedlings just before sowing.

◄ While the crop seedlings are becoming established, weeds can be controlled with herbicides. A farmer may use a herbicide that is absorbed more readily by broad-leaved weeds than by the narrow-leaved cereal seedlings. The herbicide behaves like a hormone and disrupts the normal growth processes in the weeds.

◄ When a crop is harvested the mineral ions that were used in its growth are permanently removed. These have to be replaced with fertilisers. Farmers may use organic fertilisers, such as manure, or chemicals.

◄ Grazing animals also remove nutrients from the soil. The nutrients are locked up in the animal products such as meat and milk. Grazing pastures therefore also have to be fertilised in order to maintain their productivity. The grazing animals generally consume young shrub and tree seedlings, so removing competitors of the grass, but they may avoid poisonous or unpalatable plants such as bracken or thistle. Farmers may need to take measures to prevent the spread of such invaders.

13.6 Climax communities

Fig. 8 Succession

As grazing is reduced →

Grassland with small flowering plants, like daisies.

Taller herbaceous plants, like willowherb and foxgloves, grow and cut off light to small ones. Tree seedlings can become established.

Bushes and shrubs, such as hawthorn and bramble, grow. Most herbaceous plants die out.

Fast-growing trees, such as birch, grow up, forming dense, low forest.

Larger, slower growing, but stronger oak trees grow above the birch and establish the climax community.

The most productive habitats tend to be tropical, where the amount of the Sun's energy reaching the Earth is greatest. In most places forest is the most productive ecosystem on land. Farmland that is left uncultivated will soon revert to forest. Until recently most areas of the world other than the Polar regions and high mountains were covered in forest. Even in Britain most land was forested 3000 years ago, and there were still large tracts of forest at the time of the Norman Conquest. Since forest is the most stable type of community for an area, it is called the **climax community**. Individual trees may die, but they will be replaced by others and the forest community is maintained.

Other types of community, such as grassland, will be replaced by a series of different communities until a stable forest develops (Fig. 8). This process is called **succession**.

12 a In some places the climax community is not forest. Suggest factors that could prevent a forest climax developing, even in undisturbed conditions.
b Explain how farming practices prevent succession.

Key ideas

- The human population is growing at an accelerating rate and could reach 10 billion by the year 2025.

- The growth in the human population is having a major impact on natural ecosystems.

- There is a limit to the amount of land available for growing food, and a limit to the productivity of that land imposed by photosynthesis.

- Weeds and pests may become resistant to herbicides and pesticides as a result of natural selection.

- Farmers have to maintain their land in order to prevent unwanted plants competing with crops.

- Nutrients removed by harvesting have to be replaced by fertilisers.

- The climax community of most uncultivated land is forest.

- If cultivated land is abandoned it is colonised by a succession of communities until a climax community is developed.

13.7 Conservation

There is a conflict between the need to produce more and more food and the protection of the natural environment. The issues are complex. For example, Chapter 6 showed the potential effects on climate and soil of removing rainforests. There may well be a short-term gain in terms of crop production for hungry people; on the other hand the longer term effects of reduced rainfall and lost soil fertility can result in a net loss in food production. Species become extinct as habitats are lost, often before their importance and potential usefulness have been appreciated. As species disappear so does a valuable portion of genetic diversity. We are only beginning to understand the complex network of relationships in ecosystems that maintain the web of life. For example, the increasing acidification of soils is tending to kill many of the mycorrhizal fungi that have a mutualistic relationship with tree roots. Without the fungi the trees are unable to absorb enough mineral nutrients and they also die.

Mycorrhiza of fungi from soil.

Many orchid seeds will not germinate unless they have been infected by mycorrhizal fungi.

Tiger trouble

The number of tigers surviving in their natural habitats is declining rapidly, and the species' very existence is seriously threatened (Table 4).

Fig. 9 Killed for a cure

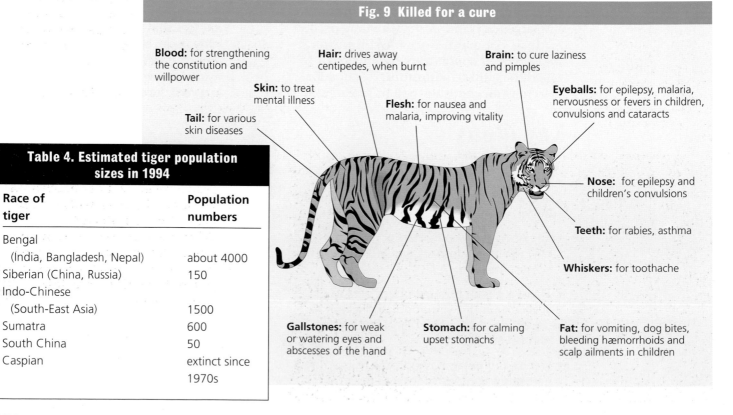

Blood: for strengthening the constitution and willpower

Skin: to treat mental illness

Tail: for various skin diseases

Hair: drives away centipedes, when burnt

Flesh: for nausea and malaria, improving vitality

Brain: to cure laziness and pimples

Eyeballs: for epilepsy, malaria, nervousness or fevers in children, convulsions and cataracts

Nose: for epilepsy and children's convulsions

Teeth: for rabies, asthma

Whiskers: for toothache

Gallstones: for weak or watering eyes and abscesses of the hand

Stomach: for calming upset stomachs

Fat: for vomiting, dog bites, bleeding hæmorrhoids and scalp ailments in children

Table 4. Estimated tiger population sizes in 1994	
Race of tiger	Population numbers
Bengal (India, Bangladesh, Nepal)	about 4000
Siberian (China, Russia)	150
Indo-Chinese (South-East Asia)	1500
Sumatra	600
South China	50
Caspian	extinct since 1970s

'The experience of meeting a tiger is stunning', says film-maker Stephen Mills. 'They're so big. And they're so beautiful – so incredibly beautiful. They've got lovely white tufts on the ears ... no tiger is the same. You know that you're seeing something that is unique.'

In May a tiger killed two buffaloes and then killed and ate a man. He killed another man in June and a woman in August. By then the villages around the Tiger Tops Lodge in the National Park were in uproar.

Source: adapted from *BBC Wildlife*, Vol. 10, No. 11, November 1992

Local people often have good reason to resent the parks. Formerly they could graze their livestock there, and collect wood and other products. That has been stopped. Outside the reserves cattle and goats have often turned grazing land to near desert. Demand for firewood has devastated wooded areas. Within the reserves people see lush grasses and forests of useful wood.

Adult tigers are solitary animals. They establish their own territories containing adequate prey, cover and water to support them. A male's territory extends from 50 to 1000 square kilometres.

Source: Jackson, *Endangered Species: Tigers*, Apple Press, 1990

The 1970 census of tigers in India showed that the population had fallen from an estimated 40 000 to under 2000. The causes were obvious – the accelerating loss of habitat (India having lost 88% of its original forests), the excessive and largely uncontrolled hunting, poaching and poisoning of tigers and the soaring prices of tiger-skin rugs and coats on the international market.

Source: Mountfort, *Project Tiger: a Review*, *Oryx*, Vol. 17, No. 1, 1983

Wiping out a wonderful animal out of carelessness or ignorance must be morally wrong. But no less important is that allowing the tiger to become extinct in this generation would represent an irreversible loss to the next.

Source: Mountfort, *Saving the Tiger*, Michael Joseph, 1981

Tigers are still valued in parts of Asia as gourmet titbits or quack medicine. Today, there is fresh evidence of well-organised poaching gangs. At a minimum of £4000 per tiger – more if all the bones reach China – it means big money. One midnight raid discovered almost 200 kg of tiger bones – all fresh, some with dried strands of meat still attached, all taken during or just before the monsoon.

Source: adapted from *BBC Wildlife*, Vol. 12, No. 1, January 1994

A tiger in a safari park, Bangkok, Thailand. The tiger is one of the world's fiercest and strongest predators. It is also one of the most beautiful and is often used a symbol of power.

13 a From the extracts and Fig. 9 summarise the reasons for the reduction in the tiger population.
  b What are the arguments for the conservation of tigers?
  c What are your own views on the desirability of conserving tigers?
  d What do you think the views of a farmer living close to a tiger reserve might be?

Blanket peat bogs, such as this in N. Uist, Scotland, provide unique habitats for many species and, like tropical rainforest, store up carbon dioxide without releasing it to the atmosphere.

The Aral Sea used to be the fourth biggest lake in the world. Over-irrigation of land by using water from rivers that flowed into the Aral Sea, and the use of pesticides on cotton crops near the lake, has turned over 68 000 km² into salt-flats and deserts.

Many species are suffering from the pressures of human activity, such as expansion of farming, over-fishing, building, road construction, leisure pursuits, as well as pollution and climate change. Clearly it is essential to satisfy the basic needs of an ever-growing human population. On the other hand, it is also essential to preserve the Earth as an environment that can sustain life.

Arguments for conservation

Living organisms are dependent on each other. For example, loss of insects reduces the number of pollinators required for the pollination of crops. Loss of predators often allows pest populations to explode out of control.

Little is known about the possible uses of many plants and animals that are becoming extinct. For example, many drugs have been derived from plants, and there may be many more still to discover. Loss of species also reduces genetic diversity. Possible sources of new genes, e.g. for crop-breeding, are therefore disappearing.

Destruction of forests is reducing the amount of fixed carbon and increasing the amount of carbon dioxide in the atmosphere, thus accelerating global warming. The loss of trees also affects the global cycling of water. This is dealt with further in Chapter 14.

It is also argued that people should protect species, habitats and landscapes for future generations to enjoy.

Each of these issues is complex. They require detailed understanding of our environment and to succeed they need the support of everyone. This combination of knowledge and determination is not achieved easily.

Key ideas

- There is increasing loss of natural habitats as more land is brought into use for farming.

- As a result many species are becoming extinct.

- A range of pressures is endangering the populations of large animals such as the tiger.

- Many other potentially useful species are also being lost.

- There are conflicting demands between the need to conserve the environment and the pressure to meet the demands of food production.

Greening the desert

Quiver trees in Namibia can shed their leaves and store water in their branches to save water during periods of extreme drought. They are called quiver trees because bushmen used to clean out the soft branches and use them to keep arrows in.

When the rains do fall, desert plants burst into flower, making the most of the water that is now available.

Some plants can survive the very harsh desert environments. Their adaptations are very specific, and often visually amazing. Desert plants have had to solve the problem of surviving long dry spells. Many of the local people have learnt to use parts of the specialised plants.

Crops that are introduced to desert environments often fail. Scientists are increasingly coming to recognise that the solution to feeding people in arid lands is to grow plants that have become adapted, over millions of years, to dry conditions. Research into the survival methods of plants from arid areas could help turn desert into productive land. Some deserts, and the subsequent lack of food resources, are the result of humans misusing the land. While science cannot solve the political and economic causes of famine, it can help to increase food production in some of the poorest areas of the world. In arid areas this can mean the difference between life and death.

14.1 Learning objectives

After working through this chapter, you should be able to:

- **explain** how external and internal factors affect the rate of transpiration;

- **explain** how stomata regulate the rate of transpiration;

- **describe** some of the ways in which desert plants reduce their transpiration rates;

- **recall** the internal structure of the root and shoot of a young plant;

- **describe** the path water takes through the plant;

- **explain** how the carbohydrates produced by the leaves are transported to the rest of the plant;

- **relate** the functioning of xylem and phloem to their structure.

14.2 Water loss from leaves

Many desert trees, such as the quiver tree, drop their leaves to prevent death from **desiccation** – drying out. Desiccation occurs when leaves lose water faster than roots can absorb it. However, dropping leaves is a drastic solution. If the tree drops its leaves it can no longer photosynthesise, so it must rely on the store of carbohydrates made during the 'fat' years so that it can survive the 'lean' years.

What is it about the structure of leaves that makes water loss inevitable? Leaves have holes called **stomata** to allow the carbon dioxide needed for photosynthesis to enter. Each stoma is surrounded by two cells called **guard cells**. But holes that allow carbon dioxide to pass into a leaf also allow precious water vapour to pass out. Stomata are, for desert plants, a 'necessary evil'.

The loss of water vapour by evaporation from a plant to the air surrounding it, through the open stomata, is called **transpiration**. This loss of water vapour via the stomata is due to the water potential (ψ) gradient between cells in a leaf and the air outside the leaf (Fig. 1). Water molecules diffuse along a water potential gradient towards areas with a more negative water potential value. The greater the gradient the faster the rate of movement.

An increase in temperature, a decrease in humidity and an increase in wind speed all increase the rate of transpiration. An increase in temperature causes a higher rate of evaporation from the leaf surface. Any decrease in humidity in the atmosphere makes the water potential gradient steeper between the leaf and the atmosphere. Any wind moving the air and water vapour away from around the leaf makes the water potential gradient steeper.

1 Explain why these three factors result in a more negative value of water potential for the air just outside the leaf in terms of the number of water molecules per unit volume of air.

Except when air is fully saturated with water vapour, it always has a value of water potential more negative than that of the leaf cells. So water molecules will always diffuse out through the open stomata. The only way to stop the loss of water is to close the stomata.

Most plants close their stomata during the night. Some plants can close their stomata during the middle of the day, when the temperature is highest, and can open them at night. One such desert plant is the unarmed saltwort (Fig. 2). The effect of this lunch-time closing is dramatic: transpiration almost ceases!

2 What are the advantages and disadvantages to a desert plant of opening its stomata during the night and closing them during lunch-time?

The guard cells surrounding the stoma have two special features that enable the plant to open and close a stoma (Fig. 3).

3 What factors will affect the water potential of the guard cells?

What is the mechanism of this stomatal opening and closing? Any hypothesis for the mechanism of stomatal opening must account for the more negative water potential of the guard cells during the day, and also why some plants can keep their stomata closed during the day.

Fig. 1 Water potential

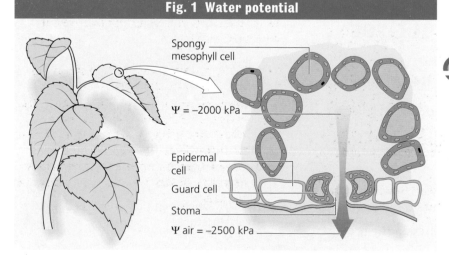

Spongy mesophyll cell

$\psi = -2000$ kPa

Epidermal cell

Guard cell

Stoma

ψ air $= -2500$ kPa

Fig. 2 Rates of transpiration

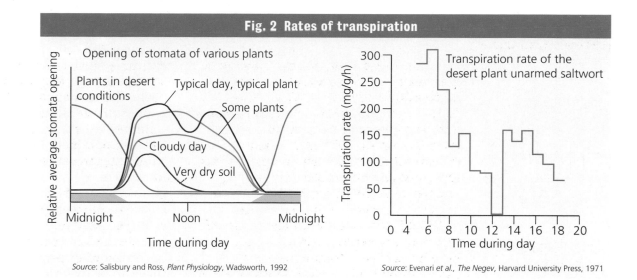

Opening of stomata of various plants

Plants in desert conditions — Typical day, typical plant — Some plants — Cloudy day — Very dry soil

Relative average stomata opening

Midnight   Noon   Midnight

Time during day

Source: Salisbury and Ross, *Plant Physiology*, Wadsworth, 1992

Transpiration rate of the desert plant unarmed saltwort

Transpiration rate (mg/g/h)

Time during day

Source: Evenari et al., *The Negev*, Harvard University Press, 1971

Fig. 3 Vertical section through a stomata

1. The guard cells are not connected along the whole of their length.

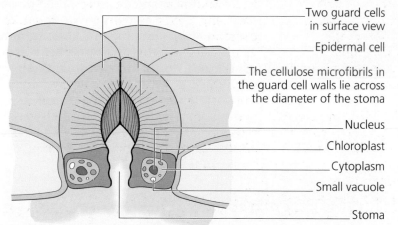

- Two guard cells in surface view
- Epidermal cell
- The cellulose microfibrils in the guard cell walls lie across the diameter of the stoma
- Nucleus
- Chloroplast
- Cytoplasm
- Small vacuole
- Stoma

2. When guard cells take in water and become turgid, they cannot expand in diameter because the microfibrils will not stretch. Therefore they increase in length, particularly along the thinner, outer walls.

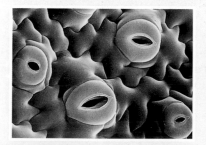

Each stomata is controlled by the turgidity of the guard cells. When the guard cells are full of water, the pore is open.

Magnification x 356.

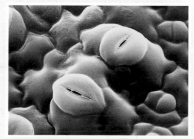

Stomatal closure is a natural response to darkness or drought, as a means of conserving water.

Magnification x 570.

There have been several hypotheses over the years. One was the 'starch–sugar' hypothesis, which suggested the following.

- The value of water potential of the guard cells depends on the balance between sugar and starch in the guard cells. The more sugar, the more negative the value of water potential.
- The enzymes that convert starch to sugar (**amylase**) and sugar to starch (**phosphorylase**) each has a different optimum pH. Amylase has a high optimum pH, phosphorylase has a low optimum pH.
- During the night, carbon dioxide from respiration dissolves in the cells to produce carbonic acid, which decreases the pH of the cell contents and favours the action of phosphorylase.
- During the day photosynthesis in the guard cell uses carbon dioxide, resulting in an increase in pH and favouring the action of amylase.

4 a Draw a flow chart that summarises the starch–sugar hypothesis.

b Explain how photosynthesis and the action of amylase could together affect the value of water potential of the guard cells.

c How would this change in the value of water potential cause the stomata to open?

159

Fig. 4 Potassium flow hypothesis

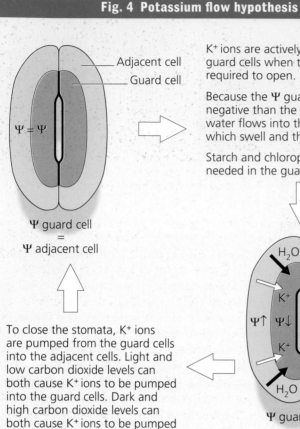

K⁺ ions are actively pumped into guard cells when the stomata are required to open.

Because the Ψ guard cell is more negative than the Ψ adjacent cell, water flows into the guard cells, which swell and the stoma opens.

Starch and chloroplasts are not needed in the guard cells.

Ψ = Ψ

Ψ guard cell
=
Ψ adjacent cell

To close the stomata, K⁺ ions are pumped from the guard cells into the adjacent cells. Light and low carbon dioxide levels can both cause K⁺ ions to be pumped into the guard cells. Dark and high carbon dioxide levels can both cause K⁺ ions to be pumped out of the guard cells.

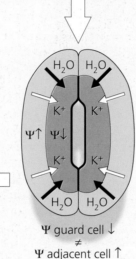

Ψ guard cell ↓
≠
Ψ adjacent cell ↑

The starch–sugar hypothesis is no longer acceptable, some of the reasons being:
- some guard cells do not have starch;
- the change in sugar–starch content is not quick enough to account for the speed at which stomata open in the light;
- some guard cells do not have chloroplasts;
- it cannot explain lunch-time closing.

A better hypothesis involves the movement of potassium ions (K^+) into and out of the guard cells. To open the stomata, adjacent cells pump K^+ ions into the guard cells (Fig. 4).

Light and carbon dioxide both affect the opening and closing of stomata. However, they can be over-ridden by a plant hormone called **abscisic acid** (ABA). ABA is produced when the plant suffers from **water stress**. This happens when a plant loses much more water through transpiration than can be absorbed through the roots, e.g. in a desert environment. ABA causes a rapid pumping of K^+ ions from the guard cells into the adjacent cells. This explains the lunch-time closing of the stomata of desert plants such as unarmed saltwort. It also explains the complete closing of stomata when the soil is very dry (Fig. 2).

Key ideas

- In most plants, stomata open during the day to allow the entry of the carbon dioxide needed for photosynthesis.

- Open stomata allow water vapour to diffuse out of the leaf, a process called transpiration.

- Water vapour diffuses out through stomata down a water potential gradient between the leaf cells and the air outside.

- Stomata open when water enters the guard cells and pushes against their cell walls.

- Water enters the guard cells by osmosis when the value of the water potential of the guard cells becomes more negative than adjacent cells due to the active transport into them of K^+ ions.

- The stomata of most plants are open during the day and closed during the night because both light and low concentrations of carbon dioxide stimulate adjacent cells to pump K^+ ions into the guard cells.

- The hormone ABA causes K^+ ions to be rapidly pumped from the guard cells into the adjacent cells. This means that stomata can be closed during the day, to conserve water, if a plant comes under water stress.

14.3 Desert plants

Deserts such as the Namib Desert in Africa are among the harshest environments in the world. Humans try to live in such areas and often fail.

The teddybear cactus, found in Arizona, USA, no longer has leaves as photosynthetic organs, but has reduced them to spines.

Much of the land that is now desert was once fertile. The change to desert began about 5000 years ago, when a change in the Earth's climate caused the rains to move away from these regions. The land became drier and drier, the cover of grass and trees withered. The soil blew away and all that was left was drifting sand.

In some areas, humans have damaged the environment, e.g. by growing the wrong crops, and caused fertile land to become too **arid** (dry and barren) for many animals and plants to survive.

Because the land is so dry no clouds form, so there is no shade during the day. Temperatures can rise as high as 50°C during the day, but because of the lack of clouds for insulation they can fall to freezing at night. Water from occasional rain collects underground and wherever this happens there will be plants. But these plants need to conserve this precious water. Plants that have adapted to arid conditions are called **xerophytes**.

Some desert plants, such as the *Pachypolium* in Madagascar, can survive dry spells by using stored carbohydrates and water. The stems and roots can become swollen with the water and carbohydrates; animals, including humans, can use these stores as a source of food and water for themselves. Some plants have adapted so successfully to arid environments that they can live for hundreds of years.

Cacti are adapted for life in the desert with the following xerophytic adaptations:
- the spines trap a layer of moist air next to the plant;
- the **epidermal** cells are covered by a thick layer of wax;
- the stems are **succulent**;
- the outer layers of cells of the stems have chloroplasts;
- the plants have a special way of obtaining carbon dioxide for photosynthesis called **crassulacean acid metabolism** (CAM).

The spines on a cactus trap a layer of water vapour next to the plant, and prevent the wind from moving the moist air layer away from around the plant. Many cacti also have a dense covering of hairs that traps even more water vapour.

The layer of wax on the epidermal cells prevents water loss by evaporation. Plants that store water are called succulent. The spines and stiff hairs also protect these plants from animals that try to get at the stored water.

Because the stem epidermal cells have chloroplasts, they can photosynthesise. CAM means they open their stomata at night to absorb carbon dioxide, and store it as malic acid. During the day the stomata are closed to conserve water, and the malic acid is broken down to release carbon dioxide so that it is available for photosynthesis.

Q5 Although cacti seem well adapted to life in deserts, their rate of growth is usually very slow. What is the factor that is limiting their rate of growth? Explain your answer.

Fig. 5 Cross-sections of gray sagebrush leaves

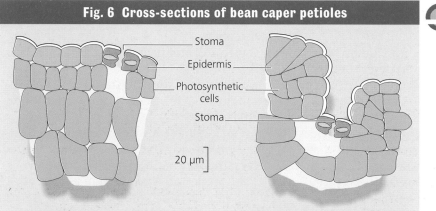

Winter leaf

Epidermis
Photosynthetic cells
Intercellular spaces

50 μm

Summer leaf

The winter and summer leaves differ in size, shape and structure

Sagebrush during winter in the Yellowstone National Park, Wyoming, USA.

Source: Evenari *et al.*, *The Negev*, Harvard University Press, 1971

Fig. 6 Cross-sections of bean caper petioles

Stoma
Epidermis
Photosynthetic cells
Stoma

20 μm

In dry conditions, the bean caper can shed its leaf blades. The leaf stalks, called **petioles**, are kept. They contain chlorophyll so can photosynthesise.

The epidermal cells elongate and divide, pushing the stomata into pits. Within the pits the stomata cannot open fully, and the air becomes saturated with water.

Source: Evenari *et al.*, *The Negev*, Harvard University Press, 1971

6 a Many desert plants manage to keep their leaves during the dry summer season, but they are smaller than those produced in the winter. Explain the advantage to the sagebrush of having smaller leaves during the summer (Fig. 5).

b Explain how the petiole and stomata adaptations of the bean caper means it can reduce its rate of transpiration by 96% during the summer (Fig. 6).

c Explain the advantage to grasses, e.g. marram grass and cereals, of rolling their leaves into cylinders during dry spells (Fig. 7).

Fig. 7 Marram grass

Marram grass is often found on sand dunes. You have probably felt the sharp end of the tight cylinder that the leaves form.

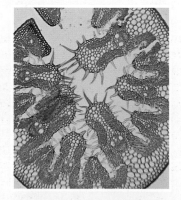

**Light micrograph of a transverse section of marram grass leaf.
Magnification x 66.**

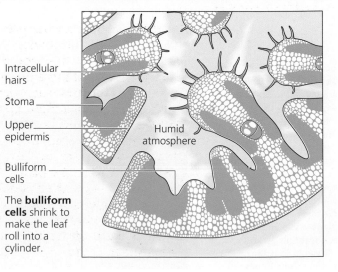

Intracellular hairs
Stoma
Upper epidermis
Bulliform cells

Humid atmosphere

The **bulliform cells** shrink to make the leaf roll into a cylinder.

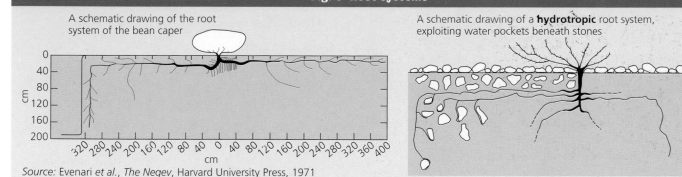

Fig. 8 Root systems

A schematic drawing of the root system of the bean caper

A schematic drawing of a **hydrotropic** root system, exploiting water pockets beneath stones

Source: Evenari *et al.*, *The Negev*, Harvard University Press, 1971

Collecting every drop of available water is vitally important to desert plants. Often the roots of these plants spread over a very wide area (Fig. 8).

Q7 Explain how the root systems in Fig. 8 are xerophytic adaptations.

Key ideas

- Cacti have reduced leaves to spines to conserve water.

- CAM plants open their stomata only at night, store the carbon dioxide absorbed at night as malic acid, then release it during the day for use in photosynthesis.

- Some desert plants reduce the area for transpiration by producing smaller leaves during the summer or modifying the shape of the leaves.

- Some desert plants shed the leaf blades, adapting the petioles for photosynthesis.

- Many desert plants sink their stomata into pits.

- Roots of desert plants often spread out over a wide area and can be hydrotropic.

14.4 Movement of water through the plant

Desert plants have a widespread root system that can collect water from a large volume of soil, but how does water get into the roots and from there up to the leaves? There is a gradient of water potential from a very negative value for air (approximately –2500 kPa) to a value approaching 0 Pa for soil water. So water moves along a gradient of water potential, mainly through the non-living parts of the plant. These non-living parts include the spaces between cells, the intercellular spaces, but also parts of the cells themselves, the cell walls. The non-living parts of the plants are known as the **apoplast**.

Everything inside the outer membrane of a cell is called the **symplast.** Minute strands of cytoplasm, called **plasmodesmata**, pass through the cell walls, connecting the symplast of adjacent cells. So, the apoplast and the symplast are separate, continuous systems.

Some cells, e.g. **xylem** vessels, have no living contents at maturity. The whole of such cells is therefore apoplast. Xylem cells form the part of the **vascular tissue** that transports water and dissolved mineral ions upwards through the plant. Water therefore moves mainly through the apoplast system of the plant on its way from the soil water to the air (Fig. 9).

163

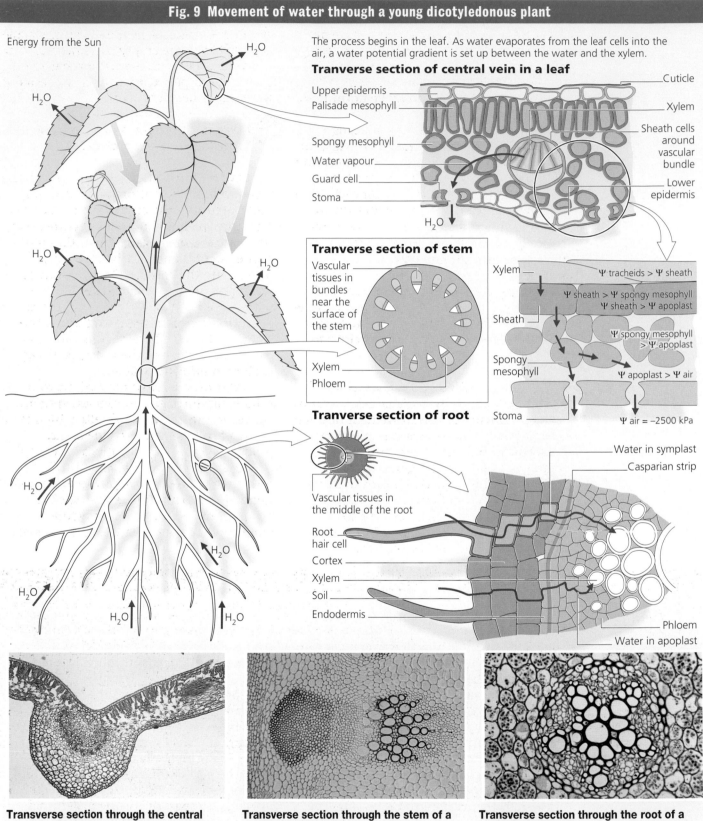

Fig. 9 Movement of water through a young dicotyledonous plant

Energy from the Sun

H₂O

H₂O

H₂O

H₂O

H₂O

H₂O

H₂O

H₂O

H₂O

H₂O

H₂O

The process begins in the leaf. As water evaporates from the leaf cells into the air, a water potential gradient is set up between the water and the xylem.

Tranverse section of central vein in a leaf

Upper epidermis

Palisade mesophyll

Spongy mesophyll

Water vapour

Guard cell

Stoma

Cuticle

Xylem

Sheath cells around vascular bundle

Lower epidermis

H₂O

Tranverse section of stem

Vascular tissues in bundles near the surface of the stem

Xylem

Phloem

Xylem

Ψ tracheids > Ψ sheath

Sheath

Ψ sheath > Ψ spongy mesophyll
Ψ sheath > Ψ apoplast

Spongy mesophyll

Ψ spongy mesophyll > Ψ apoplast

Ψ apoplast > Ψ air

Stoma

Ψ air = −2500 kPa

Tranverse section of root

Vascular tissues in the middle of the root

Root hair cell

Cortex

Xylem

Soil

Endodermis

Water in symplast

Casparian strip

Phloem

Water in apoplast

Transverse section through the central vein in a leaf of a dicotyledonous plant.

Transverse section through the stem of a dicotyledonous plant.

Transverse section through the root of a dicotyledonous plant.

Source: adapted from *New Scientist*, 18 February 1989

The xylem cells are joined to form continuous tubes that stretch from the roots right up to the leaves (Fig. 10). The tubes formed by the xylem cells have the same function as the water pipes in your home. Therefore their walls must be waterproof and there should be nothing to block the flow of water.

To move water along a stem needs a difference in water potential of 100 kPa for every 10 m to overcome the resistance. Add to this a difference of 100 kPa needed to overcome the force of gravity for each 10 m in height, and a difference of 200 kPa in water potential is required to move water 10 m up a tree. Pulling water up to this height needs a lot of energy.

Q 8 **If the difference in water potential between the air next to a leaf and the water in the soil is 2500 kPa, what is the theoretical maximum height to which a tree could grow?**

As water is pulled out of a vessel in a leaf, the column of water is pulled upwards. The mechanism for this movement of water up the xylem is known as the **cohesion-tension mechanism**. There are forces, hydrogen bonds, holding one water molecule to another. This means there is a cohesive attraction between the water molecules. Water molecules are also attracted to the sides of the xylem vessels. This creates a tension between the molecules of the vessel walls and water molecules. As a molecule of water evaporates from the leaf, the next molecule is pulled in to the empty place next to it in the xylem cells, and the water molecule below that is pulled along after the moving water molecule, and so on.

Q 9 **What is the source of energy for pulling water up a plant?**

As water leaves the xylem at the top, the xylem cells at the bottom of the column pull water from the cells in the root cortex. The water potential of the root cortex now has a value more negative than that of the root epidermis and root hairs so water moves into the cortex cells. The value of water potential for the epidermis is now more negative than that of the soil water and water moves automatically from the soil into the root. Mineral ions can enter the root dissolved in the water, or along their own diffusion gradient.

Water moves across most of the root principally through the apoplast system. However, the endodermal cells, which form a ring of cells around the xylem and phloem, have a strip of **suberin**, a water-repellent substance, in their walls. This forms the **Casparian strip**. The water and mineral ions have to pass through the symplast of endodermal cells before entering the apoplast of the xylem vessels.

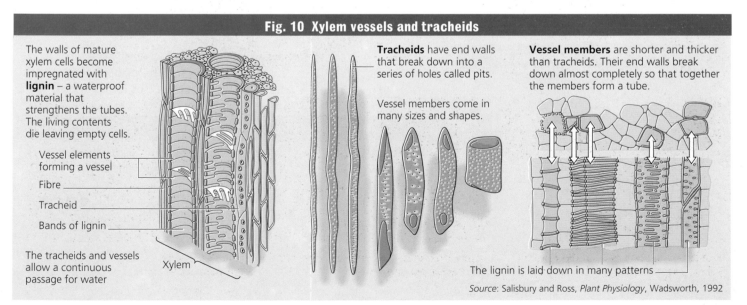

Fig. 10 Xylem vessels and tracheids

The walls of mature xylem cells become impregnated with **lignin** – a waterproof material that strengthens the tubes. The living contents die leaving empty cells.

Vessel elements forming a vessel

Fibre

Tracheid

Bands of lignin

The tracheids and vessels allow a continuous passage for water

Xylem

Tracheids have end walls that break down into a series of holes called pits.

Vessel members come in many sizes and shapes.

Vessel members are shorter and thicker than tracheids. Their end walls break down almost completely so that together the members form a tube.

The lignin is laid down in many patterns

Source: Salisbury and Ross, *Plant Physiology*, Wadsworth, 1992

Key ideas

- Water moves through a plant, from the soil to the air, because of a water potential gradient. The air has a much more negative water potential than the water in the soil. Water moves from the roots to the leaves mainly through the xylem vessels and tracheids.

- The cohesion-tension mechanism describes how water is pulled up through the xylem to replace the water lost by evaporation from the leaves.

- The energy which drives the movement of water is heat from the Sun which causes water in the apoplast of the leaf to evaporate.

- As water is pulled up the xylem, water is drawn across the root cortex to replace it.

- Water is drawn out of the soil solution because the root epidermal cells have a more negative value for water potential than the soil solution.

14.5 Sources and sinks

Desert plants can store large amounts of carbohydrate, e.g. in tuberous roots, to use as an energy source during dry spells. This carbohydrate was made by leaves of the tree. The leaves in this case are known as the **source** of the carbohydrate and the roots as the **sink**. When the rains return carbohydrate from the roots is transported up the stem to provide materials for developing leaves. This time the roots are the source and the leaves the sink.

The one-way transport system provided by the xylem cannot cope with these changes of direction. The transport of solutes is mainly done by the other vascular tissue of plants, the **phloem.**

Much of our knowledge about phloem comes from ringing experiments. In ringing experiments the xylem and phloem are separated and the amount of radioactive substances passing through each is measured. In 1951 Chen separated the xylem of the geranium from its phloem with waxed paper (Fig. 11). He applied radioactive phosphate solution to a leaf below the separated region and he allowed a leaf above the separated region to photosynthesise using radioactive carbon dioxide. Fifteen hours later he measured the amounts of radioactivity at various positions (Table 1).

10 a What do the results show about the direction of movement of:
(i) radioactive phosphate;
(ii) radioactive sugars in the phloem?
b Suggest what was the source and the sink for the phosphate and for the sugars in this experiment.

Fig. 11 Chen's experiment

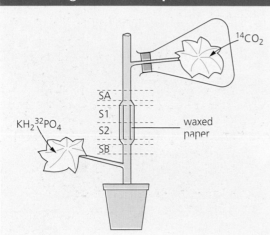

Table 1. Chen's results		
Position of phloem analysed	**Radioactivity of carbon and phosphorous in phloem**	
	^{14}C/ppm	^{32}P/µg KH$_2$^{32}PO$_4$
SA (above waxed paper)	44 800	186
S1	3480	103
S2	3030	116
SB (below waxed paper)	2380	125

To understand how phloem transports substances, sometimes in different directions at the same time, you first need to know the essential features of the structure of phloem (Fig. 12).

There are three important features of phloem cells that are different to xylem cells:

- sieve tubes do not have lignified walls, so their walls are permeable to water and to solutes;
- sieve tube elements usually do not have a nucleus when mature, but they retain most of the organelles of the cytoplasm and so are living;
- each sieve tube element has one or more companion cells associated with it – these companion cells have dense cytoplasm and abundant mitochondria in them.

11 What does the structure of companion cells suggest about the mechanism of transport in the phloem?

Chen's experiment showed that sugars were loaded into the phloem in the leaf, then passed down the phloem towards the roots. How are the sugars loaded into the phloem and how do they move downwards towards the roots? The **mass flow hypothesis** is one attempt to explain how the phloem works.

The carbohydrate sucrose is actively transported into the sieve tube cells, probably through the symplast of the mesophyll cells and companion cells. The sucrose pumped into the sieve tube elements reduces the value of the water potential of these cells. As a result, water diffuses from the surrounding cells into the sieve tube cells (Fig. 13). The increased volume of solution in the sieve tube members results in an increase in pressure, which forces the solution along the sieve tubes. This pressure can cause the solution in the phloem to move very rapidly, particularly in crop plants. Speeds of 660 cm h^{-1} have been recorded for movement of the solution in the phloem of maize plants! Large amounts of solutes can also be transported into sinks. Rates as high as $252 \text{ g h}^{-1} \text{ cm}^{-2}$ of phloem have been recorded in the castor bean plant.

In the sinks, the reverse process takes place. Sucrose is actively pumped out of the phloem into the surrounding cells. The water potential of these cells drops and water leaves the phloem by osmosis. In some xerophytic plants, the sugar is converted immediately into starch in the root cells. Starch has little or no effect on the water potential of the cells.

Fig. 12 Phloem structure

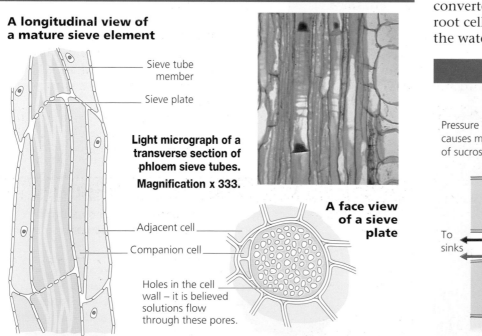

A longitudinal view of a mature sieve element

- Sieve tube member
- Sieve plate

Light micrograph of a transverse section of phloem sieve tubes. Magnification x 333.

- Adjacent cell
- Companion cell

A face view of a sieve plate

- Holes in the cell wall – it is believed solutions flow through these pores.

Source: Salisbury and Ross, *Plant Physiology*, Wadsworth, 1992

Fig. 13 Loading of sugars

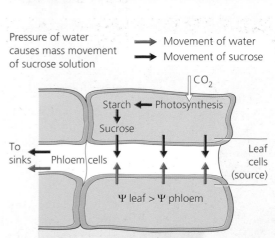

Pressure of water causes mass movement of sucrose solution

→ Movement of water
→ Movement of sucrose

CO_2

Starch ← Photosynthesis
Sucrose

To sinks ← Phloem cells

Leaf cells (source)

Ψ leaf > Ψ phloem

When the sink is a young leaf, sugars are converted into new cell materials such as cellulose, again effectively lowering the sugar concentration of the sink and keeping the process going. The water is now free to pass from the phloem into the xylem and back to the leaves. Water therefore circulates between the source and the sink (Fig. 14).

12 Look again at Fig. 11. Explain in terms of mass flow how phosphate moves up the stem in the phloem.

Although some mineral ions are moved through phloem, others are carried up the stem in the xylem passively in the transpiration stream.

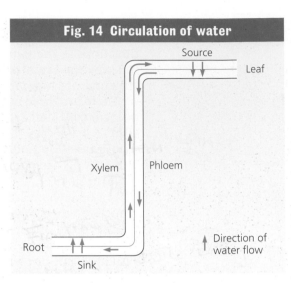

Fig. 14 Circulation of water

Source
Leaf
Xylem
Phloem
Root
Sink
Direction of water flow

Greening the desert

The deserts of the world are expanding. Changes in climate and inappropriate farming techniques mean that 3.3 billion hectares of previously useful land are now classified as desert. If we can learn to understand how plants manage their water economy we might be able to reclaim some of the land and make it fertile again.

13 List the characteristics you would look for in a new crop to grow in very dry areas.

Key ideas

- Solutes such as sugars and some mineral ions are moved through the plant in the sieve tubes of the phloem.

- These solutes are moved from areas of high concentration, sources, to areas of low concentration, sinks.

- Solutes are moved into sieve tubes by active transport with the help of companion cells.

- Water follows the solutes into the sieve tubes osmotically, the presence of high concentrations of sugars in the sieve tubes gives them a very negative value for water potential.

- Water entering the sieve tubes creates a pressure that causes the solution in the phloem to move away from the source towards the sink.

- Mass flow describes the mechanism by which the solutes are transported to the sinks.

- Sugars arriving at a sink are usually converted into storage material or new cell material. This ensures a concentration gradient between source and sink to keep the sugars moving.

Running to win

K. Merry preparing to run
at the Pearl Assurance
International in 1989.

Roger Black leads Kriss
Akabussi.

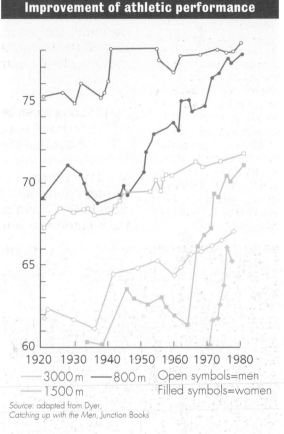

Improvement of athletic performance

75

70

65

60

1920 1930 1940 1950 1960 1970 1980

—— 3000 m   —— 800 m   Open symbols=men
—— 1500 m   Filled symbols=women

Source: adapted from Dyer,
Catching up with the Men, Junction Books

The performance of female athletes has
improved dramatically since 1920. They are
literally 'catching up with the men'. The
improvement relative to men is most
noticeable in middle and long distance
races. This improvement is almost entirely
due to improved motivation and training.
Today's athletes, men and women, are
much fitter because they are better coached.
And the coaches have a much better
understanding of how the body takes in
oxygen and gets it to the muscles when it is
needed. With the right training, would
men and women be able to compete on
equal terms?

15.1 Learning objectives

After working through this chapter, you should be able to:

- **describe** the ventilation mechanisms of
  humans, insects and fish;

- **relate** the structure and location of
  respiratory surfaces in humans, fish,
  terrestrial insects and dicotyledonous plants
  to their function;

- **explain** how the brain, the aortic bodies
  and the carotid bodies control ventilation in
  humans;

- **explain** how the development of respiratory
  systems has enabled larger organisms to
  cope with a reduction in their surface area
  to volume ratios.

15.2 Ventilation

You have probably, at least once in your life, suffered from muscle fatigue when running. You get muscle fatigue when a muscle cannot get enough oxygen to produce all the ATP it needs.

You may need to look back at Chapters 2 and 4 to revise respiration before you can answer these questions.

1 a What is ATP?
b Where in a muscle cell is ATP produced?
c What is the function of ATP?

During muscle fatigue, there is a build-up in the muscles of a poisonous substance called **lactic acid**. Lactic acid is produced when pyruvic acid accepts electrons from NADH, rather than being converted to acetylcoenzyme A. This happens when there is a shortage of oxygen. This is a form of **anaerobic** respiration. Anaerobic respiration does not need oxygen.

Aerobic respiration does need oxygen. When there is plenty of oxygen available, the electrons from NADH are transferred to ATP. Aerobic respiration is much more efficient that anaerobic respiration. For every glucose molecule that is oxidised, aerobic respiration produces 38 molecules of ATP, while anaerobic respiration produces 2 molecules of ATP.

The main aim of training for long distance running is to improve the oxygen supply to the muscles so that lactic acid is not produced, and so that the muscles do not get fatigued. One way of doing this is the improve the rate at which oxygen gets into the blood in the lungs.

When a person is training or taking part in any aerobic exercise, they are trying to increase the:
• vital capacity of the lungs;
• breathing rate;
• maximum breathing capacity.

Getting air in and out of the lungs is known as **ventilation**. Breathing is the mechanical ventilation of the lung. Getting air into the lungs (breathing in) is called **inspiration**, and getting air out of the lungs is called **expiration**. Notice the difference between ventilation and respiration. Respiration is a series of oxidation reactions that occur in cells.

The **vital capacity** of the lungs is the maximum volume of air that can be exhaled from the lungs. It depends on the volume of the lungs but it also depends on the strength of the muscles that move air in and out of the lungs. Training can increase the strength of these muscles and raise the vital capacity from an average of under five litres in an untrained person to six litres in a trained athlete.

Fig. 1 Human ventilation

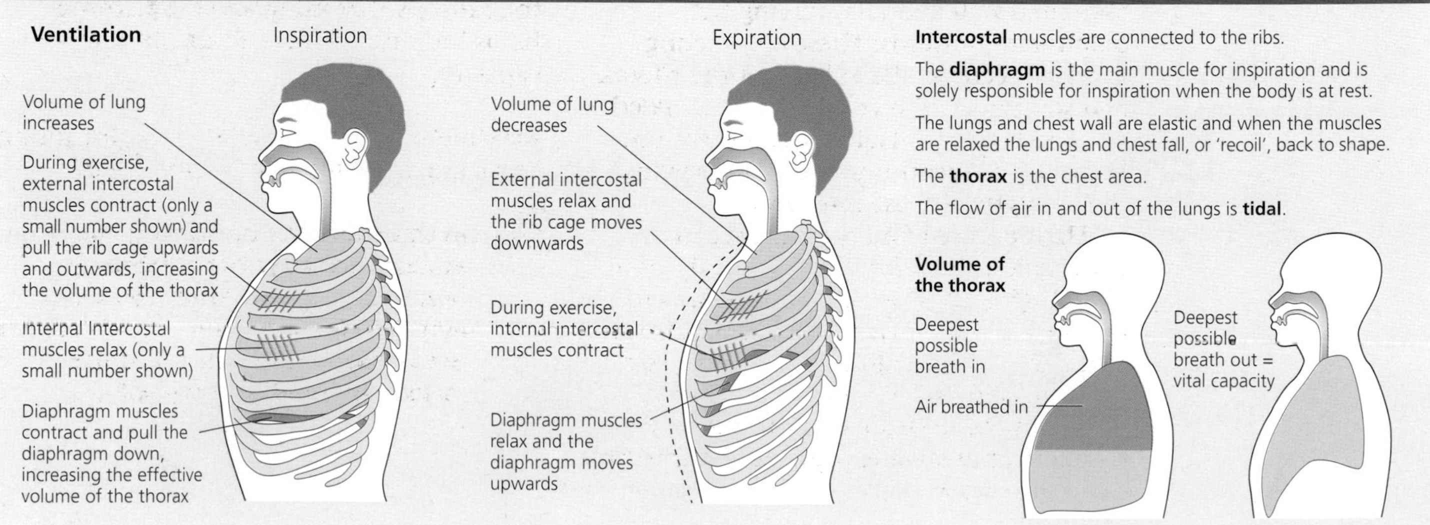

Ventilation

Inspiration

Volume of lung increases

During exercise, external intercostal muscles contract (only a small number shown) and pull the rib cage upwards and outwards, increasing the volume of the thorax

Internal intercostal muscles relax (only a small number shown)

Diaphragm muscles contract and pull the diaphragm down, increasing the effective volume of the thorax

Expiration

Volume of lung decreases

External intercostal muscles relax and the rib cage moves downwards

During exercise, internal intercostal muscles contract

Diaphragm muscles relax and the diaphragm moves upwards

Intercostal muscles are connected to the ribs.

The **diaphragm** is the main muscle for inspiration and is solely responsible for inspiration when the body is at rest.

The lungs and chest wall are elastic and when the muscles are relaxed the lungs and chest fall, or 'recoil', back to shape.

The **thorax** is the chest area.

The flow of air in and out of the lungs is **tidal**.

Volume of the thorax

Deepest possible breath in

Air breathed in

Deepest possible breath out = vital capacity

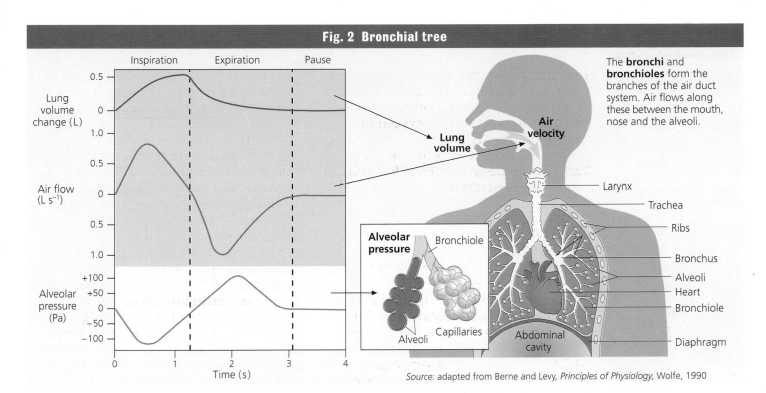

Fig. 2 Bronchial tree

The **bronchi** and **bronchioles** form the branches of the air duct system. Air flows along these between the mouth, nose and the alveoli.

Source: adapted from Berne and Levy, *Principles of Physiology*, Wolfe, 1990

There are three sets of muscles actively concerned with breathing (Fig. 1):
• the muscles of the diaphragm;
• the external intercostal muscles;
• the internal intercostal muscles.

Inspiration is an active process. When the body is at rest, expiration is a passive process. The diaphragm muscles relax and the elastic recoil of the lungs and chest wall returns the thorax to its original shape. But when the body is exercising the internal intercostal muscles contract, pulling the ribs downwards, and the muscles in the abdomen wall contract, forcing the diaphragm upwards. These contracting muscles decrease the volume of the thorax and so increase the volume of air exhaled with each breath. Training can therefore increase the breathing rate by improving the strength of these muscles.

The purpose of all these muscular contractions is to force air into and out of **alveoli** (Fig. 2). These are tiny air sacs in the lung where oxygen can diffuse into the blood and carbon dioxide can diffuse out.

Increasing the volume of the thorax decreases the pressure of air in the alveoli to below atmospheric pressure. Air is forced into the lungs until the pressure in the alveoli equals that of the atmosphere. This inflow of air inflates the lungs. Decreasing the volume of the thorax has the reverse effect. As the pressure of air in the alveoli rises above atmospheric air pressure, air is squeezed out until the alveolar pressure equals atmospheric pressure.

Training for a long distance race also improves the **maximum breathing capacity**, the maximum amount of air that can be moved in and out of the lungs over a period of time. Improving the strength of the muscles that bring about breathing helps increase the maximum breathing capacity.

$$\text{Maximum breathing capacity} = \text{vital capacity} \times \text{breathing rate}$$

Q2 In three months of training, an athlete increased her maximum breathing capacity from 130 litres min^{-1} to 180 litres min^{-1}. Calculate the percentage improvement in her maximum breathing capacity.

15.3 The human respiratory surface

Fig. 3 Alveoli

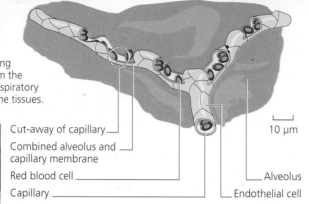

The membranes of the capillaries and the endothelial cells of the alveolus form a very thin membrane, separating air in the alveoli from the blood that carries respiratory gases to and from the tissues.

Cut-away of capillary

Combined alveolus and capillary membrane

Red blood cell

Capillary

10 μm

Alveolus

Endothelial cell

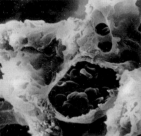

A coloured scanning electron micrograph of red blood cells flowing through a capillary in the wall of the alveoli. The cavities around the blood vessel are the air spaces inside the lung.

Ventilating the lungs has one function, to maintain diffusion gradients for oxygen and carbon dioxide between air and blood. The greater the difference between oxygen concentrations in air and blood, the faster oxygen will diffuse. Inspiration maintains a higher level of oxygen in the air in the lungs than is dissolved in the blood.

The surface of the alveoli provides a connection, an interface, between the blood and air (Fig. 3). The alveoli are a human's **respiratory surface**.

The alveoli are composed of **endothelial** cells, which support a network of blood capillaries. Collectively the alveoli and capillaries provide a very extensive surface area for **gaseous exchange**, the diffusion of gases.

As the volume of an organism increases, its surface increases by less, so that the **surface area to volume ratio** reduces. If the ratio falls below a certain value, gaseous exchange through the outer surface alone cannot occur fast enough to supply the organism's needs. Larger organisms have had to evolve systems and organs that increase the surface area to volume ratio. The respiratory surface has to be large enough to allow gaseous exchange to supply enough oxygen for the body's needs, and to remove carbon dioxide before it harms the body.

3 Explain how a reduced surface area to volume ratio slows down the rate at which molecules reach the centre of an organism.

The thinness of the membrane in the alveoli separating the blood from air is also important. It provides a short diffusion pathway for the respiratory gases. The shorter the distance, the greater the rate of diffusion.

The membrane of the endothelial cells in contact with air is covered by a thin layer of liquid. This liquid is necessary for the oxygen to dissolve in so that it can then diffuse into the blood. However, the layer of liquid has a high **surface tension**. Surface tension is a property of water that makes it 'stick' to surfaces it is next to. The water acts like stretched elastic, and can make the sides of the alveoli shrink together, reducing the area available for gaseous exchange. To prevent this, the liquid contains a chemical called a **surfactant**. Surfactants reduce surface tension.

Training increases the rate at which oxygen is taken into the blood in the lungs, from three litres of oxygen per minute in a normally active person to over six litres per minute in a long distance runner. This increase in rate depends both on the capacity of the lungs and on the rate of blood flow through the lungs. Chapter 17 discusses the flow of blood in the human body.

The rate of oxygen uptake also depends on the size of the athlete. The bigger the athlete the greater the potential oxygen uptake rate because the surface area of the lungs will be greater.

4 What would be a fairer unit (than litres of oxygen per minute) to compare the improvement in rate of oxygen uptake into the blood by athletes during a training programme?

Key ideas

- Ventilation is brought about by the diaphragm muscles, intercostal muscles and abdominal muscles.

- These muscles change the volume of the thorax and hence the pressure of air inside the lungs.

- The flow of air in human lungs is tidal.

- To maintain diffusion gradients for oxygen and carbon dioxide, the air in the lungs is changed regularly by breathing.

- The human respiratory surface is the alveoli of the lungs.

- The respiratory surface allows efficient gaseous exchange system because it has a large surface area that is thin, moist and well supplied with blood vessels.

15.4 Control of ventilation

Yoga exercises like this one can help you to change your rate of ventilation. But you do not usually have to think about this. You breathe automatically for 24 hours a day. The more active you are the higher your ventilation rate. If you have been inactive for some time you might yawn, or even fall asleep!

A part of the brain called the **medulla oblongata** maintains ventilation twenty-four hours a day (Fig. 4).

The ventilation cycle begins with **inspiratory cells**. These are a group of cells at the top of the medulla oblongata that pass impulses along efferent nerve cells to the diaphragm muscles and the external intercostal muscles. In the walls of the bronchi and bronchioles are **stretch receptor** cells that are sensitive to stretch. They send impulses along afferent nerve cells to the medulla oblongata.

Q5 Explain why the impulses from the stretch receptors act as a negative feedback mechanism.

Fig. 4 24-hour-a-day breathing

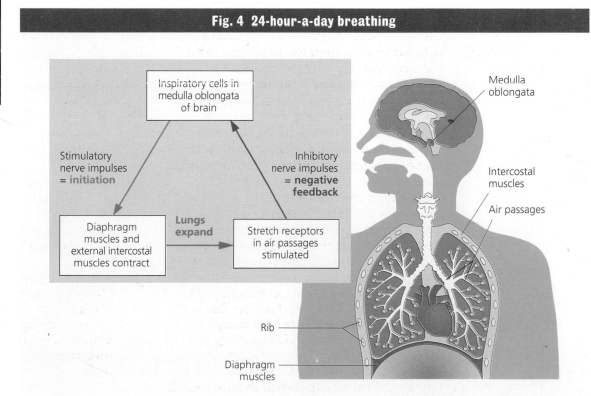

Fig. 5 Central receptors

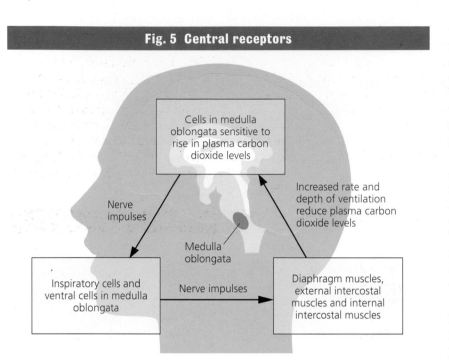

Varying the ventilation rate

When you begin to exercise your ventilation rate increases. The control mechanism for this depends on receptor cells that are sensitive to chemical changes in the blood. These receptors are called **chemoreceptors**. Some chemoreceptors are sensitive to oxygen concentration, others to carbon dioxide concentration, and others to pH. These receptors are found in three parts of the body – in the medulla oblongata in the brain and in two bodies associated with blood vessels, the **aortic bodies** and **carotid bodies**.

The chemoreceptors in the medulla oblongata are called the **central receptors**. These are sensitive to the carbon dioxide concentration of the blood in the capillaries which pass through the medulla oblongata (Fig. 5). During exercise the carbon dioxide concentration of the blood rises. The central chemoreceptors detect this rise and send impulses to the inspiratory cells and another group of cells called the **ventral group**, in the medulla oblongata.

Both the inspiratory cells and the ventral group send nerve impulses to the diaphragm and intercostal muscles. The effect of all these impulses is to increase the rate and the strength of the contractions of the intercostal muscles and so to increase

the rate and depth of ventilation. This increases the diffusion gradient for carbon dioxide in the alveoli by lowering the level of carbon dioxide in the lungs. When the blood plasma carbon dioxide levels return to normal the central chemoreceptors stop sending impulses and the ventilation rate returns to normal.

The carotid bodies and the aortic bodies are collectively known as the **peripheral receptors** (Fig. 6). Some of these receptors are also sensitive to the carbon dioxide concentration in the blood plasma. It has been estimated that the response to increased carbon dioxide in the blood is 80% due to the central receptors and 20% to the peripheral receptors.

Some of the peripheral receptors send impulses to the medulla if they detect falling oxygen concentrations in the blood plasma. Others are sensitive to decreases in the pH of the plasma. Carbon dioxide is acidic, so rising carbon dioxide concentrations cause a decrease in plasma pH. This triggers the pH-sensitive peripheral receptors to send impulses to the medulla.

Fig. 6 Peripheral receptors

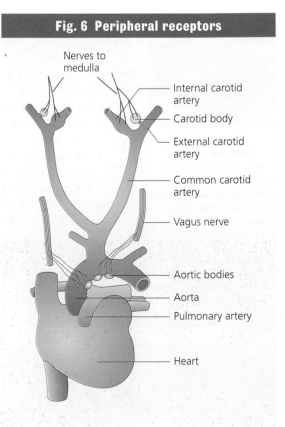

When impulses from the peripheral receptors reach the inspiratory and the ventral cells in the medulla, the effect is the same as that of impulses from the central receptors. There is an increase in the rate and depth of ventilation until the carbon dioxide levels return to normal.

6 a Draw a flow diagram of the impulses generated by the peripheral receptors.
b From Fig. 7, which of the aortic and carotid bodies is the more sensitive to increasing levels of carbon dioxide in the plasma?
c Which of the two bodies is the more sensitive to falling oxygen concentrations in plasma?

The effects of a low concentration of oxygen in the blood plasma can have dramatic effects on breathing. At high altitudes, the atmospheric pressure of oxygen falls. This makes it more difficult for the lungs to ventilate and less oxygen diffuses through the alveoli. If a person's blood is inadequately oxygenated, they suffer from **hypoxia**. The chemoreceptors respond to the falling levels of oxygen in the blood plasma and ventilation increases to reduce the carbon dioxide levels. However, such large quantities of carbon dioxide can be expelled that the blood becomes more alkaline. This increase in pH inhibits the activity of the chemoreceptors.

Chris Bonington and Ang Lhakpa, on the summit of Everest, are wearing oxygen masks so that they do not suffer from lack of oxygen.

7 a Explain the effect that inhibiting the pH-sensitive chemoreceptors will have on the rate of ventilation.
b From Fig. 8, which person, A or B, could be suffering from hypoxia?

All the control mechanisms come into play during a long distance race, to increase the rate and depth of ventilation. The maximum rate, however, depends on the amount of training. Training increases the strength of the respiratory muscles. These stronger muscles can bring more air into the body with each breath and can maintain a high ventilation rate for longer periods. The performance of the athlete is enhanced!

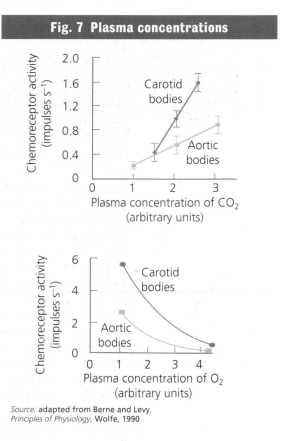

Fig. 7 Plasma concentrations

Source: adapted from Berne and Levy, *Principles of Physiology,* Wolfe, 1990

Fig. 8 Hypoxia?

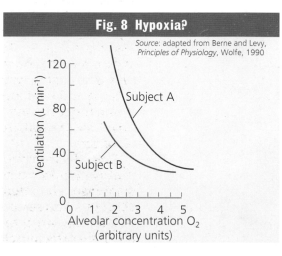

Source: adapted from Berne and Levy, *Principles of Physiology,* Wolfe, 1990

Key ideas

- The medulla oblongata controls the rate of breathing 24 hours a day.

- The ventilation cycle involves inspiratory cells and stretch receptor cells.

- Central receptors in the medulla oblongata are sensitive to the carbon dioxide concentrations in the blood.

- Peripheral receptors in the aortic bodies and the carotid bodies are sensitive to carbon dioxide and oxygen concentrations in the blood and to blood pH.

- An increase in carbon dioxide levels or a decrease in oxygen levels in the blood brings about increases in the rate and depth of ventilation.

15.5 How other organisms do it

The cichlids, like all fish, have to open and close their mouths in order to breathe.

Fish

Obtaining oxygen is far more difficult for fish than for humans. The water they live in contains only one thirtieth as much oxygen per unit volume as air. This is because oxygen is not very soluble in water. Water also has a higher density than air, making it much more difficult to move it through the body during ventilation. However, carbon dioxide is very soluble in water, so its removal from the blood does not pose such a problem.

Fig. 9 Fish ventilation

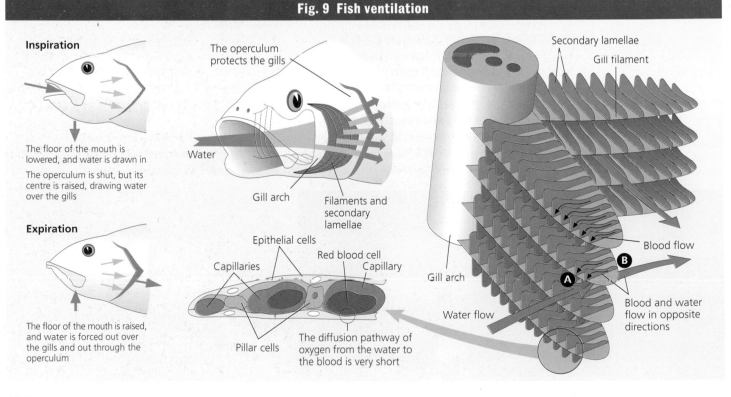

Inspiration

The floor of the mouth is lowered, and water is drawn in

The operculum is shut, but its centre is raised, drawing water over the gills

Expiration

The floor of the mouth is raised, and water is forced out over the gills and out through the operculum

The operculum protects the gills

Water

Gill arch

Filaments and secondary lamellae

Epithelial cells

Capillaries

Red blood cell

Capillary

Pillar cells

The diffusion pathway of oxygen from the water to the blood is very short

Secondary lamellae

Gill filament

Gill arch

Water flow

Blood flow

Blood and water flow in opposite directions

A

B

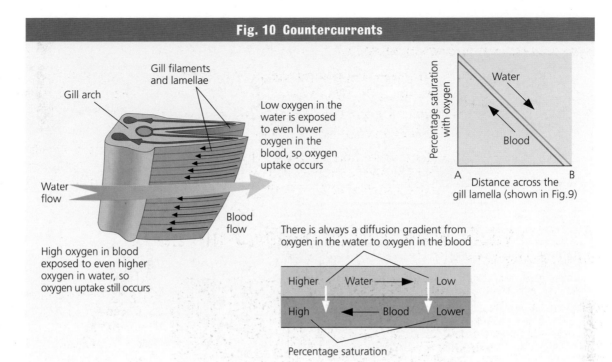

Fig. 10 Countercurrents

Gill arch

Gill filaments and lamellae

Low oxygen in the water is exposed to even lower oxygen in the blood, so oxygen uptake occurs

Water flow

Blood flow

High oxygen in blood exposed to even higher oxygen in water, so oxygen uptake still occurs

Percentage saturation with oxygen

Water

Blood

A   Distance across the gill lamella (shown in Fig.9)   B

There is always a diffusion gradient from oxygen in the water to oxygen in the blood

Higher   Water →   Low

High   ← Blood   Lower

Percentage saturation

The respiratory surface of fish is the **gills**, in particular projections called **secondary lamellae** (Fig. 9). The total surface area of these secondary lamellae is enormous.

Q 8 Why do fish require a large area of respiratory surface?

The length of the diffusion path for oxygen is very short, because there is only a thin membrane separating the blood from the outside water. However, to obtain maximum oxygen uptake from the water, fish have also developed another strategy: the **countercurrent flow** (Fig. 10). The currents of water and of blood flow in opposite directions. This increases the opportunity for the oxygen to diffuse into the blood. Up to 80% of the oxygen

dissolved in the water is extracted by the gills. This is a far higher proportion than humans can extract from air. We only extract 25% of the oxygen in the air we breathe. The diffusion of carbon dioxide from the blood into the water is also helped by the countercurrent flow.

The countercurrent mechanism requires that the ventilation current should move in one direction only – not in a tidal manner as in humans. The fish uses muscles in the floor of its mouth to pump the water and uses the mouth and the opercula as valves to ensure this unidirectional flow (Fig. 9).

Q 9 List the ways in which humans and fish differ in the way that they obtain oxygen.

Fig. 11 Locust ventilation

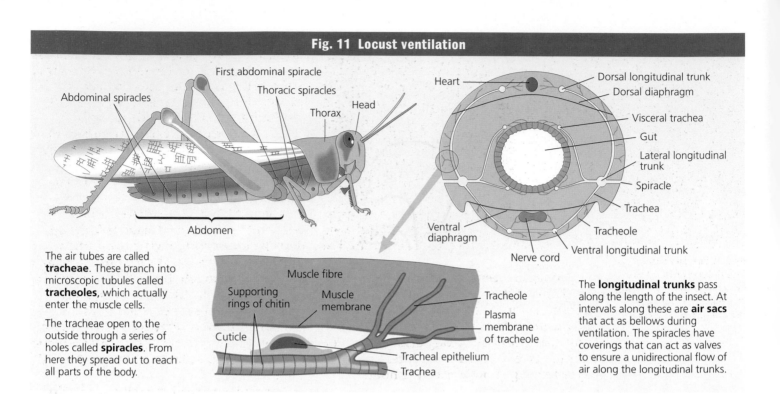

Abdominal spiracles · First abdominal spiracle · Thoracic spiracles · Head · Thorax · Head · Abdomen

Heart · Dorsal longitudinal trunk · Dorsal diaphragm · Visceral trachea · Gut · Lateral longitudinal trunk · Spiracle · Trachea · Tracheole · Ventral longitudinal trunk · Ventral diaphragm · Nerve cord

The air tubes are called **tracheae**. These branch into microscopic tubules called **tracheoles**, which actually enter the muscle cells.

The tracheae open to the outside through a series of holes called **spiracles**. From here they spread out to reach all parts of the body.

Muscle fibre · Supporting rings of chitin · Muscle membrane · Cuticle · Tracheole · Plasma membrane of tracheole · Tracheal epithelium · Trachea

The **longitudinal trunks** pass along the length of the insect. At intervals along these are **air sacs** that act as bellows during ventilation. The spiracles have coverings that can act as valves to ensure a unidirectional flow of air along the longitudinal trunks.

Insects

Insects do not have respiratory organs such as gills or lungs and they do not use the blood system to carry oxygen round the body. Instead they use a system of air tubes to carry air directly to the respiring tissues (Fig. 11). The respiratory surface of an insect is therefore actually inside most of its cells.

During ventilation when the insect is at rest, air is drawn in through spiracles 1, 2 and 4 (Fig. 12). When these close air is expired through spiracle 10. When the insect is more active expiration takes place through spiracles 5-10. The ventilation movements are synchronised with the opening and closing of the spiracles.

Carbon dioxide is removed from insects mainly by diffusing into blood and then out through the cuticle which covers the body. Some carbon dioxide does leave the body through the spiracles.

Fig. 12 Ventilation movements

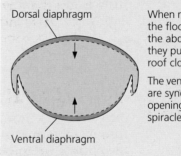

Dorsal diaphragm

Ventral diaphragm

When muscles attached to the floor and the roof of the abdomen contract, they pull the floor and the roof closer together.

The ventilation movements are synchronised with the opening and closing of the spiracles.

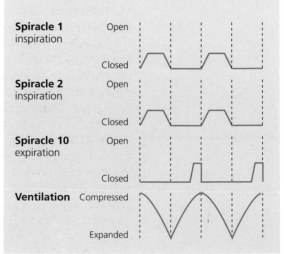

Spiracle 1 inspiration — Open / Closed

Spiracle 2 inspiration — Open / Closed

Spiracle 10 expiration — Open / Closed

Ventilation — Compressed / Expanded

Insects like this desert locust differ greatly from humans and fish in the way in which they exchange their respiratory gases.

Although it seems to be primitive, the ventilation system of an insect is very efficient. During flight a locust can take in and use up to 180 litres of oxygen per kg of body mass per hour. A long distance runner can only take in and use five litres of oxygen per kg of body mass per hour!

 10 a **List the ways in which the method of obtaining oxygen differs between insects and humans.**

b **List the ways in which the method of obtaining oxygen differs between insects and fish.**

Dicotyledonous plants

Being sedentary, plants do not need to take in anything like the amount of oxygen that active animals do. But they do need surfaces for gaseous exchange for both cell respiration and photosynthesis.

The main gaseous exchange surface in dicotyledonous plants is inside the leaves. Root and stem cells obtain most of their oxygen as dissolved oxygen in the water absorbed by the roots.

The leaf has a large surface area in relation to its volume. Chapters 5 and 14 described how both oxygen and carbon dioxide enter the leaf through the stomata and diffuse through the intercellular spaces in the mesophyll. The gaseous exchange surface is therefore the surface of the mesophyll cells themselves. The surface of the mesophyll cells is moist. This allows the oxygen to dissolve before diffusing through the cell wall.

Since they have no muscles, plants do not have a ventilation mechanism in leaves. Instead, the leaf must be thin to reduce the length of the diffusion path of the oxygen and carbon dioxide.

15.6 Surface area to volume ratio

Living organisms, plant and animal, have to exchange substances with the environment. In small organisms, such as cyanobacteria, the exchanges can take place by diffusion, osmosis and active transport across the cell membranes.

The larger an organism is the smaller the ratio of its surface area to its volume. This means the diffusion pathways of gases and nutrients to the internal cells could be so vast that a large organism could not survive without providing extra surfaces for gaseous exchange. Humans, fish, insects and plants have all evolved mechanisms to provide large surface areas for exchanging gases and other molecules. This means they can grow bigger.

Animals need mechanisms to transport oxygen to the body cells and remove carbon dioxide. Humans and fish have

Pavarotti and other opera singers, like athletes, have to train to increase their lung capacity.

respiratory organs with a large, thin surface area for exchanging gases. Chapter 17 describes how the respiratory gases are transported between the respiratory surface and the tissues by the blood system.

To maintain diffusion gradients, humans, fish and insects use muscles to ventilate their breathing systems. They all respond to exercise by using their muscles to increase their ventilation rates. Humans can train to increase the strength of the muscles of the breathing system and so enhance athletic performance by increasing the rate of oxygen uptake into the blood.

Q 11 Do you think a male and female human of the same size could reach the same level of athletic performance? Explain your answer in terms of surface area to volume ratio.

Key ideas

- Fish use a countercurrent system to maximise the rate of gaseous exchange across the respiratory surface.

- A countercurrent multiplier ensures the oxygenating medium flows in the opposite direction to the blood. This means that a diffusion gradient exists across the whole length of the exchange membrane.

- Insects have a system of air tubes called tracheoles that carry air directly to the tissues.

- The main gaseous exchange surfaces of a dicotyledonous plant are found in the leaves.

- Animals and plants have developed systems of gaseous exchange that allow them to cope with their reduced surface area to volume ratio.

16 Balancing your sugar

People with diabetes can take part in all sports, but they have to make sure their blood sugar levels do not fall too low. This is particularly important if swimming, because of the danger of drowning.

'I suffer from diabetes mellitus, which means I cannot regulate the levels of sugar in my blood automatically. I have to use regular injections of insulin and a special diet to control my blood sugar. The more I understand about how my body digests carbohydrates and the part insulin plays in regulating blood sugar levels, the easier it will be for me to live as normal a life as possible. I could even end up with a healthier lifestyle than people who have not had to find so much out about their body!'

Most diabetics have a good understanding of the importance of carbohydrates in the diet, and the role of insulin. They can then keep their blood sugar levels as near normal as possible, as to have too much or too little can be dangerous. The general advice to diabetics about diet is 'to eat starchy kinds of food to slow down the movement of sugar into the blood'. The advice given to a diabetic suffering from a 'hypo' is to take some 'easily digested sugar', e.g. in the form of glucose tablets and sugary drinks. Why the difference?

16.1 Learning objectives

After working through this chapter, you should be able to:

- **recall** the generalised structure of the mammalian gut wall;

- **relate** the modifications of this generalised structure in the oesophagus, stomach, ileum and colon to the functions of these organs;

- **recall** the mechanism of peristalsis;

- **recall** the sites of production of amylases, endopeptidases, exopeptidases, lipase, maltase and bile;

- **describe** the mechanisms involved in the absorption of food in the ileum;

- **describe** the structure of a liver lobule;

- **describe** the process of transamination and the role of the liver in the production of albumins and globulins;

- **describe** the role of the liver in fat metabolism including the production of cholesterol;

- **describe** the role of nervous reflexes and the role of the hormones gastrin, cholecystokinin and secretin in the control of digestive secretions;

- **describe** the role of the liver in glycogenesis, glycogenolysis and gluconeogenesis;

- **describe** the roles of insulin and glycogen in the control of blood sugar, including the importance of membrane receptors and their effect on enzyme-controlled processes.

16.2 Getting food into the blood

Foods like these can be eaten freely by diabetics, if they are not overweight. Starchy carbohydrate food, like wholemeal bread and pulses, is very important in a diabetic diet as it provides fibre which slows down the absorption of sugar into the blood.

Q 1 a What type of reaction joins sugar molecules together to form polymers?
 b What molecule is given out by the sugars when two molecules link?

Digestion of starch involves the opposite reaction, hydrolysis. Starch is hydrolysed by enzymes to form sugars.

Starch + water → sugars

Q 2 From your work in Chapter 5 suggest why sugars can be absorbed into cells but starches cannot.

Chapter 1 explained that starch is a polymer composed of glucose molecules linked together. Glucose can be absorbed into the blood stream as it is, but starch has to be digested to glucose before it can be absorbed, a much slower process.

The digestive system produces enzymes that hydrolyse foods into soluble products, which can then be absorbed by cells and passed into the blood stream.

Table 1. Structure and function of the gut				
Region of the gut	**Main functions**	**Adaptations of muscle layer**	**Adaptaton of submucosa**	**Adaptation of mucosa**
Oesophagus	Peristalsis of solid food.	Two layers – thick in order to force solid food into stomach.	Contains glands which secrete mucus to lubricate passage of food. Elastic to allow expansion.	Lining composed of several layers of flattened cells; outer cells are rubbed off continually as solid food passes down. Folded to allow expansion as solid food passes down.
Stomach	Temporary storage of food intake. Mixing up of stomach contents (churning). Some digestion.	Three layers – their action brings about churning of the stomach contents.		Contains abundant glands: different types produce enzymes, mucus and acid.
Ileum (small intestine)	Digestion. Absorption of soluble food products.	Two layers – for peristalsis.	Contains many blood and lymph vessels. Absorbed food products pass into these vessels to be transported around the body.	Contains abundant glands which secrete enzymes. Folded and has numerous projections called villi to increase surface area for the absorption of food products.
Colon	Absorption of water and some soluble food. Movement of faeces.	Two layers – outer layer thick and subdivided into three layers to aid peristalsis.		Numerous tubular glands which secrete mucus to aid passage of faeces.

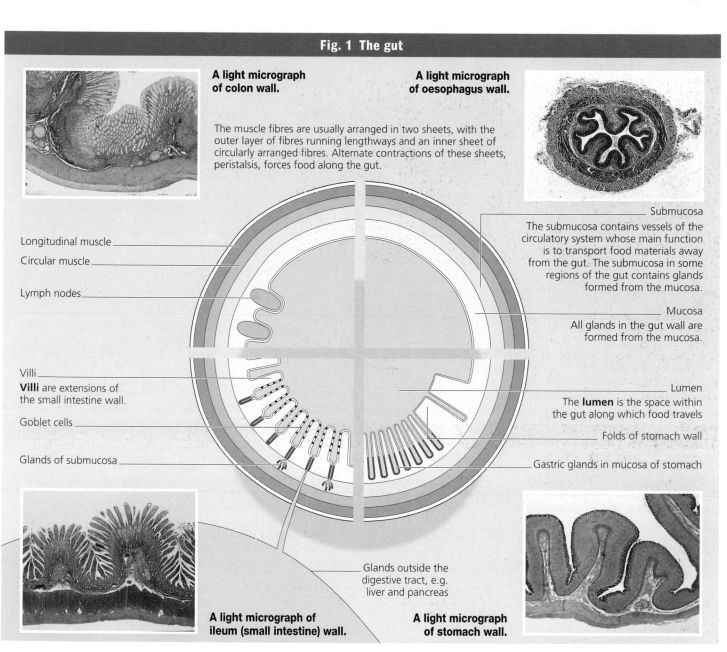

Fig. 1 The gut

A light micrograph of colon wall.

A light micrograph of oesophagus wall.

The muscle fibres are usually arranged in two sheets, with the outer layer of fibres running lengthways and an inner sheet of circularly arranged fibres. Alternate contractions of these sheets, peristalsis, forces food along the gut.

Longitudinal muscle

Circular muscle

Lymph nodes

Villi

Villi are extensions of the small intestine wall.

Goblet cells

Glands of submucosa

Submucosa

The submucosa contains vessels of the circulatory system whose main function is to transport food materials away from the gut. The submucosa in some regions of the gut contains glands formed from the mucosa.

Mucosa

All glands in the gut wall are formed from the mucosa.

Lumen

The **lumen** is the space within the gut along which food travels

Folds of stomach wall

Gastric glands in mucosa of stomach

Glands outside the digestive tract, e.g. liver and pancreas

A light micrograph of ileum (small intestine) wall.

A light micrograph of stomach wall.

The gut

In humans the site of digestion is the gut. As food passes along the gut it travels through several different regions. Each region is adapted to carry out a specific function:

• to break large lumps of food into smaller lumps, a process called **mechanical digestion**;
• to break down the food compounds by hydrolysis, a process called **chemical digestion**;
• to absorb the soluble products of digestion;
• to get rid of waste products.

The gut wall itself is also divided into three main layers:

• an outer muscle layer;
• a middle layer called the **submucosa**;
• an inner layer called the **mucosa**.

The structure of these layers is modified in each part of the gut (Table 1 and Fig. 1). The food passes through the gut by **peristalsis**. Peristalsis is a slow, continuous sequence of muscular contraction and relaxation. It travels like a wave along the gut, pushing food in front of it.

Fig. 2 Digestive glands

Stomach
Endopeptidase ● is secreted into the gastric glands and passes into the lumen of the stomach.

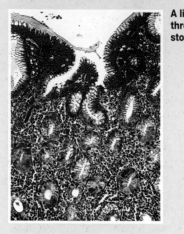

A light micrograph of a section through the mucosa of the stomach, showing gastric glands.

- ● Carbohydrate digestion
- ● Protein digestion
- ○ Fat digestion

Small intestine
Maltase ● and **exopeptidases** ● in the outer membrane of the surface cells of the microvilli.

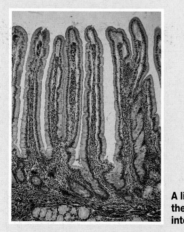

A light micrograph of a section of the epithelial lining of the small intestine, showing many villi.

Buccal cavity
Mouth
Salivary glands
Pharynx
Oesophagus

Liver
Stomach
Gall bladder
Spleen
Duodenum
Pancreas
Colon

Appendix
Ileum (small intestine)
Rectum
Anus

A high power light micrograph of islet cells in pancreas.

Salivary glands
Amylase ● is secreted into the salivary duct and passes into the mouth.

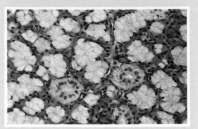

A light micrograph of parotid salivary glands.

Liver
Bile ○ is secreted into the bile duct and passes into the duodenum.

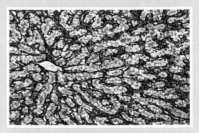

A light micrograph of liver cells.

Pancreas
Lipase ○ **amylase** ● and **endopeptidases** ● are secreted into the pancreatic duct and pass into the duodenum.

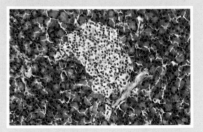

Some parts of the gut secrete digestive enzymes but there are several other **glands**, which are not part of the gut wall, that also secrete digestive enzymes (Fig. 2). Glands are organs that contain cells that secrete substances. These glands pass enzymes along tubes or ducts into the gut.

The liver also secretes a fluid called bile which enters the gut. This fluid does not contain enzymes but contains bile salts which help the body to digest fats. It is an alkaline fluid that helps to create the optimum pH for the enzymes that digest food in the intestine. Bile is stored in the gall bladder until food enters the small intestine, when it is forced down the bile duct to mix with food in the duodenum. Bile also contains several waste products formed when the liver breaks down old red blood cells.

The salivary glands, gastric glands and pancreas secrete enzymes that pass into the lumen of the gut. This part of digestion in **extracellular**, because it happens outside the cells that make up the gut wall.

Carbohydrates and proteins

The enzymes break down polymers into smaller molecules. But some of these molecules are not monomers, they are short chain polymers. The digestion of short chain polymers of carbohydrates and proteins is completed by enzymes in the **microvilli** on villi cells in the small intestine (Fig. 3). The villi increase the surface area of the gut wall. The microvilli in turn increase the surface area of the cells. The enzymes are found either in the outer membranes or in the **cytosol** of these cells. The cytosol is the solution in the cell cytoplasm. This part of digestion is therefore happening within the cells and is called **intracellular**.

Carbohydrate and protein monomers are absorbed from the lumen of the small intestine by both facilitated diffusion and active transport. These processes were described in Chapter 5.

The monomers pass into the blood capillaries in the mucosa and then on, into the larger vessels in the submucosa and finally into the blood in the hepatic portal vein which takes them to the liver.

Because glucose does not need to be digested it is quickly absorbed by the microvilli. It therefore has an immediate effect on the blood sugar level. Starch needs to be digested before its monomers can be absorbed. The sugar is therefore 'released' slowly from carbohydrate food, and this is easier for diabetics to control. In wholemeal foods the outer surfaces of the cells need to be digested by protein- and fat-digesting enzymes to release the starch grains before the starch can be digested. This slows down the rate of sugar absorption even more.

 3 What is the difference between facilitated diffusion and active transport?

4 a Draw a flow chart that shows the stages in the digestion of starch.
  b Draw a flow chart that shows the stages in the digestion of protein.

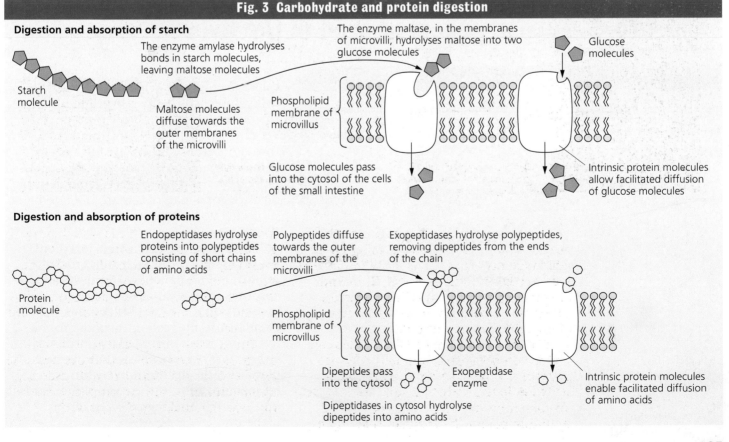

Fig. 3 Carbohydrate and protein digestion

Digestion and absorption of starch

Starch molecule

The enzyme amylase hydrolyses bonds in starch molecules, leaving maltose molecules

Maltose molecules diffuse towards the outer membranes of the microvilli

Phospholipid membrane of microvillus

The enzyme maltase, in the membranes of microvilli, hydrolyses maltose into two glucose molecules

Glucose molecules

Glucose molecules pass into the cytosol of the cells of the small intestine

Intrinsic protein molecules allow facilitated diffusion of glucose molecules

Digestion and absorption of proteins

Protein molecule

Endopeptidases hydrolyse proteins into polypeptides consisting of short chains of amino acids

Polypeptides diffuse towards the outer membranes of the microvilli

Phospholipid membrane of microvillus

Exopeptidases hydrolyse polypeptides, removing dipeptides from the ends of the chain

Dipeptides pass into the cytosol

Exopeptidase enzyme

Dipeptidases in cytosol hydrolyse dipeptides into amino acids

Intrinsic protein molecules enable facilitated diffusion of amino acids

Fats

The digestion of fats follows a slightly different pattern. The stomach secretes a fat-digesting enzyme called a lipase, but very little digestion of the fats occurs in the stomach. The warmth and the churning actions of the stomach turn solid fats into a fatty liquid.

Fig. 4 Fat digestion

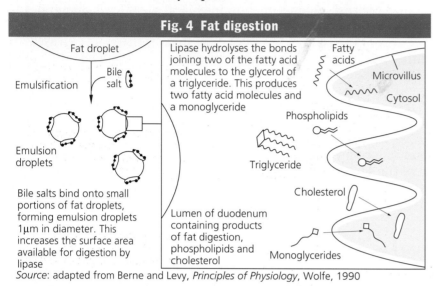

Fat droplet

Emulsification

Bile salt

Emulsion droplets

Bile salts bind onto small portions of fat droplets, forming emulsion droplets 1 µm in diameter. This increases the surface area available for digestion by lipase

Lipase hydrolyses the bonds joining two of the fatty acid molecules to the glycerol of a triglyceride. This produces two fatty acid molecules and a monoglyceride

Lumen of duodenum containing products of fat digestion, phospholipids and cholesterol

Fatty acids

Microvillus

Cytosol

Phospholipids

Triglyceride

Cholesterol

Monoglycerides

Source: adapted from Berne and Levy, *Principles of Physiology*, Wolfe, 1990

In the duodenum, bile and lipase play a part in fat digestion (Fig. 4). The products of fat digestion together with any phospholipids and cholesterol in the food can diffuse very quickly through the outer membrane of the microvilli.

5 **Suggest why these molecules move quickly through the membrane whereas carbohydrate and protein monomers only move through by facilitated diffusion and active transport.**

Once inside the cells the monoglycerides and fatty acids are recombined, by condensation reactions, to form triglycerides. The triglycerides and phospholipids together form droplets called **chylomicrons**. These droplets are too large to enter the blood capillaries. Instead they enter vessels called **lacteals**. The lacteals drain into vessels called **lymph vessels**. These eventually drain into the blood system through veins in the chest. From here the chylomicrons pass to the liver.

16.3 Fate of digested food in the liver

Fig. 5 Liver lobules

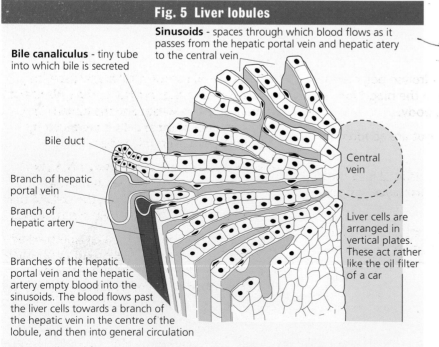

Bile canaliculus - tiny tube into which bile is secreted

Sinusoids - spaces through which blood flows as it passes from the hepatic portal vein and hepatic atery to the central vein

Bile duct

Branch of hepatic portal vein

Branch of hepatic artery

Branches of the hepatic portal vein and the hepatic artery empty blood into the sinusoids. The blood flows past the liver cells towards a branch of the hepatic vein in the centre of the lobule, and then into general circulation

Central vein

Liver cells are arranged in vertical plates. These act rather like the oil filter of a car

Source: adapted from Berne and Levy, *Principles of Physiology*, Wolfe, 1990

The liver is made up of groups of cells called liver lobules (Fig. 5). The products of digestion reach the liver by different routes: the carbohydrate and protein monomers via the hepatic portal vein, and fats through lacteals and the lymph system before they enter the bloodstream. As the blood flows past the liver cells much of the digested food materials is absorbed to be subjected to a range of chemical processes (Fig. 6).

The liver is the organ that coordinates the body's use of sugar. It is of crucial importance to diabetics. All the sugar absorbed from food passes along the hepatic portal vein to the liver before being circulated to the rest of the body. In the liver, processes controlled by hormones either store sugar or release it to keep the blood sugar concentration within reasonable limits. If the control mechanism breaks down, the person suffers from diabetes.

Fig. 6 Fate of food

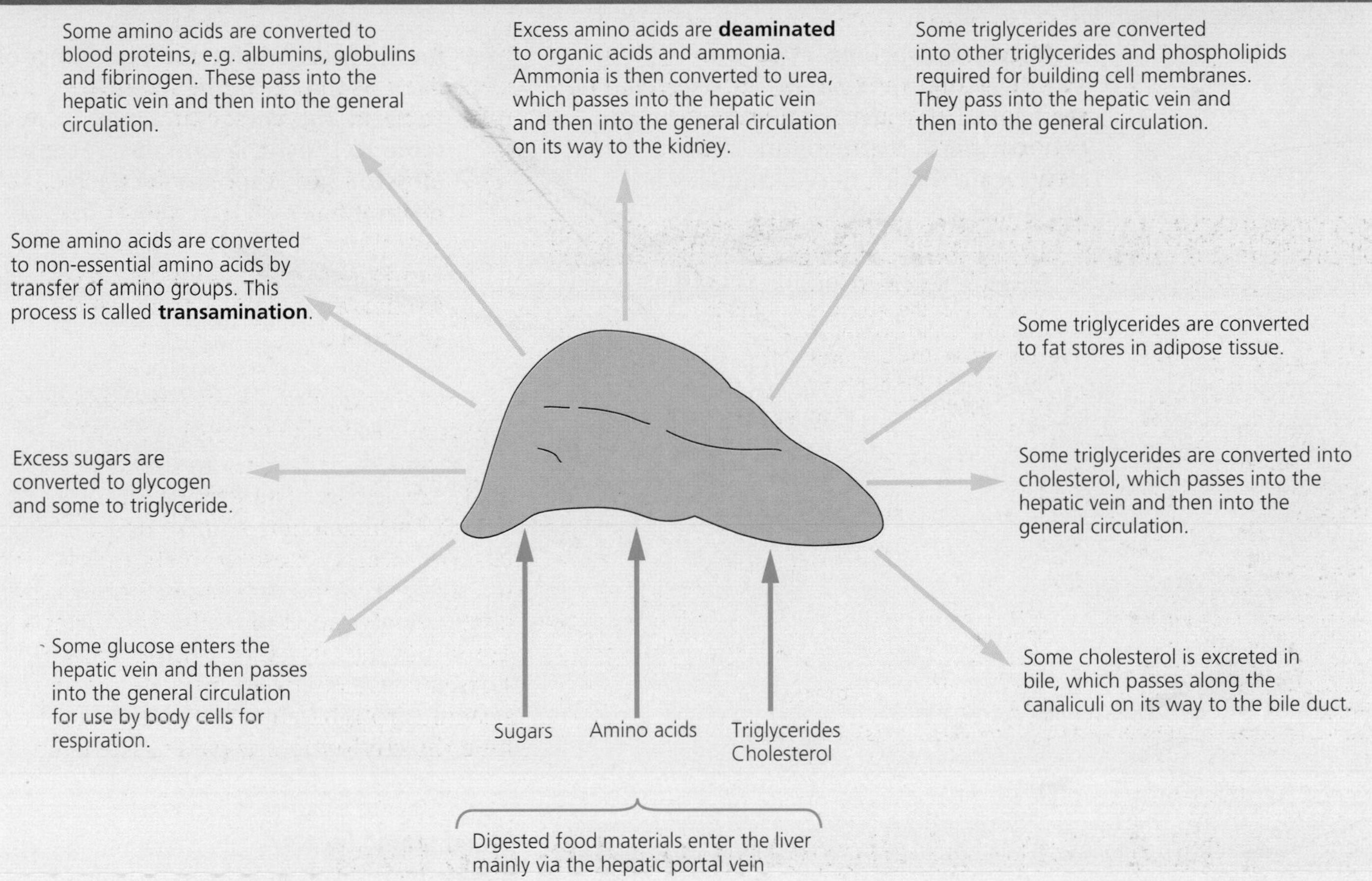

Some amino acids are converted to blood proteins, e.g. albumins, globulins and fibrinogen. These pass into the hepatic vein and then into the general circulation.

Excess amino acids are **deaminated** to organic acids and ammonia. Ammonia is then converted to urea, which passes into the hepatic vein and then into the general circulation on its way to the kidney.

Some triglycerides are converted into other triglycerides and phospholipids required for building cell membranes. They pass into the hepatic vein and then into the general circulation.

Some amino acids are converted to non-essential amino acids by transfer of amino groups. This process is called **transamination**.

Some triglycerides are converted to fat stores in adipose tissue.

Excess sugars are converted to glycogen and some to triglyceride.

Some triglycerides are converted into cholesterol, which passes into the hepatic vein and then into the general circulation.

Some glucose enters the hepatic vein and then passes into the general circulation for use by body cells for respiration.

Some cholesterol is excreted in bile, which passes along the canaliculi on its way to the bile duct.

Sugars   Amino acids   Triglycerides Cholesterol

Digested food materials enter the liver mainly via the hepatic portal vein

Key ideas

- Digestive enzymes hydrolyse polymers into monomers that pass to the blood for transport around the body.

- Different parts of the gut are adapted for different functions.

- The mammalian gut is divided into three layers: the outer muscular layer, mucosa and submucosa.

- The first stages in the digestion of protein and carbohydrate polymers take place extracellularly in the lumen of the gut.

- Digestion of carbohydrates and proteins is completed in the cytosol of the cells of the small intestine which line the lumen. The surface area of these cells is increased by projections called microvilli.

- Triglycerides are emulsified by bile salts before being partially hydrolysed and absorbed into the cytosol of the cells of the small intestine. They are then resynthesised.

- All absorbed food materials are transported to the liver, where they are used to produce the chemicals needed for growth and maintenance of the body tissues.

16.4 Hormonal control

Digestive secretions

The digestive enzymes are only secreted by the glands when there is food in the gut. The control of the secretion is very complicated. Both nerve impulses and hormones are involved (Fig. 7).

Q6 Analyse the production and effect of each of the hormones gastrin, secretin and cholecystokinin. Draw a table to show the stimulus, receptor, effector and response for each hormone.

Fig. 7 Control of enzyme secretion

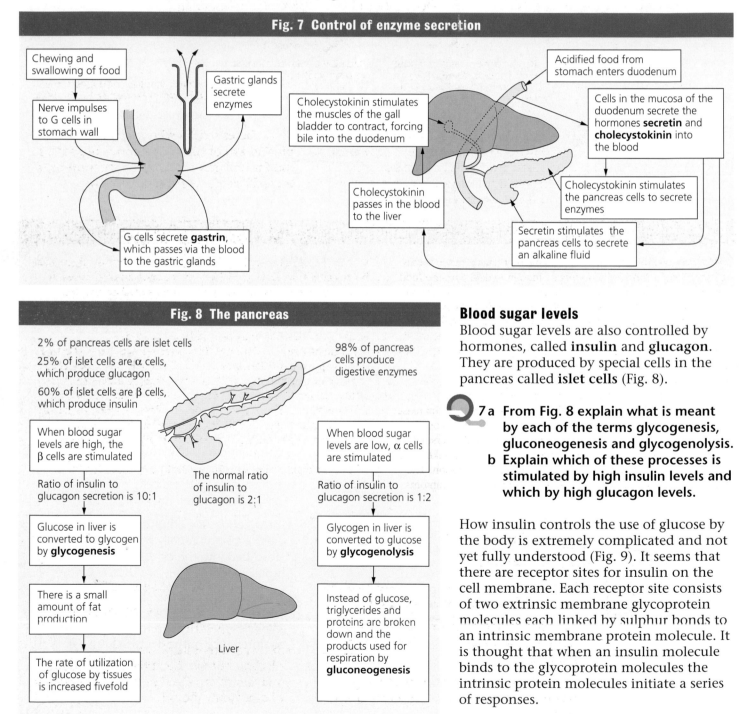

Chewing and swallowing of food

Gastric glands secrete enzymes

Nerve impulses to G cells in stomach wall

G cells secrete **gastrin**, which passes via the blood to the gastric glands

Cholecystokinin stimulates the muscles of the gall bladder to contract, forcing bile into the duodenum

Cholecystokinin passes in the blood to the liver

Acidified food from stomach enters duodenum

Cells in the mucosa of the duodenum secrete the hormones **secretin** and **cholecystokinin** into the blood

Cholecystokinin stimulates the pancreas cells to secrete enzymes

Secretin stimulates the pancreas cells to secrete an alkaline fluid

Fig. 8 The pancreas

2% of pancreas cells are islet cells

25% of islet cells are α cells, which produce glucagon

60% of islet cells are β cells, which produce insulin

98% of pancreas cells produce digestive enzymes

When blood sugar levels are high, the β cells are stimulated

Ratio of insulin to glucagon secretion is 10:1

Glucose in liver is converted to glycogen by **glycogenesis**

There is a small amount of fat production

The rate of utilization of glucose by tissues is increased fivefold

The normal ratio of insulin to glucagon is 2:1

When blood sugar levels are low, α cells are stimulated

Ratio of insulin to glucagon secretion is 1:2

Glycogen in liver is converted to glucose by **glycogenolysis**

Instead of glucose, triglycerides and proteins are broken down and the products used for respiration by **gluconeogenesis**

Liver

Blood sugar levels

Blood sugar levels are also controlled by hormones, called **insulin** and **glucagon**. They are produced by special cells in the pancreas called **islet cells** (Fig. 8).

Q7 a From Fig. 8 explain what is meant by each of the terms glycogenesis, gluconeogenesis and glycogenolysis.
b Explain which of these processes is stimulated by high insulin levels and which by high glucagon levels.

How insulin controls the use of glucose by the body is extremely complicated and not yet fully understood (Fig. 9). It seems that there are receptor sites for insulin on the cell membrane. Each receptor site consists of two extrinsic membrane glycoprotein molecules each linked by sulphur bonds to an intrinsic membrane protein molecule. It is thought that when an insulin molecule binds to the glycoprotein molecules the intrinsic protein molecules initiate a series of responses.

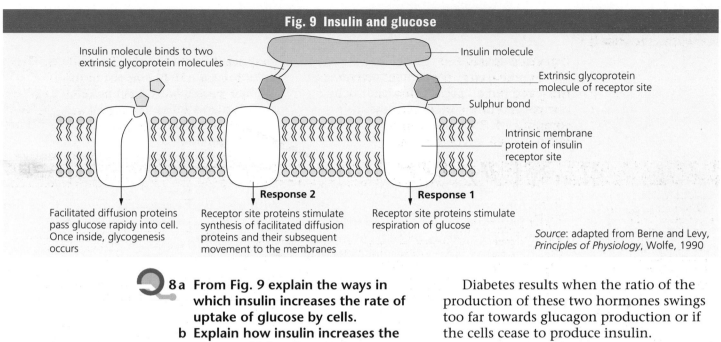

Fig. 9 Insulin and glucose

Insulin molecule binds to two extrinsic glycoprotein molecules

Insulin molecule

Extrinsic glycoprotein molecule of receptor site

Sulphur bond

Intrinsic membrane protein of insulin receptor site

Response 2

Response 1

Facilitated diffusion proteins pass glucose rapidy into cell. Once inside, glycogenesis occurs

Receptor site proteins stimulate synthesis of facilitated diffusion proteins and their subsequent movement to the membranes

Receptor site proteins stimulate respiration of glucose

Source: adapted from Berne and Levy, *Principles of Physiology*, Wolfe, 1990

Q 8 a From Fig. 9 explain the ways in which insulin increases the rate of uptake of glucose by cells.

b Explain how insulin increases the rate at which cells use glucose.

Diabetes results when the ratio of the production of these two hormones swings too far towards glucagon production or if the cells cease to produce insulin.

" Life with insulin "

If a person without diabetes eats a meal or snack, the pancreas produces just the right amount of insulin to deal with the food eaten. The carbohydrates are digested and moved into the blood stream. Insulin then allows this food to be used for energy. In this way the level of blood sugar is kept normal. If someone has diabetes, the level of sugar in the blood must be kept as near normal as possible. The amount of carbohydrate being eaten must balance the amount of insulin being injected. Sugary types of carbohydrate must be avoided. Starchy kinds of carbohydrate, particularly those with a lot of fibre, are very important.

The major effect of high insulin:glucagon ratios is to increase the use of glucose by the body tissues. This lowers the blood sugar levels. This can happen in diabetics because the person has taken too much insulin, missed or been late for a meal, taken more exercise than normal, or even for no apparent reason. The reaction is known as **hypoglycaemia**, or 'hypo'. The symptoms

include sweating, trembling, hunger, blurring of vision, difficulty in concentration. Eating quickly absorbed sugars soon raises the blood sugar level and the symptoms disappear. An untreated 'hypo' can lead to unconsciousness.

A low insulin:glucagon ratio means that tissues are unable to utilise glucose sufficiently and the blood sugar levels consequently rise. In diabetics this can result in **hyperglycaemia**. It can happen if the person is not keeping to their diet and eating too much carbohydrate, or if they are taking too little insulin, or after an infection or illness. The symptoms include feeling sick, drowsiness and stomach pain. It can also lead to unconsciousness if left untreated. Injection of insulin or taking drugs which stimulate the cells leads to lowering of the blood sugar levels.

Source: adapted from *Life with Insulin* by Plymouth Health Authority

---

Key ideas

- Nerve impulses and hormones are involved in the control of digestive secretions.

- The blood sugar level is controlled by two hormones produced in the islets of the pancreas.

- Insulin is produced in response to high blood sugar, glucagon in response to low blood sugar.

- Insulin promotes glycogenesis.

- Glucagon promotes glycogenolysis and gluconeogenesis.

- Insulin attaches itself to extrinsic glycoproteins in the outer cell membrane and causes increased uptake and utilisation of glucose by the cell.

16.5 Other ways of getting food

Other organisms also need to digest food to provide the energy for cellular activity. However, not all organisms need such complex control systems as humans.

Fungi

Chapter 6 showed how fallen leaves in the rainforest decayed rapidly. One of the principal groups of decay organisms is the mould fungi.

The body of a mould fungus consists of extremely thin threads called **hyphae** (Fig. 10). The hyphae have a wall made out of a polymer similar to cellulose but inside the hyphae are all the organelles which can be found in animal cells.

To obtain food the hyphae secrete enzymes that diffuse through the wall onto the food. These enzymes hydrolyse the materials in the food into monomers. These monomers are then absorbed into the hyphae, probably by both facilitated diffusion and active transport.

Digestion, then, is extracellular; it occurs outside the body of the fungus. This is similar to the first stage in the digestion of proteins and carbohydrates in the human gut. Enzymes secreted by gastric glands mix with food in the lumen of the gut. Only the later stages of our digestion take place inside our cells.

9 a Suggest what stimulates the fungus to secrete digestive enzymes.

b Fungal hyphae are long and very thin. What does this tell you about the surface area to volume ratio of a mould fungus?

Fig. 10 Fungus digestion

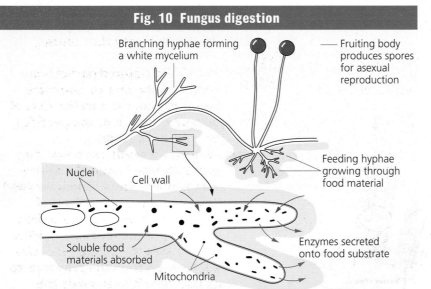

Branching hyphae forming a white mycelium

Fruiting body produces spores for asexual reproduction

Feeding hyphae growing through food material

Nuclei

Cell wall

Soluble food materials absorbed

Mitochondria

Enzymes secreted onto food substrate

Source: adapted from Green *et al.*, *Biological Science 1 & 2*, Cambridge, 1990.

The mould *Aspergillus* growing on Papaya fruit.

Mussels

Mussels are aquatic animals. They feed on food particles suspended in the water (Fig. 11). They are usually **sedentary**, which means they move very little. So, they have adopted a method of drawing large volumes of water through their bodies and sieving food particles out of this. The current is called a **feeding current**, but the animal also uses the same current to ventilate its respiratory surface.

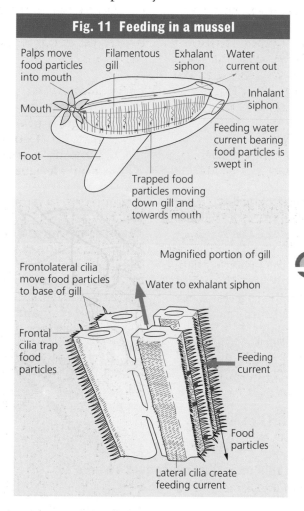

Fig. 11 Feeding in a mussel

Palps move food particles into mouth

Filamentous gill

Exhalant siphon

Water current out

Mouth

Inhalant siphon

Foot

Feeding water current bearing food particles is swept in

Trapped food particles moving down gill and towards mouth

Magnified portion of gill

Frontolateral cilia move food particles to base of gill

Water to exhalant siphon

Frontal cilia trap food particles

Feeding current

Food particles

Lateral cilia create feeding current

A white mussel with its siphons extended.

The feeding current is created by the synchronised beating of hair-like projections on the gill cells called **cilia**. Other cilia trap particles from the feeding current. A third type wafts the trapped particles towards the palps. The palps transfer the particles into the mouth.

10 a Not all the trapped particles are wafted to the mouth, some are rejected. Suggest how the mussel recognises which of the particles are worth digesting.

b Although mussels can move they generally stay in one place. This means they cannot search for food. Suggest how their method of feeding overcomes this problem.

c The body of the mussel has a low surface area to volume ratio. Use information from the drawings to explain how it overcomes this problem in relation to respiration.

Key ideas

- Fungi obtain food by extracellular digestion.
- Mussels obtain food by using one set of cilia to create a current of water, from which they trap particles using another set of cilia.

Controlling the flow

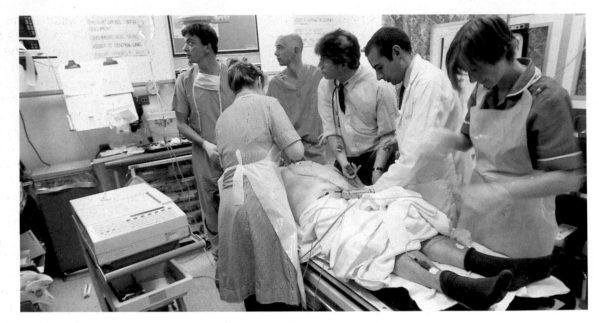

Most hospitals have a team of doctors and nurses who can respond within a few minutes to a patient with a heart attack. They are known as the crash team.

Doctors in accident and emergency departments of hospitals are very skilled in coping with emergencies such as heart attacks. However, a heart attack can cause a great deal of damage to the heart and other parts of the body. Roughly 40% of patients who have a heart attack die as a result. So the best way to survive a heart attack is not to have one in the first place.

Chest pains can provide an early warning of a heart attack. Much of the work of a cardiology department in a hospital tries to prevent heart attacks and the damage they cause. A related department, haematology, diagnoses any problems with the blood itself and advises the cardiologists.

The staff in all these hospital departments work together to keep the heart healthy and maintain the flow of blood. Hopefully, an understanding of the heart can help to overcome one of the biggest killers in the United Kingdom.

17.1 Learning objectives

After working through this chapter, you should be able to:

- **relate** the structure of the mammalian heart, arteries, veins and capillaries to their functions;

- **explain** the role of chemoreceptors, pressure receptors, the cardiovascular centres in the medulla and the sinoatrial node in the control of the cardiac cycle;

- **explain** the relationship between blood, plasma, tissue fluid, lymph and serum;

- **recall** how the lymphatic system returns tissue fluid to the blood system;

- **explain** how oxygen and carbon dioxide are loaded, carried and unloaded by the blood;

- **interpret** oxygen–haemoglobin dissociation curves;

- **describe** the buffering effect of haemoglobin.

17.2 Heart attacks

Coronary arteries are the blood vessels that supply blood to the muscles in the walls of the heart. These vessels may become partly blocked by a build up of fatty tissue, forming an **atheroma.** A blood clot, called a **thrombosis,** may develop on the surface of an atheroma. The thrombosis can cause pain in the chest during exercise. This pain is known as **angina.** Any muscle in the body gives rise to pain if it is short of oxygen and the heart muscle is no exception. In more severe cases the pain may be experienced even at rest. Worst of all, the thrombosis may completely block a coronary vessel and cause a **myocardial infarction.** This is a heart attack. The muscle supplied by the vessel beyond the thrombosis receives no blood and will die.

Death from heart attacks is usually due to a disturbance in the electrical activity of the healthy muscle. This disturbance is caused by the death of the heart muscle beyond the thrombosis. By diagnosing angina early, the effects of atheroma and thrombosis can be controlled.

17.3 Structure and function of the heart

The lungs maintain diffusion gradients for oxygen and carbon dioxide between the blood in the body and the air in the lungs.

 1 **Explain two ways in which the lungs maintain these diffusion gradients.**

The blood transports oxygen and other materials to the tissues where they are needed, e.g. muscles. It is the heart that maintains the rapid flow of blood through the blood vessels in both lungs and muscles (Fig. 1).

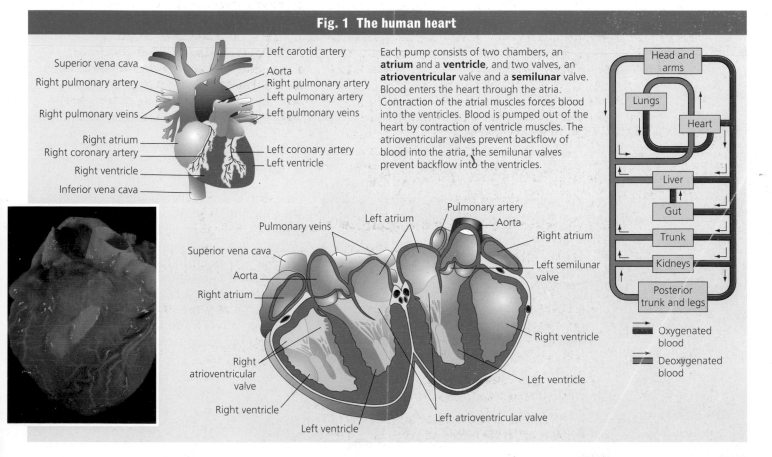

Fig. 1 The human heart

Superior vena cava
Right pulmonary artery
Right pulmonary veins
Right atrium
Right coronary artery
Right ventricle
Inferior vena cava

Left carotid artery
Aorta
Right pulmonary artery
Left pulmonary artery
Left pulmonary veins
Left coronary artery
Left ventricle

Each pump consists of two chambers, an **atrium** and a **ventricle**, and two valves, an **atrioventricular** valve and a **semilunar** valve. Blood enters the heart through the atria. Contraction of the atrial muscles forces blood into the ventricles. Blood is pumped out of the heart by contraction of ventricle muscles. The atrioventricular valves prevent backflow of blood into the atria, the semilunar valves prevent backflow into the ventricles.

Pulmonary veins
Superior vena cava
Aorta
Right atrium
Right atrioventricular valve
Right ventricle
Left ventricle

Left atrium
Pulmonary artery
Aorta
Right atrium
Left semilunar valve
Right ventricle
Left ventricle
Left atrioventricular valve

Head and arms
Lungs
Heart
Liver
Gut
Trunk
Kidneys
Posterior trunk and legs

→ Oxygenated blood
→ Deoxygenated blood

The heart contains two muscular pumps. The right side of the heart pumps **deoxygenated** blood from the body along the pulmonary artery to the lungs. Deoxygenated blood is poor in oxygen. The left side of the heart pumps **oxygenated** blood from the lungs along the aorta to the rest of the body. Oxygenated blood is rich in oxygen.

The muscles of the heart themselves need food and oxygen. This is supplied by the blood in the coronary arteries. If atheroma develops in the coronary arteries the oxygen supply to the heart muscle may be cut off and the muscle may die.

Q 2a Suggest why the wall of the left ventricle is thicker than the wall of the right ventricle.

b Surgeons can often replace defective left atrioventricular valves. Suggest what effect this defective valve might have on a patient. Explain your answer.

Contraction of atrial muscle is called **atrial systole**, and contraction of ventricle muscle is known as **ventricular systole**. Relaxation of heart muscle is called **diastole** (Fig. 2).

Q 3a Using Fig. 2, calculate how many complete cardiac cycles (heartbeats) there are per minute.

b Suggest what causes the:
(i) atrioventricular valves to close;
(ii) semilunar valves to open;
(iii) semilunar valves to close;
(iv) atrioventricular valves to open.

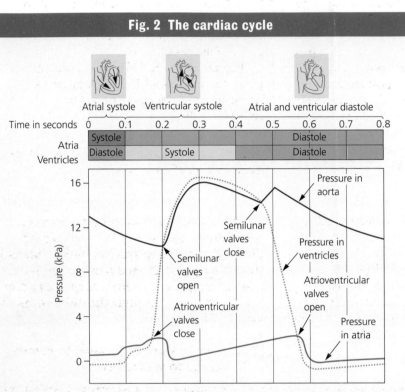

Fig. 2 The cardiac cycle

17.4 Arteries, capillaries and veins

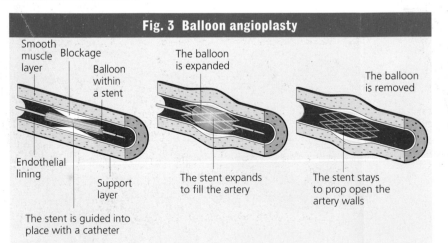

Fig. 3 Balloon angioplasty

Source: adapted from an article in *New Scientist*, 25 June 1994

One way in which cardiologists can keep the blood flowing through blood vessels is to clear them of any blockage. The technique is called **balloon angioplasty** (Fig. 3). It is essentially the same technique as that used to unblock drains! Once the blockage is clear, sufficient oxygenated blood can enter the capillaries of the heart muscle to allow them to contract normally and respond to exercise without causing angina.

Purging arteries of the fatty deposits that clog them is rather like clearing the muck from a blocked drain: a simple task requiring a long pole, a brush and brute force. Doctors use this technique to clear blocked arteries that restrict blood circulation and cause the painful chest pains called angina. The pole is a thin wire with a tiny balloon at its tip. The balloon is inflated to push the artery walls apart.

This technique, called angioplasty, is used in more than 500 000 patients a year around the world. Yet within 6 months 40% of patients go back to have their pipes unblocked a second time. This is because the pressure of the balloon can damage the wall of the artery, causing the muscle underneath the lining to swell up and block the vessel.

An alternative approach that is now winning widespread support, is the use of a stent to keep the blood vessel open during the critical first 6 months after angioplasty. This involves inserting tiny metal tubes inside the artery with the balloon. The hope is that when the balloon is removed, these tubes will support the muscle cell layer, and prevent it from growing into the centre of the vessel.

In trials involving 520 patients, patients given stents were 40% less likely to need a repeat operation than those treated by angioplasty alone.

Source: adapted from an article by John Bonner, *New Scientist*, 25 June 1994

Surgeons can insert the probes used in angioplasty into veins and pass them to the coronary arteries to deal with atheroma, because the pressure of blood in veins is low. If they tried to insert the probes through arteries, the high pressure in the arteries could squirt large amounts of blood into the body tissue. This is called **haemorrhaging**.

The pressure of blood in the arteries never drops below 10 kPa, even during diastole. But the pressure of blood entering the atria from the veins barely rises above 0 kPa. This pressure difference is caused as the blood flows through the different blood vessels (Fig. 4).

 4 **What feature is common to arteries, veins and capillaries?**

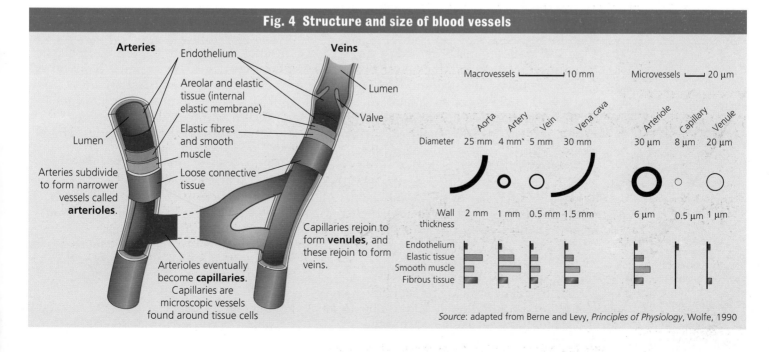

Fig. 4 Structure and size of blood vessels

Source: adapted from Berne and Levy, *Principles of Physiology*, Wolfe, 1990

Arteries

The wall of the aorta contains a thick layer of elastic tissue. This is stretched by the pressure produced by the left ventricle during systole. During diastole the elastic recoil of the walls of the aorta and large arteries maintains the high blood pressure. This expansion and recoil of the arteries does a lot to smooth the surges in blood flow caused by contraction of the left ventricle. But the surges can still be felt, as the pulse, where arteries pass over a bone near to the skin, e.g. in the wrist and at the temple.

In the arterioles the thickest layer is composed of muscle fibres. This muscle enables the arterioles to act as the stopcocks of the blood system. By contracting, the muscle can restrict the flow of blood through a particular blood vessel.

5 From your work on temperature regulation in Chapter 7, what name is given to this restriction of blood flow to an organ?

As the arteries subdivide to form ever narrower vessels, the pressure of blood in the vessels decreases. This is because the total cross-sectional area of all the smaller vessels is greater than that of all the larger vessels (Fig. 5).

Capillaries

Capillary walls are made up from a single layer of cells called endothelial cells. Capillaries have a diameter of only 8 µm and a wall thickness of only 2 µm. Blood flow and velocity are slowest through the capillaries (Fig. 5). The velocity of the blood describes how fast it is moving, while the flow describes how much blood moves past a particular point. The flow depends on the velocity and the size of the blood vessel. You can see how a large, slow-moving river (low velocity) can shift much more water than a small, fast moving stream (high velocity) in the same time. Blood flow follows the same rules.

The capillaries exchange materials such as oxygen, carbon dioxide and soluble food molecules between the blood and the tissues.

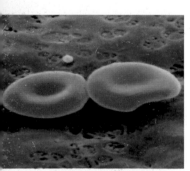

A false colour scanning electron micrograph of red blood cells travelling through a capillary in the liver. The fenestrated endothelium of the capillary is characterised by a number of small holes through which nutrients can reach all the liver cells. Magnification x 1600.

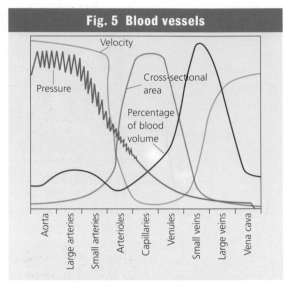

Fig. 5 Blood vessels

Velocity
Pressure
Cross-sectional area
Percentage of blood volume

Aorta · Large arteries · Small arteries · Arterioles · Capillaries · Venules · Small veins · Large veins · Vena cava

Some capillaries have small gaps inbetween adjacent endothelial cells. These gaps, called **fenestrations**, allow even faster rates of diffusion between the capillaries and the tissues.

6 a Suggest two organs other than the liver where these fenestrations may occur. Give reasons for your choices.
b How does the size and the rate of blood flow through the capillaries suit them for their function?

Veins

Some large veins have walls almost as thick as arteries. These walls contain both elastic and muscle tissue. The pressure of blood in the veins is lower than in either arteries or capillaries, falling almost to zero in the largest vein, the vena cava. Veins are the only blood vessels that have **valves**. These prevent backflow of blood.

7 a Use information from Fig. 5 to explain why the velocity of blood decreases as the blood flows from arterioles into capillaries.
b Explain why the velocity increases as the blood flows from the smaller veins into the larger veins.

The 'secondary heart'

The action of the leg muscles and the valves in the veins means they act as a 'secondary heart' (Fig. 6).

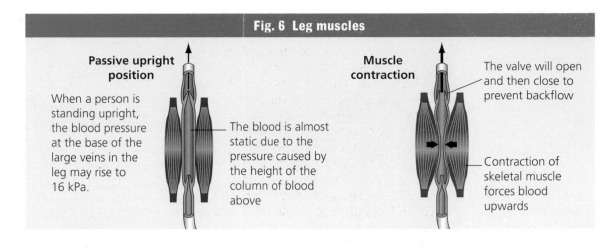

Fig. 6 Leg muscles

Passive upright position

When a person is standing upright, the blood pressure at the base of the large veins in the leg may rise to 16 kPa.

The blood is almost static due to the pressure caused by the height of the column of blood above

Muscle contraction

The valve will open and then close to prevent backflow

Contraction of skeletal muscle forces blood upwards

Key ideas

- The heart consists of two muscular pumps: one that pumps blood to the lungs to be oxygenated; and one that pumps oxygenated blood around the rest of the body. Blood is kept moving in the right direction by valves in the heart.

- Muscle layers in the walls of arteries control the supply of blood to each organ. Elastic tissue smoothes surges of blood pressure.

- Capillaries have walls one-cell thick to enable the exchange of materials between the blood stream and the tissues.

- Valves in veins prevent backflow of blood. Contractions of the skeletal muscles which surround veins help to return blood to the heart.

17.5 Pacemakers

" Pacemakers "

In Britain about 10 000 people a year receive an artificial pacemaker. The operation takes less than an hour under local anaesthetic and yet it can transform the quality of a patient's life for many years.

Heartbeats are triggered by a small group of cells in the wall of the right atrium called the sinoatrial node. This node is the heart's natural pacemaker. It generates electrical impulses which spread through all the muscles of the heart, causing first the atria then the ventricles to contract and produce a heartbeat.

One of the most common heart problems is known as a heart block. Damage to the electrically conductive tissue of the heart means that electrical impulses are not conducted from the atria to the ventricles. The pacemaker overcomes this by sensing the level of electrical activity in the atrium and delivering an electrical impulse (pacing) at the corresponding rate to the ventricle. Thus the pacemaker can mimic the natural activity of the heart, making it speed up or slow down, according to what the body is doing.

Source: adapted from an article by Helen Davies, *Guardian Education*, 30 November 1993

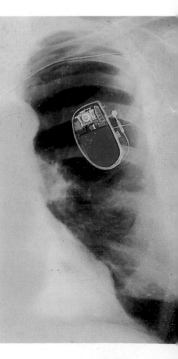

A coloured X-ray of the chest of a patient, showing a fitted heart pacemaker. The electronic battery-run device can be seen above the ribcage, with a yellow lead connecting it to the heart (also yellow), which is at the lower right, taking up part of one lung. A pacemaker can be external (worn on a belt) or internal (implanted in the chest, as here). It supplies electrical impulses to the heart to maintain the heartbeat at a regular rate. Pacemakers can supply a fixed rate impulse or discharge only when a heartbeat is missed.

Fig. 7 Conduction system of the heart

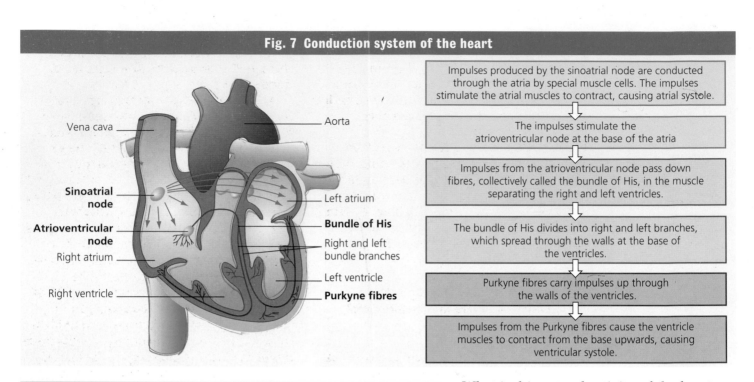

Impulses produced by the sinoatrial node are conducted through the atria by special muscle cells. The impulses stimulate the atrial muscles to contract, causing atrial systole.

The impulses stimulate the atrioventricular node at the base of the atria

Impulses from the atrioventricular node pass down fibres, collectively called the bundle of His, in the muscle separating the right and left ventricles.

The bundle of His divides into right and left branches, which spread through the walls at the base of the ventricles.

Purkyne fibres carry impulses up through the walls of the ventricles.

Impulses from the Purkyne fibres cause the ventricle muscles to contract from the base upwards, causing ventricular systole.

Fig. 8 Electrocardiogram

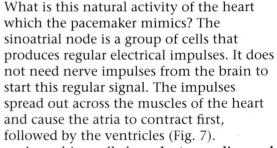

R shows the contraction of the ventricle muscles.

The T wave shows the relaxation of the ventricle muscles

The P wave shows the contraction of atrial muscles.

The P-R interval shows the time taken for an electrical impulse to travel from the sinoatrial node to the Purkyne fibres.

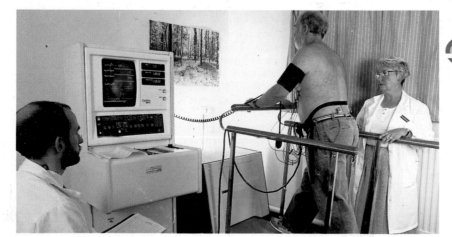

What is this natural activity of the heart which the pacemaker mimics? The sinoatrial node is a group of cells that produces regular electrical impulses. It does not need nerve impulses from the brain to start this regular signal. The impulses spread out across the muscles of the heart and cause the atria to contract first, followed by the ventricles (Fig. 7).

A machine called an **electrocardiograph** (ECG) can record these electrical impulses as they pass through the heart (Fig. 8).

If a thrombosis cuts off the blood supply to Purkyne fibres, they die and prevent electrical impulses from passing to healthy muscle cells. This is the main cause of deaths from heart attacks. Damage to any part of the heart's muscle can be recognised by changes to the ECG of the patient.

Q 8 Explain why the ECG is so useful to a doctor.

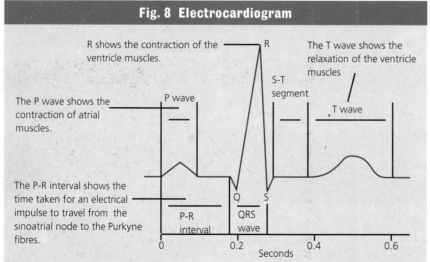

This patient is exercising whilst an ECG records the electrical activity of his heart. The various electrodes taped over his chest and back are connected to the ECG machine.

If an ECG shows a large P–R interval, it probably means that there has been damage to the conducting fibres in the region of the atrioventricular node. On seeing such a trace a doctor would consider fitting the patient with a pacemaker.

Modification of the rate of heartbeat

Although the heart can beat without nerve impulses, nerves are needed to change the rate of the heartbeat. A resting healthy adult has a heartbeat rate of about 70 min^{-1}. During exercise the rate may rise to over 100 min^{-1}. During sleep it may fall as low as 50 min^{-1}.

Q9 What are the advantages to an athlete in a rise in heartbeat rate during a race?

There are two cardiovascular centres in the brain that modify the rate of the heartbeat. They are located in the medulla oblongata of the brain. They are called the **cardioacceleratory centre** and the **cardioinhibitory centre**. Nerve fibres pass from each of these centres to both the sinoatrial node and the atrioventricular node (Fig. 9).

What causes the cardioacceleratory centre to produce these impulses is not fully understood. What is known is that it is usually linked to an increased rate of ventilation of the lungs (see Chapter 15).

Chemoreceptors and pressure receptors

There are chemoreceptors, sensitive to oxygen and carbon dioxide concentrations, present in the walls of the aorta and **carotid sinuses**. Sinuses are large cavities that contain blood. However, the chemoreceptors do not control the rate of the heartbeat directly. If the oxygen concentration of the blood is low, or if the carbon dioxide concentration is high, these receptors cause an increase in the rate of ventilation and it is this that, somehow, results in an increase in the rate of heartbeat. It is still not know exactly how this works.

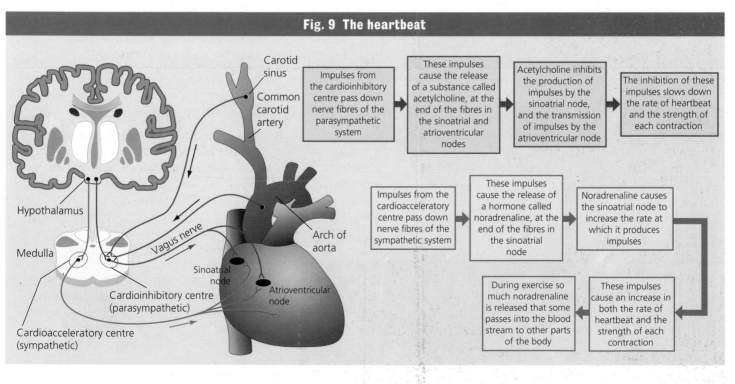

Fig. 9 The heartbeat

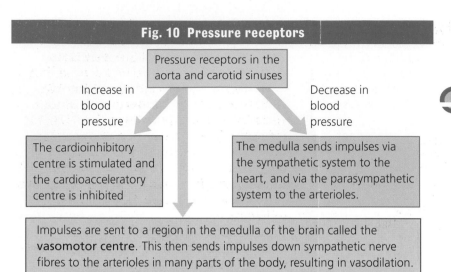

Fig. 10 Pressure receptors

Pressure receptors in the aorta and carotid sinuses

Increase in blood pressure

Decrease in blood pressure

The cardioinhibitory centre is stimulated and the cardioaccelerary centre is inhibited

The medulla sends impulses via the sympathetic system to the heart, and via the parasympathetic system to the arterioles.

Impulses are sent to a region in the medulla of the brain called the **vasomotor centre**. This then sends impulses down sympathetic nerve fibres to the arterioles in many parts of the body, resulting in vasodilation.

There are also pressure receptors in the walls of the aorta and the carotid sinuses. These affect the cardioaccelerary and cardioinhibitory centres directly (Fig. 10).

10 a What effect will an increase in blood pressure have on the rate of heartbeat?
b What effect will this have on blood pressure?
c What is the effect of:
(i) sympathetic impulses on the heart;
(ii) parasympathetic impulses on the arterioles?

Key ideas

- The sinoatrial node is the 'natural' pacemaker of the heart. It does not require impulses from the nervous system to initiate electric impulses.

- Impulses are conducted from the sinoatrial node, first to the atria and then to the ventricles. These impulses cause the atria to contract, followed by the ventricles.

- The rate at which the sinoatrial node sends out impulses can be modified by the nervous system and by hormones. This modification is controlled by the medulla of the brain.

- Impulses via sympathetic nerve fibres speed up the rate at which the sinoatrial node sends out impulses; impulses via parasympathetic nerve fibres slow down the rate at which the sinoatrial node sends out impulses.

- The medulla of the brain is influenced by impulses from pressure receptors and chemoreceptors in the walls of the aorta and carotid sinuses.

- There is no direct relationship between the oxygen and carbon dioxide concentration of the blood and the rate of heartbeat.

17.6 Exchange of materials

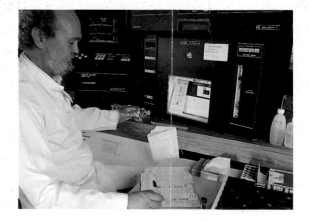

This haematologist in a hospital pathology laboratory is using a computer-controlled machine that counts and measures the sizes of red and white blood cells and platelets in a sample of blood. It can also estimate the haemoglobin content of red blood cells. The results are presented as histograms on the computer screen or on a print-out.

A sister department to the cardiology department in a hospital is the haematology department. Haematologists are consulted if there is something wrong with the blood itself, as opposed to the heart and blood vessels. One of the most common problems haematologists have to deal with is **anaemia**. A patient with anaemia appears pale and has little energy. This may be because the blood is not transporting enough oxygen around the body due to a shortage of red blood cells.

Fig. 11 Composition of blood

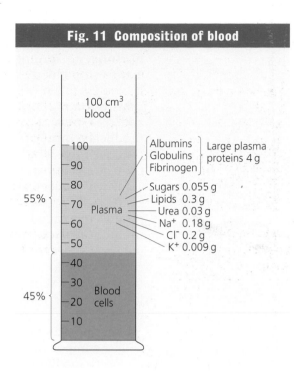

100 cm³ blood

Albumins, Globulins, Fibrinogen — Large plasma proteins 4 g

Sugars 0.055 g
Lipids 0.3 g
Urea 0.03 g
Na⁺ 0.18 g
Cl⁻ 0.2 g
K⁺ 0.009 g

55% — Plasma

45% — Blood cells

The main function of the blood system is to transport materials such as oxygen and glucose to and from the cells of the body. An important aspect of this transport is maintaining diffusion gradients at sites such as the alveoli of the lungs and the villi of the small intestine. To understand how the exchanges take place we first need to consider the composition of blood (Fig.11).

It is through the endothelial cells of the capillaries that exchange of materials occurs between the blood and the tissues. But how do substances needed by the body cells get out of the blood capillaries? For water, the answer is that it is literally forced out by the pressure of the blood. For other materials, such as sugar and mineral ions, the answer is facilitated diffusion. The two processes produce **tissue fluid**. Tissue fluid has a similar composition to blood plasma, but does not have plasma proteins (Fig. 12).

Similarly, waste products such as urea enter the blood capillaries by facilitated diffusion. The composition of tissue fluid does vary depending on its position in the body. For example, tissue fluid in the small intestine might contain a high concentration of sugars in the hours following a meal.

Red blood cells and platelets remain inside the blood capillaries. But some types of white cells can squeeze out of the capillaries through the fenestrations. These white cells combat infection by ingesting bacteria or producing chemicals such as **antibodies** to combat the effects of bacteria and viruses.

11 Suggest why the plasma proteins do not pass out into the tissue fluid.

Water re-enters the capillaries by osmosis. The protein molecules in the plasma are generally too large to leave the capillaries. After water has been forced out the water potential of the blood becomes very negative due to the large solute potential of the protein molecules and the loss of water. The value of water potential for the tissue fluid is less negative than this, mainly because there are no plasma proteins present. Water diffuses to the region with the more negative value for water potential, in this case back into the blood.

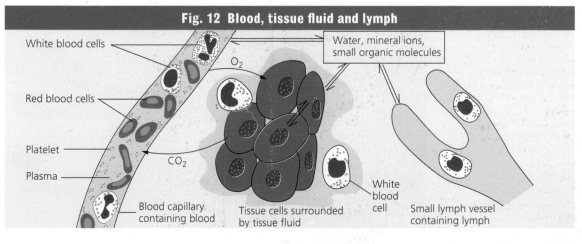

Fig. 12 Blood, tissue fluid and lymph

White blood cells

Red blood cells

Platelet

Plasma

O₂

CO₂

Water, mineral ions, small organic molecules

White blood cell

Blood capillary containing blood

Tissue cells surrounded by tissue fluid

Small lymph vessel containing lymph

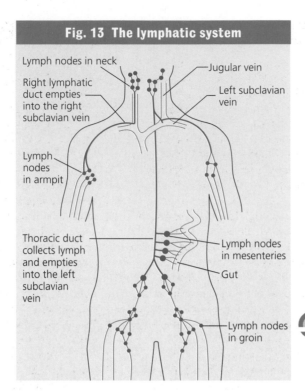

Fig. 13 The lymphatic system

Lymph nodes in neck

Jugular vein

Right lymphatic duct empties into the right subclavian vein

Left subclavian vein

Lymph nodes in armpit

Thoracic duct collects lymph and empties into the left subclavian vein

Lymph nodes in mesenteries

Gut

Lymph nodes in groin

Serum

One of the proteins in the plasma is **fibrinogen**. Fibrinogen helps blood to clot, and so stop blood escaping from a wound. If blood is taken from the body for transfusion purposes, **anti-coagulants** are added to prevent it clotting. Some blood products require only the plasma. To produce these, the blood cells are centrifuged out and the plasma retained.

The fibrinogen is then removed to prevent the plasma clotting. The liquid produced is called **serum**. Serum is very useful in replacing the blood plasma lost by patients with extensive burns. In these patients, the loss of the outer waterproof outer layer of skin means that tissue fluid is lost from their wounds very rapidly.

12 Construct a table to compare the compositions of blood, plasma, tissue fluid, lymph and serum.

Serum is useful for burns patients but, for patients who have lost a lot of whole blood, only a whole blood transfusion will suffice. But uninfected blood is difficult to obtain in some parts of the world. That is why a recent development, artificial blood, is exciting doctors.

Some of the tissue fluid passes into small capillary-like vessels, which drain into lymph vessels (Fig. 12). Once inside a lymph capillary the tissue fluid is known as **lymph**. Lymph has the same composition as tissue fluid. The lymph vessels form a secondary drainage system that eventually empties the lymph back into the blood system (Fig. 13). The larger lymphatics have valves to prevent fluid flowing backwards.

This man is donating blood. His blood can be used to provide serum or whole blood for transfusions.

Blood transfusion has probably saved more lives than any other medical procedure. But too many people are dying each year because the right type of blood cannot be found in time, or worse, because they are given infected blood.

The function of blood given in a transfusion is to maintain fluid pressure and, above all, to carry oxygen to the tissues. The red cells are the oxygen transporters and therefore usually the most crucial part of transfused blood. Red cells carry on their surface the blood-type antigens that can lead to rejection if the wrong kind of blood is used. These cells have a brief shelf-life, so that donated blood becomes useless after 5 weeks. Any remaining white cells and plasma may also be infected.

A blood substitute with high oxygen affinity may be excellent at picking up oxygen in the lungs, but incapable of releasing it in the tissues. Human blood can achieve the best of both worlds, so recent research has focused on the prime ingredient of our blood – the intricate and extraordinary protein, haemoglobin.

One red cell contains 280 million haemoglobin molecules. Pure haemoglobin carries no information that might cause rejection and would seem an ideal candidate for artificial

blood; but when it was tried in experiments 50 years ago, it caused acute kidney failure.

The problem is haemoglobin's natural instability when removed from its cell: it tends to split into two amino chains small enough to slip through the glomerular membrane in the kidney, clogging it up on the way to the bladder.

Free haemoglobin was also found to be reluctant to release its oxygen to the tissues. It was discovered that each red blood cell has a crucial extra component, a molecule called DPG, that encourages the haems to unload their cargo. The trick, it seemed, was to reduce the oxygen affinity of the haemoglobin molecule while increasing its stability.

Ten years ago Dr Kiyoshi Nagai and fellow researchers at the Medical Research Council's Laboratory of Molecular Biology in Cambridge introduced the haemoglobin gene into the DNA of a bacterium and 'tricked' it into producing large amounts of the protein.

Once they could make haemoglobin, the MRC scientists set about altering its properties. 'We joined two genes of the sub-units, and this solved the problem of molecules splitting,' Dr Nagai said. 'We also

introduced a mutation, found in natural abnormal haemoglobin and known to reduce oxygen affinity, so that we could adjust it to normal levels.'

The process stemmed directly from pioneering work on DNA by Professor Michael Smith of the University of British Columbia, Canada, who was awarded a share of the 1993 Nobel Prize for Chemistry. 'We could not have done it without that work', Dr Nagai said.

The MRC's partner, the American company Somatogen, is seeking approval for its product from the US Food and Drug Administration, and has begun clinical tests. Healthy volunteers have been given up to a pint of the artificial haemoglobin, known as rHbl.l. So far no toxic effects have been reported.

The manufacturer will have to be able to compete with donated blood on price. It may irritate blood donors to hear that what they give freely soon after acquires a market price: about £60 a litre in Britain and much more in America. If the artificial product does not compete, says one researcher, it will be just another amazing discovery with no practical purpose.

Source: adapted from an article by Owen Dyer, *The Independent*, 1994

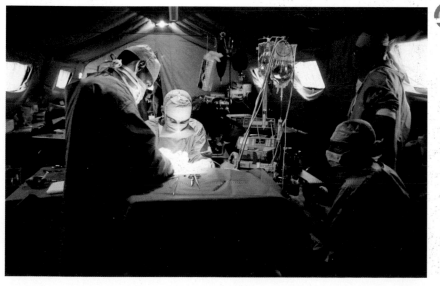

Operations such as this one in Rwanda need supplies of blood from donors.

Q13 Do you think that people should be paid to donate blood, or that blood donated freely should be sold? Give reasons for your answer.

Haemoglobin

The key molecule responsible for transporting oxygen around the body is **haemoglobin**. Haemoglobin is the 'Robin Hood' molecule; it combines with oxygen in oxygen-rich situations, e.g. in the capillaries of the lungs, but it releases this oxygen in oxygen-poor situations, e.g. in the capillaries of exercising muscles.

oxygen + haemoglobin $\rightleftharpoons$ oxyhaemoglobin

To understand why this happens we have to consider its oxygen **dissociation curve**. The curve shows how the percentage of haemoglobin molecules that have combined with oxygen to form oxyhaemoglobin varies with the external partial pressures of oxygen (Fig. 14).

14a What is the advantage in the part of the curve labelled X being flat?
b The region labelled Y shows what happens as blood flows through an oxygen-poor region, e.g. a respiring muscle. Why is it an advantage for the curve to fall sharply in such regions?

The tissue fluid in an active muscle has a high partial pressure of carbon dioxide due to the high rate of respiration in the muscle cells. The effect of this is to 'shift' the dissociation curve to the right (Fig. 14).

15 Explain the advantage to the muscle cells of this shift of the curve to the right.

Organisms that live in anaerobic conditions often have haemoglobin with a slightly different dissociation curve to that of humans. The worm *Tubifex* lives in mud at the bottom of lakes and rivers. The oxygen dissociation curve of its haemoglobin is shifted to the left compared with human haemoglobin (Fig. 15).

16 What is the advantage to *Tubifex* in having haemoglobin with a dissociation curve of this shape?

Fig. 15 Tubifex dissociation curve

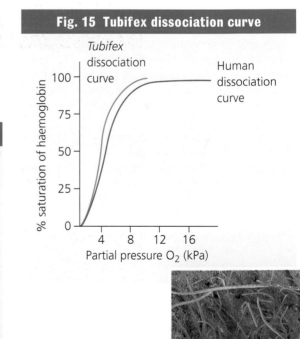

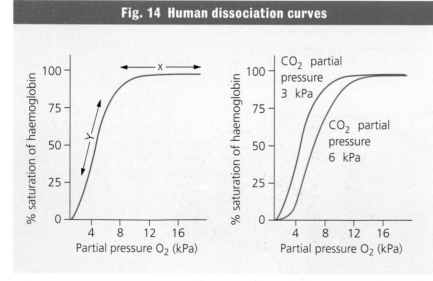

Fig. 14 Human dissociation curves

Tubifex worms in mud at the bottom of a lake.

Besides carrying oxygen to the tissues, blood also carries carbon dioxide from the tissues to the lungs. Carbon dioxide is much more soluble than oxygen in water. This means about 5% of the carbon dioxide is transported in simple solution in the plasma. Some of the carbon dioxide dissolved in the plasma is converted into carbonic acid, which then dissociates to form hydrogen ions and hydrogencarbonate ions.

$$CO_2 + H_2O \rightarrow H_2CO_3 \rightarrow H^+ + HCO_3^-$$

This reaction occurs very slowly in the plasma, but there is an enzyme in the red cells called **carbonic anhydrase** which increases the rate ten thousandfold. The hydrogencarbonate ions produced by the red cells diffuse into the plasma. As they do so, chloride ions (Cl^-) diffuse from the plasma into the red cells to maintain electrical neutrality (Fig. 16).

In the lungs the reverse series of reactions occurs, to release carbon dioxide, which is breathed out.

$$H^+ + HCO_3^- \rightarrow H_2CO_3 \rightarrow CO_2 + H_2O$$

Haemoglobin on its own, instead of whole red blood cells, can be successfully transfused to help oxygen transport in patients who have lost a lot of blood.

17 **Explain how the blood is still able to transport carbon dioxide satisfactorily even though the number of red cells is greatly reduced.**

Haemoglobin has one other important function in addition to the transport of gases: it helps to keep the pH of the plasma constant. It does this by 'taking' up any excess H^+ ions and thus preventing the blood from becoming too acidic.

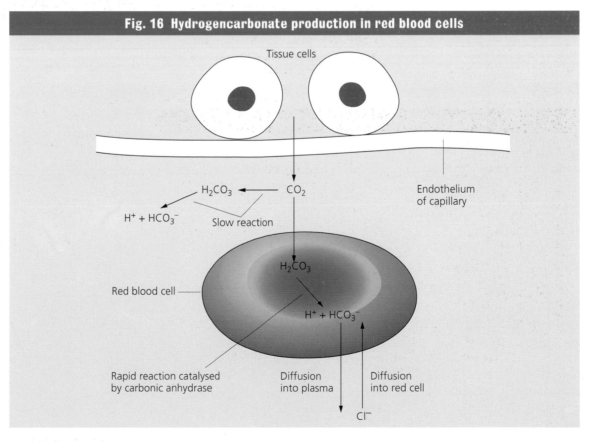

Fig. 16 Hydrogencarbonate production in red blood cells

Tissue cells

Endothelium of capillary

H_2CO_3 ← CO_2

$H^+ + HCO_3^-$ Slow reaction

H_2CO_3

Red blood cell

$H^+ + HCO_3^-$

Rapid reaction catalysed by carbonic anhydrase

Diffusion into plasma

Diffusion into red cell

Cl^-

Key ideas

- The main function of blood plasma is the transport of materials, in solution, around the body.

- Plasma is forced out of the capillaries to form tissue fluid. Tissue fluid does not contain plasma proteins, but may contain white blood cells.

- Tissue fluid returns to capillaries by osmosis.

- Lymphatics drain some tissue fluid.

- Fibrinogen, a plasma protein, can be removed from plasma so that the liquid will not clot. The resultant liquid is called serum.

- Red cells contain haemoglobin whose principal function is to carry oxygen as oxyhaemoglobin.

- Haemoglobin has an oxygen dissociation curve that allows it to become fully saturated as it passes through the lungs and to release oxygen as it passes through the tissues.

- The oxygen dissociation curve can be 'shifted' to the right in muscle to allow more oxygen to be released. It can be shifted to the left in animals which live in situations where there is reduced oxygen availability.

- Carbon dioxide is carried mainly as hydrogencarbonate ions in the plasma. The hydrogencarbonate ions are produced mainly as a result of the action of the enzyme carbonic anhydrase in the red cells.

- Haemoglobin helps to keep the pH of the plasma constant by absorbing excess hydrogen ions.

Cleaning the blood

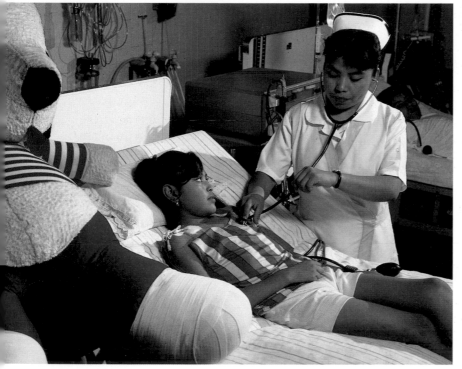

This girl is undergoing renal dialysis. A steady flow of blood is taken from an artery and passed into the dialysis machine. There the blood passes over a semipermeable membrane. Water and waste products cross the membrane, but blood cells and proteins are unable to cross. The cleaned blood then returns to the body into a vein.

" An alternative to dialysis? "

Doctors are trialling a new drug – ANP – that enhances the body's own response to kidney failure. The body produces ANP in response to increased blood volume.

In early trials, involving 53 patients, ANP halved the number of deaths compared with a control group who were given conventional treatment, and reduced the number of patients requiring dialysis from 55% to 23%. Dialysis is used in cases where the kidneys are unable to filter waste products from the blood naturally. This could be because of a drop in the flow of blood through the kidneys. The doctors warn, however, that these results were from a small sample – the trials are now being extended to a further 500 patients to find if the drug really does work.

Source: adapted from article an article by Andy Coghlan, *New Scientist*, 21 May 1994

A lack of suitable treatment for kidney failure, the kidney equivalent to a heart attack, and a shortage of donor kidneys means many people have to spend several hours each week receiving dialysis treatment. Dialysis is expensive to provide, but research into how the kidney works and how ANP helps may provide other solutions. However, a choice often has to be made between funding research into treatments of the symptoms patients already have, and funding research into organ functioning that may help prevent symptoms.

18.1 Learning objectives

After working through this chapter, you should be able to:

- **describe** the processes in the liver which form ammonia and urea;

- **describe** the processes of ultrafiltration and selective reabsorption in the kidney;

- **explain** how the kidney regulates the water and ion content of the blood;

- **explain** how the hormone ADH controls this regulation;

- **explain** how the kidney regulates the pH of the blood;

- **describe** the ways fish, insects and protozoa pass nitrogenous waste from their bodies.

18.2 Nitrogenous waste

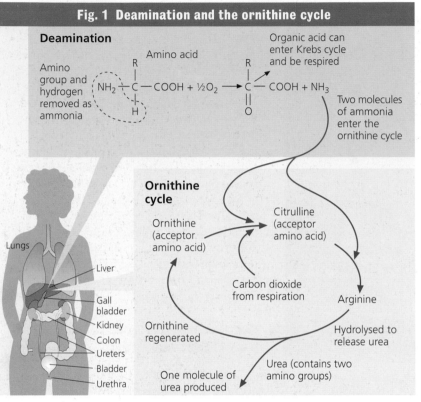

Fig. 1 Deamination and the ornithine cycle

Deamination

Amino group and hydrogen removed as ammonia

Amino acid

Organic acid can enter Krebs cycle and be respired

NH_2—C—COOH + ½O_2 → C—COOH + NH_3

Two molecules of ammonia enter the ornithine cycle

Ornithine cycle

Ornithine (acceptor amino acid)

Citrulline (acceptor amino acid)

Carbon dioxide from respiration

Arginine

Ornithine regenerated

Hydrolysed to release urea

One molecule of urea produced

Urea (contains two amino groups)

Lungs
Liver
Gall bladder
Kidney
Colon
Ureters
Bladder
Urethra

When a kidney suddenly stops working it is known as **acute renal failure**. Doctors use the word acute to describe an illness which develops quickly. Chronic conditions take longer to develop and last longer. Both acute renal failure and permanent kidney damage can cause a build up of toxins in the blood. Toxins are poisonous organic molecules and people can die when these reach a certain concentration.

One of the functions of the kidney is to remove toxins from the blood. **Ammonia** and **urea** are two toxins that are called nitrogenous waste products because they contain nitrogen. The nitrogen they contain comes from the amino group found in every amino acid. Chapter 16 described how the liver deaminates excess amino acids from the diet. This process removes an amino group and a hydrogen group from the amino acid to form ammonia.

The ammonia is highly toxic and is immediately converted, via a series of reactions called the **ornithine cycle**, into the less toxic compound urea (Fig. 1). The urea passes into the blood flowing through the liver and is carried to the kidney, where it is filtered from the blood and passed out in the urine. During acute renal failure, the urea is not filtered out of the blood and, if it is not removed by dialysis, builds up to dangerous concentrations.

A sharp drop in the flow of blood through the kidneys can cause acute renal failure. Although the kidneys constitute less than 0.5% of the body mass, the blood flow through the kidneys in a healthy person is 25% of the output of the heart, 1.25 litres per minute when the body is at rest! This blood is supplied to thousands of microscopic structures called **nephrons**, which make up the bulk of the kidney and carry out its work (Fig. 2). If the flow of blood drops sharply, the nephrons may clog up and die.

The blood vessel bringing blood into the glomerulus, the afferent arteriole, is wider than the vessel leading out of the glomerulus, the efferent arteriole. This creates a bottleneck in the capillaries of the glomerulus, which makes the blood pressure in the capillaries rise.

It is thought that ANP works by dilating the afferent arteriole and constricting the efferent arteriole, causing pressure to build up. In some cases of renal failure, this helps to start filtration again.

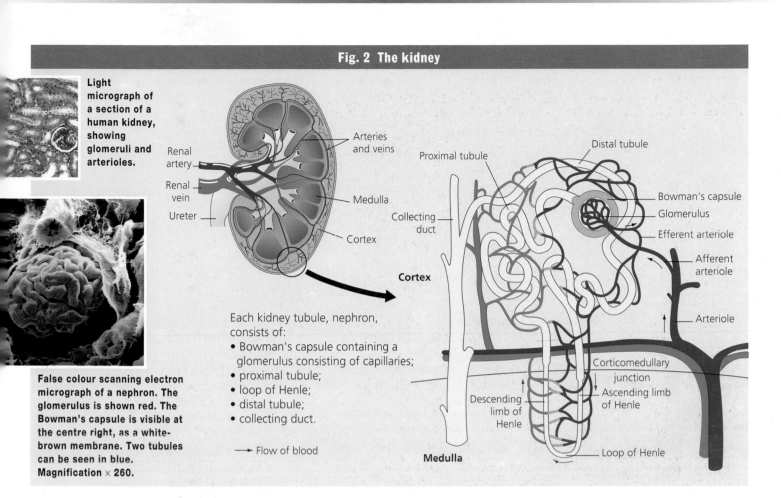

Fig. 2 The kidney

Light micrograph of a section of a human kidney, showing glomeruli and arterioles.

False colour scanning electron micrograph of a nephron. The glomerulus is shown red. The Bowman's capsule is visible at the centre right, as a white-brown membrane. Two tubules can be seen in blue. Magnification × 260.

Renal artery
Renal vein
Ureter
Arteries and veins
Medulla
Collecting duct
Cortex

Each kidney tubule, nephron, consists of:
• Bowman's capsule containing a glomerulus consisting of capillaries;
• proximal tubule;
• loop of Henle;
• distal tubule;
• collecting duct.

→ Flow of blood

Proximal tubule
Cortex
Distal tubule
Bowman's capsule
Glomerulus
Efferent arteriole
Afferent arteriole
Arteriole
Corticomedullary junction
Descending limb of Henle
Ascending limb of Henle
Loop of Henle
Medulla

18.3   Filtration

Fig. 3 Filtration into Bowman's capsule

Afferent arteriole
Endothelium of glomerulus
Pedicels
Outer layer of Bowman's capsule
Capsular space
Proximal tubule cells with microvilli
→ Flow of filtrate
Endothelial pores, which provide no barrier to the filtrate
Pedicels
Efferent arteriole
Podocytes of inner layer of Bowman's capsule
Endothelium of glomerulus
Basement membrane of glomerulus through which filtration occurs
Filtration silts, through which the filtrate passes
Podocyte of inner layer of Bowman's capsule

The cells that make up the inner layer of Bowman's capsule are called **podocytes**. These have lots of processes called **pedicels** with gaps in between them. These provide no barrier to the passage of filtrate.

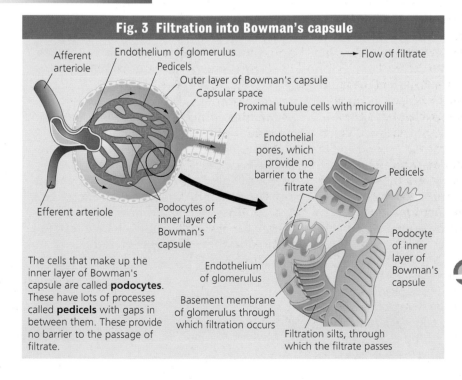

Ultrafiltration

Filtration is the first stage in getting rid of waste materials from the blood. **Ultrafiltration** is filtration caused by the high hydrostatic pressure of the blood in the glomerulus. This pressure pushes fluid from the blood in the capillaries of the glomerulus into the capsular space of the **Bowman's capsule**. The filtrate is produced rapidly because of the structure of the glomerular capillaries and Bowman's capsule (Fig. 3). Ultrafiltration is a quick way to produce tissue fluid. There is no difference between the composition of glomerular fluid and tissue fluid.

Q 1 What are the differences in composition between plasma and tissue fluid?

Table 1. Reabsorption and excretion					
Substance	Units	Filtered	Excreted	Reabsorbed	Percentage of filtered load reabsorbed
Water	litres / day	180	1.50	178.5	99.2
Na^+	mEq / day	25 200	150	25 050	?
K^+	mEq / day	720	100	620	?
Ca^{++}	mEq / day	540	10	530	?
HCO_3^-	mEq / day	4320	2	4218	?
Cl^-	mEq / day	18 000	150	17 850	?
Glucose	mEq / day	800	0.5	799	?
Urea	g / day	56	28	28	?

Source: Berne and Levy, *Principles of Physiology*, Wolfe, 1990

Selective reabsorption

Approximately 180 litres of filtrate is produced by the glomeruli in a day. But most of this is quickly reabsorbed into the blood (Table 1). The filtrate that is not reabsorbed continues through the nephrons and is eventually excreted as urine.

2 a The figure for the percentage of water reabsorbed has been completed for you. Calculate the percentage reabsorption for the remaining substances in the table.
b Suggest why this figure is so different for glucose and urea.

How does this reabsorption occur? Chapter 5 described some of the mechanisms that move substances into and out of cells. These include diffusion, facilitated diffusion and active transport using molecular pumps.

3 a From the figures in Table 1 explain which mechanisms are most likely to be involved in the reabsorption of glucose and sodium ions.
b Suggest why some urea passes back into the blood.

The materials which the body needs, glucose and most of the water and mineral ions, are reabsorbed actively into the blood by the **proximal tubule** cells. There is no active method for reabsorbing toxins such as urea, although some urea passes back into the blood by diffusion. So there is **selective reabsorption** of materials in the proximal tubule. Useful substances that are in excess may also be excreted, to maintain a constant internal environment.

The cells lining the proximal tubule have a similar structure to those lining the small intestine.

4 a Explain how the structure of proximal tubule cells is adapted to absorb materials quickly from the fluid in the tubule.
b As glucose and ions pass from the filtrate into the blood, what will happen to the water potential of the filtrate compared to that of the blood? Explain how this will affect movement of water between the filtrate and the blood.

Many poisonous substances in the blood are bound onto plasma proteins and are therefore not filtered in the glomerulus. The cells of the proximal tubule actively transport these substances from the blood into the filtrate so that they are excreted. If ANP increases the blood flow through the kidney, then there is more chance that these substances will be excreted.

Key ideas

- Excess amino acids are deaminated in the liver, producing ammonia.

- Ammonia is highly toxic. The ornithine cycle converts it via a series of reactions into a less toxic substance called urea.

- The kidneys filter urea from the blood. It leaves the body dissolved in the urine.

- Thousands of nephrons, each with its own blood supply, carry out some of the functions of the kidney.

- The afferent glomerular arteriole is wider than the efferent arteriole, which raises blood pressure in the glomerulus.

- The high pressure of the blood forces plasma, without plasma proteins, from the glomerular capillaries of the nephrons into the Bowman's capsules. This process is called ultrafiltration.

- The cells lining the proximal tubules selectively reabsorb most of this filtrate into the blood.

- Some urea passes back into the blood by diffusion, but half the urea filtered is excreted.

- Proximal tubule cells move many toxins from the blood into the filtrate.

18.4 Water and ion content

Chapter 7 explained that the loss of too much water and mineral ions from the blood could have catastrophic effects on a horse. You have probably noticed that when your body is dehydrated, e.g. after a long day on a hot beach, you produce very little urine and this urine is concentrated. However, if you have drunk a lot of liquid you produce large quantities of very dilute urine.

5 **From the photographs, which people are more likely to have urine that is hypotonic to blood. Which are more likely to have urine that is hypertonic to blood? Explain your answers.**

The kidney regulates the amount and composition of the urine in order to control the composition of the blood. It is essential to keep the amounts of water and ions in the blood within narrow limits. The control of water and ion excretion by the body is largely done by the three remaining parts of the nephron – the **loop of Henle**, the **distal tubule** and the **collecting duct**.

The filtrate entering the loop of Henle has urea and ion concentrations similar to the blood plasma. This means that it has roughly the same water potential. The different regions of the loop of Henle have different permeabilities with respect to water and sodium chloride. The whole loop is relatively impermeable to urea.

Because sodium chloride diffuses out of the filtrate in the ascending limb, the filtrate becomes more dilute. There is the same amount of water but less sodium chloride (Fig. 4). As the filtrate flows through the thick ascending limb, the loss of sodium to the tissue fluid dilutes the filtrate even more. The filtrate leaving the loop of Henle has a water potential less negative than blood plasma and its water potential is due almost entirely to urea. There is very little sodium chloride in the filtrate by this stage. This is very different to the filtrate produced in the glomerulus, which has the same water potential as

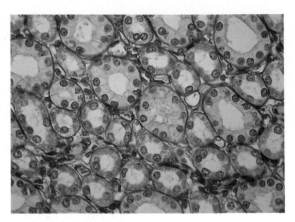

Light micrograph of kidney tubules.

blood plasma and a range of ions, including K⁺ and Na⁺.

What happens to the filtrate as it flows through the distal tubule and the collecting duct depends on the water potential of blood plasma, the total volume of blood in the body and blood pressure (Fig. 5).

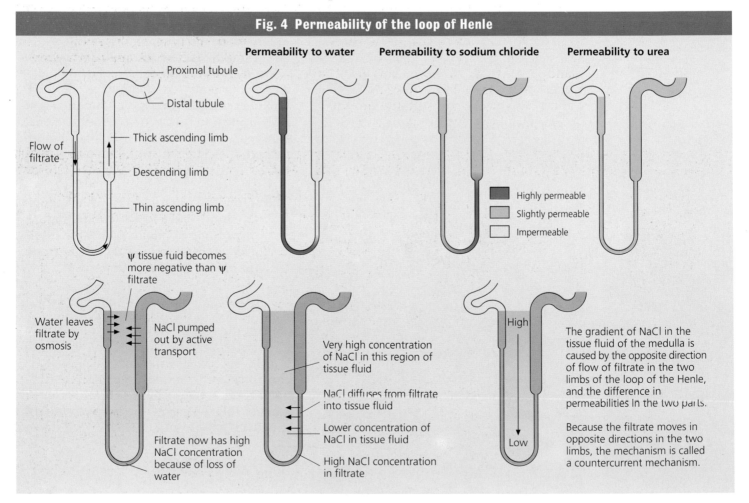

Fig. 4 Permeability of the loop of Henle

Proximal tubule
Distal tubule
Thick ascending limb
Flow of filtrate
Descending limb
Thin ascending limb

Permeability to water
Permeability to sodium chloride
Permeability to urea

Highly permeable
Slightly permeable
Impermeable

ψ tissue fuid becomes more negative than ψ filtrate

Water leaves filtrate by osmosis

NaCl pumped out by active transport

Filtrate now has high NaCl concentration because of loss of water

Very high concentration of NaCl in this region of tissue fluid

NaCl diffuses from filtrate into tissue fluid

Lower concentration of NaCl in tissue fluid

High NaCl concentration in filtrate

High

Low

The gradient of NaCl in the tissue fluid of the medulla is caused by the opposite direction of flow of filtrate in the two limbs of the loop of the Henle, and the difference in permeabilities in the two parts.

Because the filtrate moves in opposite directions in the two limbs, the mechanism is called a countercurrent mechanism.

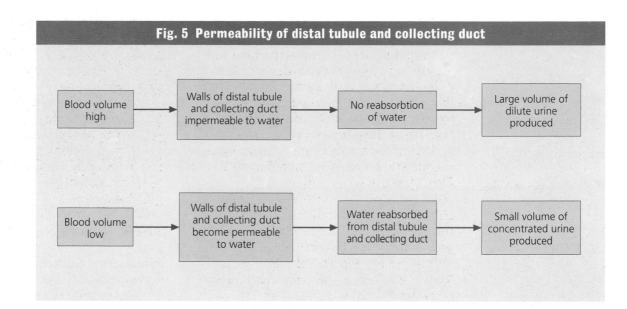

Fig. 5 Permeability of distal tubule and collecting duct

Blood volume high → Walls of distal tubule and collecting duct impermeable to water → No reabsorbtion of water → Large volume of dilute urine produced

Blood volume low → Walls of distal tubule and collecting duct become permeable to water → Water reabsorbed from distal tubule and collecting duct → Small volume of concentrated urine produced

18.5 Hormonal control

The volume and the water potential of the urine are mainly controlled by a hormone called **ADH**. The hypothalamus controls the secretion of ADH but it is the pituitary gland that actually produces it. When ADH reaches the kidneys it increases the permeability of the distal tubule and the collecting duct to water (Fig. 6).

6 The control of the production of ADH is an example of negative feedback. Draw a diagram to show how negative feedback operates to stop ADH production.

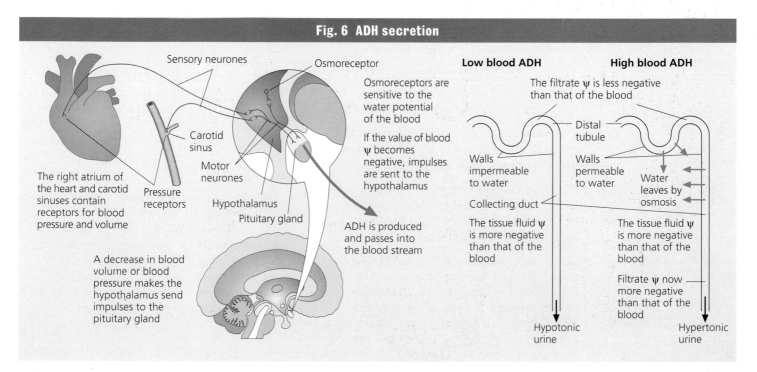

Fig. 6 ADH secretion

Sensory neurones

Osmoreceptor

Low blood ADH   **High blood ADH**

Osmoreceptors are sensitive to the water potential of the blood

If the value of blood ψ becomes negative, impulses are sent to the hypothalamus

The filtrate ψ is less negative than that of the blood

Distal tubule

Carotid sinus

Motor neurones

Pressure receptors

Hypothalamus

Pituitary gland

The right atrium of the heart and carotid sinuses contain receptors for blood pressure and volume

A decrease in blood volume or blood pressure makes the hypothalamus send impulses to the pituitary gland

ADH is produced and passes into the blood stream

Walls impermeable to water

Collecting duct

The tissue fluid ψ is more negative than that of the blood

Walls permeable to water

Water leaves by osmosis

The tissue fluid ψ is more negative than that of the blood

Filtrate ψ now more negative than that of the blood

Hypotonic urine

Hypertonic urine

213

A hormone called **aldosterone**, which is secreted by the adrenal glands, controls the sodium chloride content of the blood. Aldosterone is produced when pressure receptors in the walls of the afferent glomerular vessels detect a fall in blood pressure. Aldosterone secretion results in an increase in the permeability of the collecting ducts to sodium. Sodium ions pass from the tubule into the blood plasma.

Fig. 7 Aldosterone production

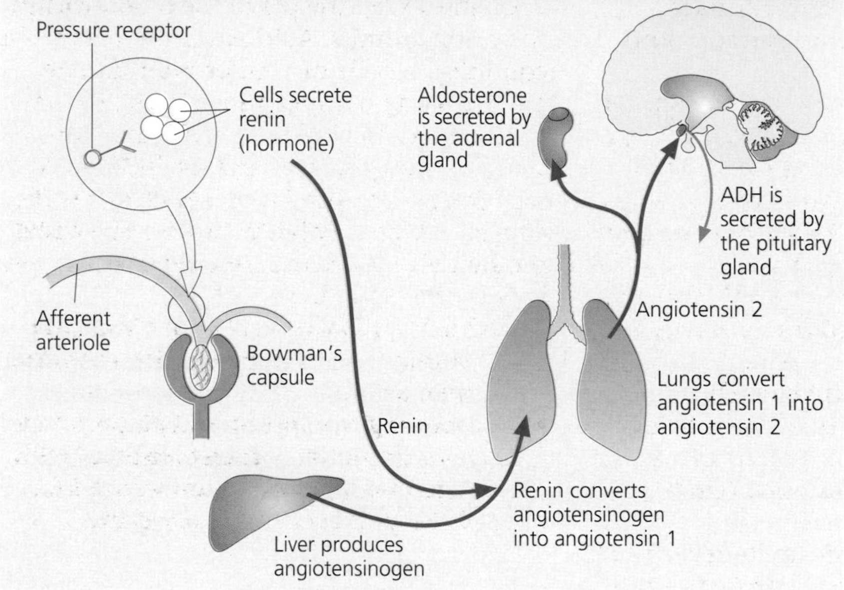

Pressure receptor

Cells secrete renin (hormone)

Aldosterone is secreted by the adrenal gland

ADH is secreted by the pituitary gland

Afferent arteriole

Bowman's capsule

Angiotensin 2

Renin

Lungs convert angiotensin 1 into angiotensin 2

Renin converts angiotensinogen into angiotensin 1

Liver produces angiotensinogen

The mechanism of the response involves two other hormones, **renin** and **angiotensin** (Fig. 7).

7 a What effect will an increase in sodium chloride have on the water potential of the blood?
  b Doctors sometimes inject patients with kidney failure with sodium chloride and glucose. Explain how this will help the kidneys to function.

ANP is produced naturally by the body in response to increased blood volume. It is antagonistic to aldosterone and ADH.
- ANP increases the amount of sodium chloride and water that are excreted by the kidney, mainly by inhibiting their reabsorption by the collecting duct.
- ANP increases the rate of glomerular filtration by dilating the afferent arteriole and constricting the efferent arteriole.
- ANP inhibits both aldosterone and ADH production.

8 Explain how these actions may help patients with renal failure.

Key ideas

- The thick ascending limb of the loop of Henle pumps sodium from the filtrate into the tissue fluid that surrounds the loop.

- The more negative water potential of the tissue fluid draws water from the filtrate flowing down the descending limb.

- The high concentration of sodium chloride in the filtrate results in sodium chloride diffusing out of the filtrate in the thin ascending limb into the tissue fluid.

- The filtrate in the distal tubule consists mainly of water, urea and sodium chloride. If the blood volume is high, the filtrate passes through the rest of the tubule relatively unchanged and flows down the ureter to the bladder as urine. The urine is hypotonic to the blood plasma.

- If the water potential of the blood is too negative, the pituitary gland secretes ADH. ADH increases the permeability of the distal tubule and the collecting duct to water. This means water can pass from the tubule into the tissue fluid, resulting in hypertonic urine.

- The sodium chloride content of the blood is controlled by aldosterone secreted by the adrenal gland. If blood pressure is too low aldosterone secretion results in an increase in the permeability of collecting ducts to sodium. Sodium ions are pumped from the tubule into the blood plasma, restoring the sodium chloride levels in the blood.

18.6 The acid–base balance

Normal diets contain more acid-producing foods than alkali-producing foods. To maintain the normal pH of the blood, 7.35 to 7.45, the body has **buffer** systems. A buffer system is a solution that resists any change in pH when an acid or an alkali is added. The buffer systems of the body usually consist of a weak acid and a weak base. There are two principal buffer systems in the body, the **hydrogencarbonate system** and the **phosphate system**. Both work in the same way.

The hydrogencarbonate system contains sodium hydrogencarbonate, a weak base, and carbonic acid, a weak acid. When a strong acid is added to this system it is immediately converted into a weak acid by the hydrogencarbonate (Fig. 8a).

If a strong base is added to this system it is immediately converted into a weak base by the carbonic acid (Fig. 8b).

A buffer system works by quickly changing a strong acid into a weak acid, or a strong base into a weak base so that the pH of the body fluids is never altered drastically.

In the phosphate buffer system the weak acid is sodium dihydrogen phosphate and the weak base disodium hydrogen phosphate (Fig. 8c).

Q9 Which is the 'strong base', 'strong acid', 'weak acid of buffer', 'weak base of buffer', 'weak acid' and 'weak base' in the two equations in Fig. 8c?

The two buffer systems are normally enough to keep the pH of the blood within the normal limits. **Acidosis** is the name of a condition people can suffer from if there are too many hydrogen ions in the blood. This makes the blood very acidic. If the acidosis is very severe, and the buffers are unable to cope with blood pH changes, the kidney acts as a 'fail-safe' device. The distal tubule cells reduce the number of hydrogen ions in the blood by:
- producing hydrogencarbonate ions that will combine with hydrogen ions to form carbonic acid;
- deaminating the amino acid glutamine to produce ammonia, which combines with hydrogen ions to form ammonium ions, which then pass out with the urine.

Fig. 8 Buffer systems

(a) Hydrochloric acid + hydrogencarbonate → sodium chloride + carbonic acid
    Strong acid + weak base of buffer → salt + weak acid

(b) Sodium hydroxide + carbonic acid → water + sodium hydrogencarbonate
    Strong base + weak acid of buffer → weak base

(c) Hydrochloric acid + disodium hydrogen phosphate → sodium chloride + sodium dihydrogen phosphate
    Sodium hydroxide + sodium dihydrogen phosphate → water + disodium hydrogen phosphate

---

Key ideas

- Buffer systems in the body prevent excessive changes to blood pH.

- The hydrogencarbonate buffer system and the phosphate buffer system each consist of a weak acid plus a weak base.

- The distal tubule acts as a further mechanism for controlling blood pH by manufacturing hydrogencarbonate and ammonia.

18.7 Different mechanisms

Rainbow trout live in freshwater habitats.

The trout and the beetle both have to get rid of nitrogenous waste materials, but their different habitats mean that they do it in a different way to humans.

The trout continually pumps water over its gills to absorb oxygen and get rid of carbon dioxide. Any other waste products will pass from the blood into the respiratory current of water in the same way as carbon dioxide. Because of this the fish has no need to convert ammonia, produced when deaminating amino acids, to urea. It is quite safe to allow the ammonia to pass into the blood because the ammonia will diffuse out of the blood into the respiratory current of water as soon as the blood reaches the gills.

Trout do have kidneys to get rid of the water that is continually diffusing into the blood through the gills. Small quantities of ammonia are excreted in the hypotonic urine.

10 Why does water continually diffuse into the blood in the gill of a trout?

Insects such as the darkling beetle have a different problem. There is very little available water in the desert, even in its food, so it cannot afford to lose water as urine. Instead it converts its nitrogenous waste into **uric acid**. Uric acid is almost insoluble in water, so the beetle can get rid of it as a solid. This solid nitrogenous waste can then be passed out, not in urine, but in the faeces! Insects do not have kidneys. The uric acid is produced in structures called **malpighian tubules**, which empty into the gut at the junction of the ileum and the colon (Fig. 9).

Darkling beetles live in desert habitats.

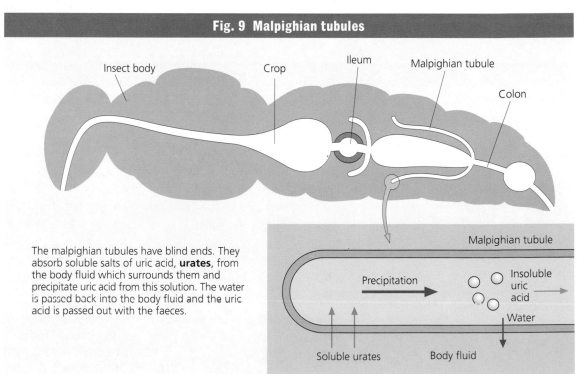

Fig. 9 Malpighian tubules

Insect body   Crop   Ileum   Malpighian tubule   Colon

The malpighian tubules have blind ends. They absorb soluble salts of uric acid, **urates**, from the body fluid which surrounds them and precipitate uric acid from this solution. The water is passed back into the body fluid and the uric acid is passed out with the faeces.

Malpighian tubule

Precipitation   Insoluble uric acid

Water

Soluble urates   Body fluid

Protozoans are single-celled organisms that live in water habitats. They usually have no problem getting rid of nitrogenous waste, ammonia diffuses into the surrounding water almost as quickly as it is produced. Multicellular animals such as insects, fish and humans find it more of a problem. Multicellular animals have therefore evolved excretory systems to keep the volume and concentrations of their body fluids within reasonable limits.

In humans, when the systems go wrong, e.g. during acute renal failure or long-term kidney damage, doctors have worked out ways of helping the body. Dialysis machines work rather like the distal tubules and collecting ducts. The dialysis fluid supplied to the machines has the same concentrations of glucose and ions as the blood plasma that leaves a healthy kidney, but no urea. This fluid is separated from the blood of a patient by a partially permeable membrane. Urea, excess ions and excess water diffuse from the blood into the dialysis fluid.

The regulation of excretion is almost entirely under the control of hormones. We are only now coming to understand fully exactly how these hormones control body processes. A full understanding might lead to new treatments for kidney failure, such as using ANP, which encourage the restoration of normal kidney function rather than relying on twice weekly dialysis for the rest of the patient's life.

Key ideas

- Freshwater fish get rid of nitrogenous waste mainly as ammonia, which diffuses from the blood into the water that flows over the gills.

- Insects conserve water by passing out a solid nitrogenous waste product, uric acid, with the faeces. The uric acid is produced by malpighian tubules from urates that are absorbed by the tubules from the body fluids.

Answers to questions

Chapter 1

1 Carbon atoms are found in every monomer because they can join with each other to form long chains.

2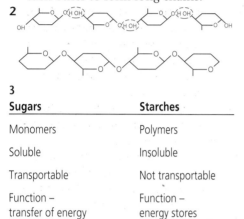

3

Sugars	Starches
Monomers	Polymers
Soluble	Insoluble
Transportable	Not transportable
Function – transfer of energy	Function – energy stores

4 a Non-essential amino acids can be produced from essential amino acids but not vice versa.

b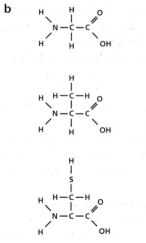

5 The 20 naturally occurring amino acids can be combined in an almost unlimited number and sequence. The two-dimensional and three-dimensional structures can be different for every combination.

6 a (i) Cereals, root vegetables and fruit are good sources of carbohydrate;
(ii) meat, eggs, milk, cereals and pulses are good sources of essential amino acids;
(iii) cereals and pulses are good sources of essential fatty acids.

b Carbohydrates are needed by the body for energy stores, for the transfer of energy and for structural components. Proteins are needed for enzymes, carrier molecules and structural components, e.g. of hair. Fats are needed for energy storage, insulation, solvents for some vitamins, and structural components, particularly in membranes.

c So that they can be transported to the cells where they are needed, then reassembled as the particular chemical compounds required by the body.

7 a The ratio of protein : carbohydrate : fat in Wysoy is 1 : 2 : 3.8; in breast milk it is 1 : 3.2 : 5.7

b The carbohydrate is needed to provide the energy transfer to synthesise the fat and proteins needed by the baby's cells.

c Yes, the difference between the milks is significant. The proportion of both fat and protein is almost 50% higher in human milk than in Wysoy.

d (i) The total mass of vitamins in 100 g Wysoy is 11.4 mg;
(ii) the total mass of minerals is 259.2 mg.

8 The parents are right to be concerned, as there is the possibility of problems when feeding infants with completely animal-free diets, e.g. they could be lacking in essential fatty acids. However, Natalie knows of the potential problems and the steps that can be taken to prevent them. The correct balance of plant foods plus some vitamin supplements can provide all the nutrients required by a growing infant, but it has to be planned carefully, and a doctor must be consulted.

Chapter 2

1 Living organisms need constant attention; the cyanobacteria would need supplies of nutrients and gas such as oxygen and carbon dioxide. There would be problems of recycling or disposing of excretory products.

2 The $NADP^+$ has been reduced to NADPH because it has accepted electrons.

3 Cyanobacteria would produce oxygen, which humans need for respiration, continuously when illuminated, eliminating the need for large stocks of oxygen, and could be a source of food.

4 a Ionisation:
water $\rightleftharpoons$ hydroxyl ions + protons.
Photolysis:
water $\rightarrow$ protons + electrons + oxygen.

b Oxygen is released; energy from excited electrons is used to produce NADPH and to operate proton pumps; hydroxyl ions attract protons, which move through chemiosmotic channels, producing ATP.

c All the energy is provided by the excited electrons.

d $NADP^+ + H^+ + 2e^- \rightarrow NADPH$.

5 Starch is used as an energy store; cellulose is a structural component of cell walls.

6 a Five-sixths of the glyceraldehyde 3-phosphate is recycled to produce acceptor molecules for carbon dioxide.

b (i) The growth of the cyanobacteria will be reduced because no new carbohydrates can be produced as ribulose bisphosphate cannot accept carbon dioxide;
(ii) the evolution of hydrogen initially will not be affected because hydrogen production is light-dependent and does not depend on ribulose bisphosphate

carboxylase. Later the evolution of hydrogen will be reduced because NADPH will not be recycled back to NADP⁺ because no glycerate will have been produced in the light-independent reaction.

7 Light-independent is a better name because if NADPH and ATP are supplied the reactions can occur in both the light and dark.

8 The net gain of ATP is 4 − 2 = 2.

9 There are two atoms of carbon.

10 a The production of ATP will be greatly reduced because there will be no supply of NADH and FADH to the electron transport chain.

b If ATP production is uncoupled from Krebs cycle, large amounts of energy from glucose will not be made available for the cell as ATP. The loss of Krebs cycle makes the cell energy transfer systems much less efficient so that the person can eat much more food. The danger with this pill is that the cycle could be permanently uncoupled and the cells might fail to get enough energy in order to work normally.

Chapter 3

1 a Yes, because their combined kinetic energy is higher than the minimum activation energy required for the reaction.

b They still react because their combined kinetic energy is still as high as the activation energy required.

2 a The reaction between the enzyme and the substrate molecules is slower because both molecules have less kinetic energy in cold rather than hot water.

b The amino acids of the enzymes may contain phosphate groups, which can help cause algal blooms. The amino acids also contain nitrogen compounds which can enter the nitrogen cycle and have similar effects to phosphates. However, the levels

of nitrates and phosphates produced are very low compared with traditional detergents.

3 a The optimum temperature is 55°C.

b The reaction rate will double for each 10°C rise, up to 50°C.

4

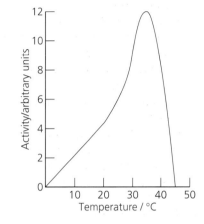

5 An enzyme with a curve similar to B will be effective over a wider pH range.

6 The curves start to flatten out when all the active sites are continually occupied by fresh substrate molecules, and the rate of the reaction cannot increase any more.

7 The rate of the reaction would increase because there would be an increased chance of substrate molecules rather than inhibitor molecules occupying the active sites.

Chapter 4

1 The overall function of an organ depends on the functions of the tissues that make up the organ. These tissues are made up of cells which contain similar organelles inside the cells. Ultimately the function of an organ depends on the organelles which carry out the specific reactions.

2 The theoretical limit due to the wavelength of the electron beam will be slightly greater than 0.0025 nm. There may be other technical factors (difficulty of focusing the electron beam, etc.) that may mean this distance is still too small to resolve even with electron microscopes.

3 a The endoplasmic reticulum and ribosomes are visible on electron but not light micrographs.

b (i) The nucleus, nucleolus, membranes, mitochondria, endoplasmic reticulum, ribosomes and cytosol can be seen in plant and animal cells; (ii) chloroplasts, cell wall, large vacuole and plasmodesmata can only be seen in plant cells; (iii) centrioles and secretary granules can only be seen in animal cells.

4 Hydrophobic means literally 'water-hating'; hydrophobic molecules will not mix with water.

5 Chloroplasts would be the second fraction, because they are smaller (have less mass) than nuclei but are larger than the other cell components.

6 ATP and NADPH are the end products of the light-dependent reactions of photosynthesis.

7 Activity needs energy, and mitochondria are the site of energy release via respiration.

8 ATP is formed when protons flow back through the thylakoids.

9 a NADH and FADH donate electrons to the electron carriers in the cristae.

b Both have outer phospholipid membranes, inner phospholipid membranes, internal spaces and DNA.

c Both mitochondria and chloroplasts are principally concerned with energy transfer.

10 Nuclear membranes, mitochondria and endoplasmic reticulum are present in eukaryotes but are absent in prokaryotes.

11 a Mitochondria have internal projections similar to the mesosomes in bacteria.

b Thylakoids of cyanobacteria are concerned with the light-dependent reactions of photosynthesis.

Chapter 5

1 The greater the sodium chloride concentration in the external solution, the smaller the volume of the cell.

2 The loss of water by sweating effectively increases the external concentration of ions, so water will move out of the red blood cells faster than it will move in.

3 a The concentration of water molecules in the two regions will become equal.

b In osmosis, the solute molecules are confined by a differentially permeable membrane; in diffusion, there is no barrier to the movement of solute molecules.

4 a (i) Speed equals distance divided by time, so the speed over 10 μm is 0.02 cm s^{-1};
(ii) the speed over 1 mm is 0.25 cm s^{-1}.

b It will take between 0.5 and 1 seconds.

5 The net direction of movement of the water would be from the cell into the solution, as the water potential of cell is (−500 + 100) = −400 kPa, i.e. less negative than −600 kPa.

6 a If the concentration of sodium was any higher, and the whole solution was absorbed into the blood, then the plasma would become hypertonic to the red cells, which would then shrink.

b Runners need sugar to provide energy.

7 The folded surface gives them a larger surface area to absorb digested food materials.

8 Much of the absorption in the intestine is against a concentration gradient, and therefore needs energy transferred from respiration. Mitochondria are the site of energy transfer in respiration.

9 The palisade cells are more closely packed and therefore more light energy is absorbed for photosynthesis.

Chapter 6

1 From a local point of view, rainforests are home to a wide variety of useful species that can be used by people in their daily lives. From a global point of view, rainforests provide raw materials for the manufacturing industry, sources of new medicines, a pool of genetic variety and can affect the climate.

2 Plant respiration, biomass decomposition and plant photosynthesis balance each other out. Human activity contributes 7 billion tonnes of carbon dioxide. Of this 2 billion is due to deforestation. The proportion of the increase in atmospheric carbon dioxide due to deforestation is 2/7 = 28.57%.

3 Carbon dioxide is a 'substrate' for photosynthesis, so increasing the concentration of the substrate would increase the rate of reaction.

4 Hibiscus → humming bird → margay
Wood from tree → termites → anteater

5 a

```
  Anteater              Margay
    ↑                ↗  ↑  ↖
  Termites    Bat  Monkey  Humming bird
    ↑          ↑     ↑        ↑
   Wood    Tree fruits   Hibiscus flower
```

b (i) Oak tree → caterpillar → titmice → weasel;
(ii) other trees and shrubs → decomposers → earthworms → beetles → moles;
(iii) herbs → decomposers → soil insects → beetles → moles → tawny owls.

6 a (i) In the tropical rainforest food web, tree fruits and leaves are producers, howler monkeys, toucans and macaws are primary consumers, margays are secondary consumers;
(ii) in the woodland food web, trees, shrubs and herbs are producers, caterpillars, adult insects, voles and mice are primary consumers, titmice, parasites, spiders, voles, mice, earthworms, soil mites and insects are secondary consumers, and weasels, moles, tawny owls and shrews are tertiary consumers.

b The higher the level of consumer, the lower the number of organisms.

7

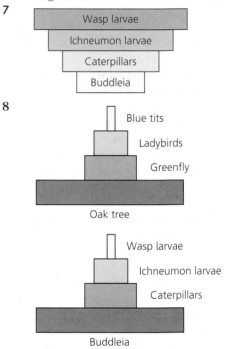

```
|        Wasp larvae        |
|     Ichneumon larvae      |
|       Caterpillars        |
|         Buddleia          |
```

8

```
|          Blue tits        |
|          Ladybirds        |
|          Greenfly         |
|          Oak tree         |
```

```
|         Wasp larvae       |
|      Ichneumon larvae     |
|        Caterpillars       |
|          Buddleia         |
```

9 There is a much higher proportion of energy from producers transferred to grazers in the grassland ecosystem. There is a much higher transfer of energy from grazers to decomposers in the grassland. There is a higher proportion of energy lost to the environment by decomposers in the forest ecosystem.

10 a The amount of energy lost depends on the proportion of food digested; because plant food contains large amounts of cellulose that cannot usually be digested, herbivores lose a large proportion of their energy intake in their faeces. Mammals respire a large proportion of their food to transfer heat energy to maintain a high, constant body temperature. Invertebrates respire little food for heat production because they use heat transfer from the environment to provide the heat

energy needed for the chemical reactions in their bodies.

b The large amount of energy loss in maintaining body temperature means that almost all the energy is lost to the environment by the time the second carnivore in the chain has grown.

11 Nitrates would be released from proteins, and phosphates from proteins and phospholipids.

12 a The proportion of nitrogen is limiting the growth of plants at point A on the graph; the proportion of phosphate is the limiting factor at point B.

b This information means a farmer can know the proportions of nitrate and phosphate to add as fertilisers.

13 The clover receives nitrogen compounds from the bacterium, and the bacterium receives carbohydrates from the clover.

14 Mineral ions are quickly leached out of the soils because the root system of grasses is not as extensive as that of the trees. The grass is likely to be eaten by domesticated animals, which in turn are eaten by humans. Most of the minerals are therefore not returned to the soil for recycling.

15 Peatbogs are enormous 'sinks' of carbon compounds. Decay is very slow, so return of carbon dioxide to the atmosphere is very slow.

Chapter 7

1 If the body temperature becomes too high, the enzymes will be denatured.

2 The loss of water by sweating will effectively increase the external concentration of ions, so water will move out of its red blood cells faster than it will move in. The horse would suffer from dehydration and heat stress. The performance of the horse would be affected, it would probably start staggering, and if left unchecked it could fall into a coma and die.

3 a There is an immediate increase in temperature in the region of the shoulders and hips, followed by a general increase in temperature.

b The bulk of the muscles associated with moving limbs is located around the shoulders and hips. Blood leaving these will be warmer due to energy release in the contracting muscles. After several minutes cantering there is a general increase in blood temperature due to muscular activity; all the body surface is now at a greater temperature.

4

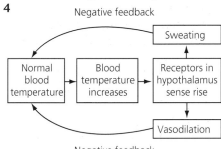

5 Isotonic fluid replaces some of the ions lost via sweating, as well as water, which is helpful in keeping the water potential of the plasma constant.

6 a Sweating is only effective in lowering body temperature if the sweat can evaporate: fur would reduce the rate of evaporation of sweat.

b When the saliva evaporates it will transfer energy from the rat, and there will be a cooling effect.

c (i) While in the water, energy will be transferred by conduction from the hippopotamus to the water;
(ii) when on the bank, evaporation of water from the wet hippopotamus will have a cooling effect.

7 Blood temperature is maintained by heat from respiration in all the body tissues. If the temperature of any organ or tissue falls, the rate of respiration will decrease, providing less heat to maintain the body and blood temperature.

8 One reason could have been that the birth rate in most developing countries is high. Another reason might have been that their lack of education may have led them not to question possible side-effects.

9 Several eggs are likely to be released, resulting in a multiple pregnancy because LH cannot target just one of the follicles.

10 This is an example of negative feedback. Increasing amounts of the follicular hormones inhibit LH production.

11 Inhibition of FSH will prevent the growth of a follicle. Inhibition of LH will prevent ovulation.

12 The continued secretion of both oestrogen and progesterone will maintain the stability and thickness of the endometrium.

13 The oestrogen and progesterone will inhibit FSH and LH production, mimicking the negative feedback that operates in the normal menstrual cycle.

Chapter 8

1

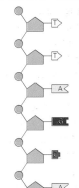

2

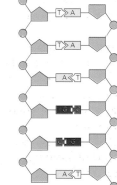

3 In each organism the percentages of adenine and thymine are the same, and the percentages of cytosine and guanine are the same. This is because they fit together as complementary pairs in DNA, so there must be the same number of adenine and thymine bases, and of cytosine and guanine.

4

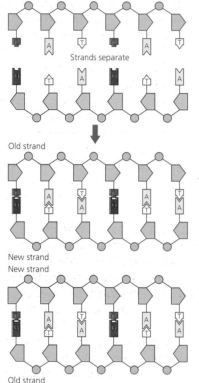

Strands separate

Old strand

New strand
New strand

Old strand

5 It would be unlikely that all the DNA, and therefore all the genes, would have been preserved intact. It would also be necessary to stimulate and control the process of development from a single cell to an adult. This involves a complex pattern of activating particular genes at particular stages, which at present cannot be done artificially for more complex organisms. However, perhaps in the future the necessary techniques will be developed!

6

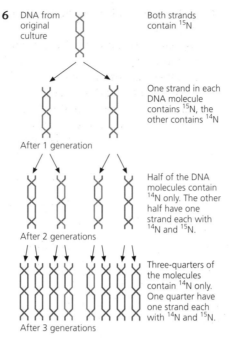

DNA from original culture — Both strands contain ^{15}N

After 1 generation — One strand in each DNA molecule contains ^{15}N, the other contains ^{14}N

After 2 generations — Half of the DNA molecules contain ^{14}N only. The other half have one strand each with ^{14}N and ^{15}N.

After 3 generations — Three-quarters of the molecules contain ^{14}N only. One quarter have one strand each with ^{14}N and ^{15}N.

7 Two equal-sized bands, one at the top level (containing ^{14}N only) and one at the lowest level (containing ^{15}N only).

8 (i) The sixth base, T, has been replaced by G (substitution);
(ii) an extra base, A, has been added (insertion);
(iii) bases 9 to 11, ATG, have been switched round to GTA (inversion);
(iv) the fourth base, C, has been removed (deletion).

9 Only mutations in developing ova in the ovaries could be passed on to children.

10 a Advantages of testing include the ability to reduce the chance of having children with a serious abnormality, either by avoiding having children with a partner carrying the same faulty gene or by testing during pregnancy; reduced pressure on health services if fewer seriously handicapped children are born. Disadvantages include the increased stress involved in choosing a partner and whether to have children; possible pressure to be tested, e.g. from insurance companies; the possibility of a government banning people with certain abnormal genes from having children.

11 a Advantages centre around the possibilities of understanding the genetic origins of diseases and disorders, and of developing appropriate treatments.

b Possible disadvantages and concerns include the prospect of a child's genetic constitution being manipulated in order to 'improve' intelligence, appearance and so on.

12 a A two-base code could identify 16 amino acids.

b A three-base code could identify 64 amino acids.

13 CAC ATT CTC

14 Cys Asn His Val His

15 a (i) Gln will be substituted for Val;
(ii) Cys and Thr will be substituted for Val and His.

b All the three-base codes that come after the missing base will be changed, as in question 8(iv). Therefore all the amino acids will differ, and the protein will have a completely different structure. If only one base is swapped, only one amino acid will be changed.

16 a UGC UAA CAC GUG CAC

b UUU GUG UAA GAG CAC AUC UGC

17

Amino acid in insulin	Gln	His	Leu	Cys
DNA code in gene	CTC	GTG	TAG	ACG
Codon in mRNA	GAG	CUC	AUC	UGC
Anticodon in tRNA	CUC	GTG	UAG	ACG

18 a Remember to give reasons for your ideas and evidence to support your viewpoint.

b Important scientific work like genetic technology probably does need legal guidelines. Suggest some guidelines and give reasons.

Chapter 9

1 a (i) Turner's syndrome has no Y chromosome, and only one X chromosome. Klinefelter's syndrome has an extra X chromosome;

(ii) an individual with Turner's syndrome would be female, because there is no Y chromosome and therefore no *SRY* gene. An individual with Klinefelter's syndrome would be male, because there is a Y chromosome.

b The embryo is genetically 'programmed' to become female, and female reproductive organs will develop unless a *SRY* gene is present. This gene stimulates the development of testes instead of ovaries.

2 A person may be physically female, but not have a Barr body, for example because there is only one X chromosome. Also abnormal development, for example untypical response to hormones, may result in some females having exceptional physical features, such as muscle strength.

3 a (i) The haploid number of chromosomes in a cat is 19;
(ii) in an onion it is 8.

b (i) There would be 23 chromosomes in a human sperm;
(ii) 14 in a leaf cell of a pea;
(iii) 20 in a mouse ovum;
(iv) 64 in a horse zygote;
(v) 10 in a maize gamete.

4 (i) $2^4 = 16$ combinations would be produced if there were four pairs;
(ii) $2^{23} = 8\,388\,608$ would be produced if there were 23 pairs.

5

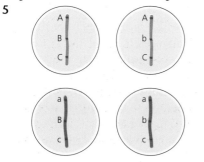

6 Mutations would provide genetic variation in an asexually reproducing species.

7 a (i) Part 2 shows the nuclei of the gametes;
(ii) part 3 shows the nuclei of the zygotes.

b (i) Part 2 would have the haploid number;
(ii) part 3 would have the diploid number.

c No, you cannot distinguish between male and female gametes. There are no differences, they are the same size and one does not move towards the other.

8 a

Ovum	Sperm
Size	
Larger than sperm, about 150 μm diameter	Small, about 10 μm long
Proportions of main parts	
Roughly spherical	Long, with small head and middle piece and extended tail
Special features	
Large proportion of cytoplasm, containing yolk droplets	Little cytoplasm, no yolk
Clear coating	Enzymes, mitochondria and contractile filaments
Numbers produced	
Few	Many
Adaptations related to function	
Yolk provides food reserves for first stages of development of embryo	Enzymes at tip enable it to penetrate coating of ovum
The coating restricts entry to one sperm	Contractile filaments in tail enable swimming
	Mitochondria provide energy for swimming

b This is a much more economical use of food reserves. The sperms have little food reserves as few of them will reach an ovum, and therefore much would be wasted. The ovum can be retained where it has the best chance of surviving and developing.

c Each can be adapted for the production of one gamete, and for successful fertilisation. The male is adapted to ensure the motile gametes find and reach the female ovum; the female is adapted to protect the ova and often to help in development of the embryo.

9 a Females are XX and do not have Y chromosomes.

b The sperm, because it may have either an X or a Y chromosome,

and it is the Y chromosome that determines maleness.

10 a Separate X sperms from Y sperms, and then use only the X sperms for artificial insemination.

b Males can assist in the development of the young and make the survival of a female's young, and therefore her genes, more likely. Such a strategy is not universal and many species do not have equal proportions of males and females.

11 a Problems could include an imbalance in the sexes; parents choosing a child's sex for reasons that would be damaging in the longer term, such as to provide help for themselves; social problems for those unable to find a partner; rejection of a child that turned out not to be the chosen sex.

b Not really; it is important to remember that many different features and many different genes may contribute to an ability like success in athletics, as well as a range of environmental factors.

12 a The amount of DNA will be doubled during interphase as the chromosomes replicate.

b The hyacinth has approximately 6 chromosomes.

c There will be twice as many chromatids as there are chromosomes, i.e. 12.

d They contract separately from each other so that they can be separated during anaphase.

e The chromatids stay together until metaphase, when they are lined up across the middle of the cell. One chromatid from each pair is then pulled towards each pole by the spindle.

13

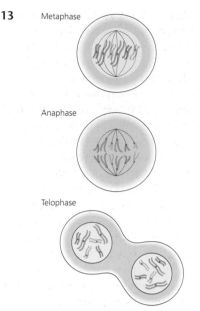

Metaphase

Anaphase

Telophase

14 Successful varieties can reproduce quickly and in large numbers. This often enables plants to colonise an area very rapidly.

15 a Advantages include the ability to produce large quantities of a particularly good or useful plant or animal; cheapness; reliability and consistency of produce for sale; ability to use low quality animals as parents for cloned embryos.

  b Issues include dangers and difficulties of selecting desirable features; the treatment of less favoured individuals; social engineering by governments; parental aspirations. Governments may have to restrict experimentation in these areas.

Chapter 10

1 a Two of Beatrice's children did not have Huntington's disease. She must therefore have carried the normal allele, which she passed on to these children. Since the normal allele is recessive, unaffected individuals must receive one normal allele from each parent.

  b Gwen's mother, Cynthia, did not develop Huntington's disease. She must have the homozygous

'normal' genotype, hh, and does not have the allele for Huntington's disease. Her children cannot possibly inherit the disease from her. Since the disease is rare, it is very unlikely that her partner, from a different family, would have the allele for the disease.

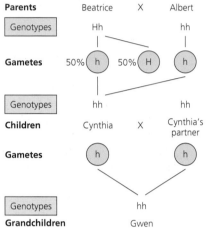

Parents	Beatrice	X	Albert
Genotypes	Hh		hh
Gametes	50% h 50% H		h
Genotypes	hh		hh
Children	Cynthia	X	Cynthia's partner
Gametes	h		h
Genotypes		hh	
Grandchildren		Gwen	

  c There is a 50% chance that a child of Jasper will develop the disease.

  d Issues to consider include the anxiety caused to the parents and the child if found to have the allele for the disease; decisions about having children; problems of life insurance.

2 a The ratio of phenotypes is 3 normal : 1 with cystic fibrosis.

  b Twenty-five per cent of the children would suffer from cystic fibrosis.

  c Fifty per cent of the children would be carriers of the cystic fibrosis allele.

  d (i) $1/25 \times 1/25 = 1$ in 625 (0.16%);
(ii) 1/4 (25%);
(iii) $1/625 \times 4 = 1$ in 2500 (0.04%).

3 a Heterozygous people have a higher resistance to malaria, but one-third of their red blood cells are sickle-shaped.

  b

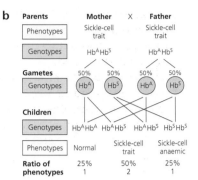

Parents	**Mother**	X	**Father**
Phenotypes	Sickle-cell trait		Sickle-cell trait
Genotypes	Hb^{A}Hb^S		Hb^{A}Hb^S
Gametes	50% 50%		50% 50%
Genotypes	Hb^A Hb^S		Hb^A Hb^S
Children			
Genotypes	Hb^{A}Hb^A Hb^{A}Hb^S	Hb^{A}Hb^S	Hb^{S}Hb^S
Phenotypes	Normal	Sickle-cell trait	Sickle-cell anaemic
Ratio of phenotypes	25% 1	50% 2	25% 1

  c There is no malaria in the USA. People with the sickle-cell trait do not have the advantage of resistance to malaria. They are likely to produce fewer children that survive, because those with sickle-cell anaemia die. The allele for sickle-cell is therefore becoming less common in the population.

4 All the cats have similar body structure, but they have very different colours and lengths of hair.

5 a (i) A Siamese cat has the genotype C^{s}C^s;
(ii) a Burmese cat has the genotype C^{b}C^b.

  b

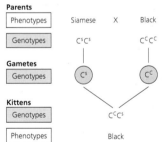

Parents	Siamese	X	Black
Phenotypes	Siamese		Black
Genotypes	C^{s}C^s		C^{c}C^c
Gametes			
Genotypes	C^s		C^c
Kittens			
Genotypes		C^{c}C^s	
Phenotypes		Black	

6 a The pale brown cats have the genotype C^{b}C^s.

  b Yes they are codominant because the heterozygote is different from either of the homozygotes.

  c The ratio of offspring would be 50% pale brown cats, 25% Burmese cats, 25% Siamese cats.

  d She will have to breed a Burmese with a Siamese each time.

7 Fifty per cent of the kittens will be tailed.

8 BBDd would be seal; bbDd would be chocolate; BBdd would be blue; BbDd would be seal.

9 a Twenty-five per cent seal; 25%

blue; 25% chocolate; 25% lilac, i.e. a ratio of 1:1:1:1.

b (i) The genotypes of these cats could be BBdd or Bbdd;
(ii) she needs to select only those cats that are homozygous, BBdd. She can only determine this by breeding them. Possible crosses are BBdd × BBdd; BBdd × Bbdd; and Bbdd × Bbdd. The last cross will on average produce 25% lilac kittens. Any parents that produce lilac kittens must be excluded from the breeding programme, since they must have the genotype Bbdd. It will be necessary to breed for several generations, since with a small number of kittens there is no certainty that a lilac kitten will be produced in the cross Bbdd × Bbdd.

Parents

| Phenotypes | Blue | X | Blue |

| Genotypes | DDdd | | BBdd |

Gametes

| Genotypes | Bd | | Bd |

Kittens

| Genotypes | | BBdd | |

| Phenotypes | | Blue | |

Parents

| Phenotypes | Blue | X | Blue |

| Genotypes | BBdd | | Bbdd |

Gametes

| Genotypes | Bd | | Bd | bd |
| | | | 50% | 50% |

Kittens

| Genotypes | BBdd | | Bbdd |

| Phenotypes | Blue | | Blue |

Parents

| Phenotypes | Blue | X | Blue |

| Genotypes | Bbdd | | Bbdd |

Gametes

| Genotypes | Bd | bd | Bd | bd |
| | 50% | 50% | 50% | 50% |

Kittens

| Genotypes | BBdd | Bbdd | Bbdd | bbdd |

| Phenotypes | Blue | Blue | Blue | Lilac |

---

10 a The F_2 plants with wrinkled seeds that produce dwarf plants will have the genotype Ttrr.

b

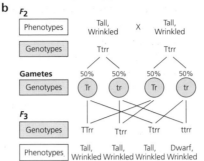

11 a Only those plants which have a desired characteristic are used for breeding. Therefore the alleles which produce other characteristics are bred out.

b These stocks will have a much wider range of alleles. If conditions change, for example the appearance of a new disease, or breeders want to develop a new feature, the older breeds may contain the alleles needed.

12 a Fifty per cent of the boys are red/green colour blind.

b The genotypes $X^CX^c × X^cY$, or $X^cX^c × X^CY$ could produce a red/green colour blind girl.

c A boy receives his X chromosome from his mother.

13 a

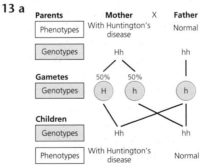

b The parents must both be carriers of the recessive gene for cystic fibrosis and have the genotype Cc. There is therefore always a 1 in 4 chance of any child having cystic fibrosis.

14 a A haemophiliac male has the genotype X^hY.

b The most likely genotypes would be X^HX^h and X^hY.

c (i) It is unlikely that the woman will be carrying the allele for haemophilia, therefore none of their children will have the disease;
(ii) none of their sons will have the gene for haemophilia and so they cannot pass it on to their children. However, their daughters will carry the haemophilia gene, because they will inherit an X chromosome from their father, which must have the gene for haemophilia. There is a 50% chance that the daughters' sons will have haemophilia.

15 a The ADA gene is not inserted into the reproductive organs, and therefore does not enter the sex cells.

b The allele for ADA deficiency is rare and recessive. It is unlikely that the patient's partner would also carry this allele.

16 Start your answer by listing the arguments on each side of an issue. You could also look at an argument on one side of the issue and see if it has an alternative interpretation that would make it fit on the other side. Once you have listed as many arguments as possible on both sides sort them carefully into an order with the most significant ones first. You can then prepare your radio script giving most time to the most important arguments on each side.

Chapter 11

1 a Twenty to 23% of Japanese, Nigerians, Russians and US blacks have blood group B; 9-10% of British and US whites have blood group B; 0% of native Americans and native Australians have blood group B.

b No; for example, Japanese and Nigerians, native Americans and native Australians have quite different skin colours.

c The black population derives from people of African ancestry, who, like the Nigerians, have a proportion of 20% with blood group B, whereas the white population is largely European in origin, where the proportion is similar to the British 9%.

2 a A male can mate with several females, and can successfully father many young. It may be a more economical use of available food resources for a population to contain a high proportion of females.

b A plant's growth may be affected by such factors as light, water and nutrient availability; temperature; wind; animal grazing; disease.

c (i) (c) Because it shows four distinct phenotypes;
(ii) (b) because it shows two distinct phenotypes;
(iii) (d) because it shows continuous variation, with a normal distribution curve;
(iv) (a) because it shows two phenotypes, each with a certain range of variation.

3 a Only gene mutation or environmental factors could produce differences in the offspring of asexually reproducing organisms.

b Environmental factors, such as differences in food intake, or gene mutations occurring during the development of certain parts of the body, could cause identical twins to differ from each other.

c Each ovum will have been produced from a different cell in the ovary by meiosis. As a result of independent assortment and crossing-over, the ova will have received different combinations of alleles.

4 a The amount of available food and space could limit the size of the population.

b The population would increase tenfold each year. There would soon be severe competition for food.

c Two young must survive.

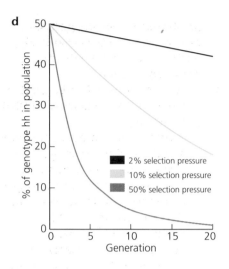

d

e At 2% selection pressure, 4200 individuals would show the phenotype of the recessive allele; at 10%, 1800; at 50% 100.

f The frequency of the recessive allele would decrease in each case.

5 Features that could show advantageous variation could include long legs, so that the rodents could escape faster; eyes giving all round vision; camouflaged fur colour; long claws, etc.

6 The melanic form could provide better camouflage on the blackened tree trunks in the polluted areas, and the speckled form could be better camouflaged in the unpolluted areas. Fewer of the camouflaged forms would be taken by predators.

7 a As well as improved camouflage, melanics might be more resistant to pollutants, better adapted to the climate in central Britain, and less easily disturbed by people.

b Make sure your reasons link your chosen explanation to the evidence. It can be difficult to decide which explanation is correct from one set of data so the reasons are often more important than the choice of answer.

8 The population of the speckled form is likely to increase again.

9 It suggests that a male with a large tail also carries genes for heavier and more successful chicks. It is therefore an advantage for the female to have such a mate because her genes are

also more likely to be passed on by the successful chicks.

10 a The extra red cells give the blood more oxygen carrying capacity. This is an advantage at high altitudes, where the oxygen concentration in the atmosphere is much lower than at sea level.

b People with larger lungs would inhale more air in each breath. Oxygen would enter their blood more rapidly and they would be better adapted to survive at high altitudes. They would be more likely to have children who would inherit the large lung capacity, and in turn pass it on to their children.

11 a Conditions vary in different parts of the world. A feature that is well suited to one set of conditions may not be desirable in other circumstances. For example, very pale, unpigmented skin is at a disadvantage in tropical areas where the intense radiation is liable to cause sunburn and cancers. Also, if every individual is the same, the genes must be homozygous so there is no possibility of adaptation if conditions change. Increasing depletion of the ozone layer may, for example, make pale skins even more disadvantageous as ultraviolet levels increase. Humans, however, unlike other organisms, are able to deal with selective disadvantages by making use of appropriate understanding and technology.

b People tend to group each other on the basis of a small number of readily identifiable features. The vast range of variation in other features is generally ignored.

Chapter 12

1 If the parents are of different species with different numbers of chromosomes, the sex cells will have different numbers too. The hybrid will have different numbers of maternal and paternal chromosomes, so some chromosomes will be unable to pair up during the prophase of meiosis. For example, a horse's egg has 33 chromosomes and a donkey's sperm has 31, so mules have two chromosomes with no partner. Even if two species have the same number of chromosomes, the chromosomes may be of different sizes and shapes and thus be unable to pair up for crossing-over during meiosis.

2 The populations would probably change in different ways, since conditions would be different. After a few million years the organisms in two locations might have very dissimilar features, and may seem to be quite distinct species.

3 One way would be to check whether the finches could interbreed and produce fertile offspring.

4 On the island there were no other predators, and plenty of prey. The prey included quite large animals, such as pigs, so the largest 'dragons' would be the most successful at capturing these. They would therefore pass on their genes for large size to their offspring.

5 If conditions change and cause the food source to decline, the species that feeds on it would also decline.

6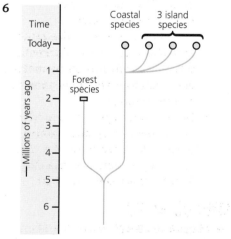

7 Box A could represent fungi, protoctists or prokaryotes; box B could represent molluscs, annelids or echinoderms; box C birds, amphibia or fish; box D rodents, cetaceans

(including whales and dolphins), carnivora (including cat and dog families) or ungulates (including horses and cattle).

8 a It took between 4 and 5 million years for a 1% difference in DNA to develop.
 b They shared a common ancestor about 9 million years ago.

9 a The hairiness of the hominid population would have a range of continuous variation. Those with the thinnest hair would cool down quickest, and would perhaps be able to sustain a longer pursuit of prey, as well as requiring less water. As a result more hominids with thin hair would survive and pass on the genes to their offspring. This process would continue until the bodies of hominids were largely hairless.
 b The active processes that maintain the brain need a continuous supply of energy from respiration, and this inevitably generates waste heat. The excess heat must be released in order to keep a constant body temperature.
 c Possible hypotheses include adaptation to swimming and feeding in a coastal or lake environment, adaptation to a dense tropical forest environment, or sexual selection.

10 a This is an opportunity to think about possibilities and there are no 'right' answers. You could suggest that human beings will start to change their genotypes to remove genetic illnesses or to improve the functioning of their bodies beyond current limits. We may see people living longer and longer. There may be fashions in genotypes with parents choosing the look of their offspring from catalogues. The only certainty is that the developments will be at least as important as any scientific advance to date.
 b Genetic material might be

obtained from related species in order to help breeding programmes, or females of closely related species might be used as surrogate mothers for eggs or embryos.

Chapter 13

1 a

Generation	Number of bacteria
1	20
2	40
3	80
4	160
5	320
6	640
7	1280
8	2560
9	5120
10	10 240

 b The shape shows an increasingly steep increase in the size of the population. This is known as exponential growth.

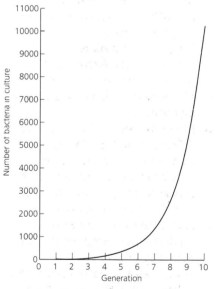

 c For the first few days this graph also shows exponential growth, i.e. an increasingly steep curve.
 d After 15 days the population stopped increasing, because it would be limited by a shortage of raw materials and space.

2 The population would fall as individuals died from food shortage, until a sustainable number was reached, when the population would stay at a stable level.

3 The Arctic fox population would follow a similar cycle, increasing in numbers as the lemming population increases, and falling sharply after the lemmings decline.

4 a The population of this colony would decline, and the colony might well die out, because the total number of rabbits at the end of the season (39) was much smaller than the number at the start (70). However, the rabbit colony can produce a large number of young very quickly and so the population could recover rapidly if the population of predators dropped.

   b Natural selection might occur, whereby the young that are better at avoiding predators survive, perhaps by being more cautious or having more acute senses. These more successful young could pass on their characteristics to their offspring. Numbers in the colony could also be increased by immigration from other colonies.

5 a The vegetation grows much taller and shows a reduction in the number of different plant species present.

   b Small plants are overshadowed and unable to photosynthesise sufficiently, so they die out.

   c The number of species declines as a few species become dominant in the plot.

6 a Sucking the sap reduces the food supply available for growth. The sooty mould reduces the amount of light available for photosynthesis, and acts as a parasite taking sugar from the host (tomato). Both effects reduce the amount of sugar available to the leaves. Blockage of the stomata reduces the uptake of carbon dioxide and thus also reduces the rate of photosynthesis.

   b A small number of *Encarsia* can infect a large number of whitefly larvae. The scales infected by a wasp can easily be identified as they turn black. The scales infected by wasps are small and easily handled and transported. The wasps find and target whitefly scales that would otherwise be difficult to detect, and they only affect whiteflies so they will not harm other useful organisms.

7 Some rabbits had alleles that made them naturally resistant to the myxomatosis virus. These rabbits would be more likely to survive and pass on these alleles to their young. After a few generations a high proportion of the rabbit population would be resistant to myxomatosis.

8 a

Billion of population	Year to reach it
2nd	97
3rd	33
4th	14
5th	13
6th	10

   b The world population might reach 10 billion by 2025.

9 a In a food chain, only a small proportion of energy is passed on from one trophic level to the next, because at each level the organisms dissipate the energy released in respiration, largely as heat. Also, only a proportion of the energy stored in a plant crop will be absorbed by a consumer, such as a cow, because parts, e.g. the roots, are not eaten and others are not digestible.

   b Humans consume different proportions of the stored energy in a plant, depending on which parts are eaten. In cereal crops only the grains are used as food; sugar beet stores relatively large quantities of sugar in its swollen root.

10 Some weed plants may contain mutant alleles that make them resistant to the effects of 2,4-D. They will survive spraying with the herbicide and will be able to produce seeds. The young plants that develop are likely to have the same resistant alleles.

11 a The bacteria involved in decay and in the nitrogen cycle require oxygen.

   b It is important that herbicides should not drift onto other areas, such as hedges, gardens or orchards. It is also difficult to ensure that the crop receives the correct dosage in windy conditions.

   c Ploughing buries plant materials that are then recycled by fungal and bacterial activity. Grazing cattle add manure to the soil.

   d Ploughing buries and kills weeds. Harrowing removes weed that would compete with young seedlings. Spraying with herbicides kills the weeds that do grow in the crop.

   e The nitrogen-fixing bacterium *Rhizobium* lives in the nodules on the roots of clover, and restores soil fertility by synthesising nitrogen compounds from atmospheric nitrogen. The farmer would still have to add other mineral fertilisers, such as phosphates.

12 a Very low average temperatures, thin soil cover, shortage of soil nutrients, waterlogging and high winds or exposed conditions can all prevent a forest community developing.

   b Regular ploughing and grazing by animals prevent shrubs and trees becoming established.

13 a Loss of habitat, e.g. due to destruction of grazing land by cattle and goats, and loss of forests for firewood; hunting and poaching due to the demand for tiger skins for rugs and coats and tiger bones for medicine, and to reduce the population of a dangerous predator of humans, could have contributed to the reduction in the tiger population.

   b Arguments for conserving tigers include the preservation of a particularly beautiful animal for future generations, maintenance of biological and genetic diversity, and the tiger's role in the ecosystem in which it lives.

c When you give your views make sure you back them up with reasonable arguments rather than just stating them. Remember to explain why you hold a viewpoint rather than simply stating it.

d A farmer living near to a tiger reserve would have a much clearer perception of the dangers posed by these creatures. However, the farmer may also be able to enjoy the beauty of the tigers at first hand and may regard the reserve as a national, or even global, asset. Try to think of how these, and other, conflicting emotions might influence the farmer's viewpoint.

Chapter 14

1 With an increase in temperature, energy is transferred to water molecules enabling them to break the bonds which hold them in a liquid, and so diffuse away from the leaves as water vapour molecules. Fewer water molecules per unit volume of air results in a more negative water potential. A decrease in humidity means there are fewer water vapour molecules outside the leaf and therefore a greater tendency for molecules to diffuse away from the leaf surface. Wind blows water vapour molecules away from the leaf, so an increase in wind would move more water molecules away; fewer water molecules results in more negative water potential.

2 The advantages of opening the stomata at night are that gaseous exchange can take place, replenishing carbon dioxide levels, without losing much water by transpiration. The disadvantage is that there is no light energy available for photosynthesis. The advantage of closing stomata at lunch-time is that the transpiration rate will be reduced. The disadvantage is that carbon dioxide intake will be reduced just when the light intensity

is at its maximum level.

3 The concentration of solutes in the cytoplasm and vacuole, and the pressure potential of the cell wall, will affect the water potential of the guard cells.

4 a

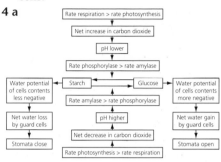

b Photosynthesis produces sugars, and amylase hydrolyses starch into sugars. An increased sugar concentration gives a more negative value of water potential.

c Water would diffuse along a water potential gradient from the cells adjacent into the guard cells, causing them to increase in volume. The unequal thickening of the guard cell walls causes them to change shape, and results in stomatal opening.

5 Because the leaves have been reduced to spines, the surface area available for the absorption of light for photosynthesis is reduced. They are also living in very dry conditions and so will suffer from heat stress, even though they are adapted to arid areas.

6 a Smaller leaves lower the surface area available for transpiration, whilst still enabling some photosynthesis to take place.

b The petioles provide a reduced surface area for transpiration. Sinking the stomata into pits results in the air in the pits quickly becoming saturated with water vapour, making the water potential less negative and therefore reducing the diffusion gradient.

c Water vapour trapped inside the rolled leaf results in the air in the rolled leaf quickly becoming saturated with water vapour, making the water potential less

negative and therefore reducing the diffusion gradient.

7 Some roots are near the surface of the soil, so any rainfall will reach them quickly. Some roots go very deep, in case there is any moisture deeper in the soil. Other root systems grow towards any moisture trapped under stones.

8 2500 kPa /200 kPa per 10 m = 12.5 × 10 m =125 m.

9 Heat energy from the Sun pulls water up a plant.

10 a (i) Most of the radioactive phosphate moves up the plant; (ii) most of the radioactive sugar moves down the plant, at the same time.

b The source for the phosphate was the application leaf, and the sink for the phosphate was the growing parts at the apex of the stem. The source for the sugar was the photosynthesising leaf, and the sink mainly the growing parts above SA but also the roots.

11 The abundance of mitochondria in the companion cells indicates that energy is important. This suggests that sugars probably move into sieve tubes by active transport.

12 The phosphate is actively loaded into the sieve tubes in the application leaf, the source, reducing the water potential of the phloem. Water then passes from the xylem to the phloem in the application leaf, causing an increase in pressure. The mass of solution in the phloem is forced to flow up to the sink. At the sink, the phosphate is actively removed into growing cells at the stem apex, and the water passes back into the xylem.

13 Desirable characteristics would include structural modifications such as sunken stomata, to prevent excess water loss in summer whilst still allowing photosynthesis at a reasonable rate for production, and biochemical modifications such as CAM, to allow carbon dioxide to be absorbed and stored during the night enabling photosynthesis during the day without opening stomata.

Chapter 15

1 a ATP is a compound that acts as a temporary energy store.

b As in any cell, most ATP is produced in the mitochondria.

c ATP transfers energy needed for muscle contraction or other energy-requiring reactions in a cell.

2 $50/130 \times 100 = 38.5\%$.

3 The rate of diffusion depends on the length of the diffusion path. The less the surface area to volume ratio, the longer the length of the diffusion path.

4 A fairer unit would be litres of oxygen per minute per kilogram of body mass.

5 The impulses from the stretch receptors stop initiation of inspiratory impulses, so the muscles relax and the lungs return to their previous size.

6 a

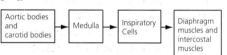

b The aortic bodies are more sensitive at lower concentrations of carbon dioxide, but the carotid bodies initiate more impulses with increasing carbon dioxide levels.

c The activity of the carotid bodies is affected far more than the aortic bodies by a decrease in oxygen concentration.

7 a There will be fewer impulses from chemoreceptors to the inspiratory cells, consequently there will be fewer impulses to the diaphragm and external intercostal muscles. There will therefore be a decrease in the ventilation rate.

b Subject A could be suffering from hypoxia, because low levels of oxygen have resulted in a large increase in ventilation rate.

8 Fish require a large area of respiratory surface because of the low dissolved oxygen content of the water they live in.

9

Fish	Humans
Oxygen obtained from water	Oxygen obtained from air
Unidirectional flow of water	Tidal flow of air
Respiratory surface surface is the gill filaments	Respiratory surface is the alveoli
Countercurrent flow of blood and water	No such flow

10 a

Insects	Humans
Air intake via spiracles	Air intake via nose and mouth
No lungs	Lungs
Oxygen diffuses as gas to tissues	Oxygen transported dissolved in blood to tissues
Intracellular air tubes (tracheoles)	No such structures

b

Insects	Fish
Air intake via spiracles	Water intake via mouth
No gills	Gills
Oxygen diffuses as gas to tissues	Oxygen transported dissolved in blood to tissues
Intracellular air tubes (tracheoles)	No such structures
Tidal flow of air	Unidirectional flow of water

11 Yes, but only if the male and female have a comparable mass of muscle. The surface area to volume ratio would then be the same; therefore the rate of oxygen delivery to the muscles would be the same. However, male hormones usually give males proportionally more muscle than females.

Chapter 16

1 a Condensation reactions join sugar molecules together.

b Water is released when two sugar molecules link.

2 Sugar molecules are small and can 'fit' facilitated diffusion proteins in membranes, whereas starch molecules cannot.

3 Active transport requires energy, facilitated diffusion does not.

4 a

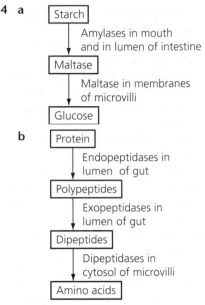

5 The products of fat digestion, phospholipids and cholesterol are soluble in the phospholipids which make up most of the membranes; carbohydrate and protein monomers are not.

6

	Gastrin	Secretin	Cholecystokinin
Stimulus	Chewing, swallowing	Acid contents of stomach entering duodenum	Acid contents of stomach entering duodenum
Receptor	Receptor cells in mouth and oesophagus	Cells in mucosa of duodenum	Cells in mucosa of duodenum
Effector	G cells secrete gastrin	Mucosal cells secrete secretin	Mucosal cells secrete cholecystokinin
Response	Gastrin stimulates gastric glands to secrete digestive enzymes	Secretin stimulates pancreas cells to secrete an alkaline fluid	Cholecystokinin stimulates pancreas cells to secrete digestive enzymes and stimulates gall bladder to contract forcing bile into duodenum

7 a Glycogenesis is the production of glycogen from glucose. Gluconeogenesis is the production of glucose by the breakdown of protein and fat.

Glycogenolysis is the breakdown of glycogen into glucose.

b High insulin levels stimulate glycogenesis, to reduce blood sugar levels. High glucagon levels stimulate gluconeogenesis and glycogenolysis, to increase blood sugar levels.

8 a Receptor site proteins stimulate the production of facilitated diffusion proteins. These move into the membrane and begin to transport glucose rapidly into the cell.

b Insulin stimulates the rate of respiration and stimulates the rate of glycogenesis.

9 a Chemicals from dead leaves could stimulate the fungus to secrete digestive enzymes.

b The surface area to volume ratio of mould fungus is very large.

10 a The mussels may have chemoreceptors that can detect chemicals present in particles.

b Instead of moving towards food, mussels effectively move food towards themselves, in the feeding current.

c The gills of the mussel have a high surface area to volume ratio.

Chapter 17

1 The movement of blood though lungs and breathing (ventilation) maintain the diffusion gradients.

2 a The left ventricle pumps blood all round body, whereas the right ventricle only pumps blood the short distance to the lungs.

b Some oxygenated blood could return to the heart when the heart muscles relax, because the valve can no longer prevent the backflow of blood.

3 a 60/0.8 = 75.

b (i) The contraction of the ventricles forcing blood against them causes the atrioventricular valves to close;
(ii) the contraction of the ventricles forcing blood against them causes the semilunar valves

to open;
(iii) ventricular diastole, and the (potential) backflow of blood against them, causes the semilunar valves to close;
(iv) the contraction of the atria forcing blood against them causes the atrioventricular valves to open.

4 They all have endothelial cells.

5 Vasoconstriction reduces the blood flow to an organ.

6 a Fenestrations may be found in the lungs and kidneys because both are organs where a high rate of exchange of materials with circulating blood is required.

b The size of the capillaries gives them a very large surface area to volume ratio, which maximises the rate of diffusion of substances into and out of the blood. The slow rate of flow also maximises the rate of exchange of materials.

7 a The capillaries have a total cross-sectional area much greater than that of the arterioles.

b The velocity increases because the larger veins have a total cross-sectional area much smaller than that of the small veins.

8 A doctor can interpret changes to different parts of the ECG to locate the probable site of the damage in the heart. This can therefore be done without an operation.

9 A rise in heartbeat rate would provide a greater rate of delivery of oxygen to muscles, a greater rate of aerobic respiration and therefore energy transfer, and a greater rate of removal of carbon dioxide and heat.

10 a An increase in blood pressure will slow the rate of heartbeat because the cardioinhibitory centre will initiate impulses that inhibit impulse production by the cardioacceleratory centre.

b This will lower the blood pressure.

c (i) Sympathetic impulses will cause the release of noradrenaline, which in turn will cause the sinoatrial node to increase its output of impulses;

(ii) parasympathetic impulses will cause the release of acetylcholine, which in turn will cause a reduction in the output of impulses by the sinoatrial node. The arterioles will vasocontrict.

11 The plasma protein molecules are too large to pass through the capillary membrane.

12

Blood	Plasma	Tissue fluid	Lymph	Serum
Contains red cells, white cells and platelets	Suspends red cells, white cells and platelets	May contain white cells	Contains white cells	Contains no cells or platelets
Contains soluble proteins	Contains soluble proteins	Contains no soluble proteins	May contain soluble proteins	Contains soluble proteins

13 Reasons against paying could include that it may increase the number of people who are desparate for money, e.g. drug addict donors with an increased risk of infected blood, donating. Reasons against selling blood could include that poorer people may not be able to afford blood. Volunteer donors may also object to the selling of the blood they have given for free.

14 a At that part of the curve, haemoglobin is fully saturated with oxygen even if the oxygen content of inspired air falls significantly.

b So that the oxyhaemoglobin will dissociate and release its oxygen rapidly.

15 If the curve is in this position, even more oxygen is released into the muscle from oxyhaemoglobin.

16 *Tubifex* can fully oxygenate its haemoglobin at low external oxygen concentrations, but still release oxygen to its muscles.

17 Because the carbon dioxide is not carried inside the red cells, the amount of carbonic anhydrase enzyme present in the reduced number of cells is sufficient to convert the carbon dioxide to hydrogencarbonate ions.

Chapter 18

1 Plasma contains proteins and suspended blood cells, whereas tissue fluid does not.

2 a

Substance	Percentage of filtered load reabsorbed
Sodium	99.4
Potassium	86.1
Calcium	98.1
Hydrogencarbonate	97.6
Chloride	99.2
Glucose	99.9
Urea	50

   b Glucose is needed by the body, urea is a waste product.

3 a Active uptake is the most likely mechanism involved in the reabsorption of glucose and sodium because it occurs ultimately against a diffusion gradient.

   b Some urea passes back into the blood along a diffusion gradient because plasma and filtrate levels are unequal.

4 a Microvilli in the proximal tubule cells provide a greater surface area for absorption, and abundant mitochondria are present to transfer the energy required for active uptake.

   b The water potential of the filtrate will become less negative than that of the blood. This will cause a net diffusion of water into the blood, from a region of less negative water potential to a region of more negative water potential.

5 The sun bathers are more likely to have hypertonic urine because their bodies will be losing water in sweat; the people drinking at a café will be more likely to have hypotonic urine because of their high water intake.

6

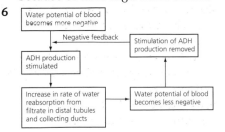

7 a An increase in sodium chloride will make the water potential of the blood more negative.

   b It will cause an increase in blood pressure that might stimulate some filtration in the kidneys, resulting in excretions of toxins such as urea.

8 Vasodilation of the afferent arteriole and vasoconstriction of the efferent arteriole will increase the rate of glomerular filtration. Inhibition of aldosterone and ADH will increase the volume of water and amount of sodium chloride in the urine and so help to flush out any toxins in the body.

9

Hydrochloric acid *Strong acid* + disodium hydrogen phosphate *weak base of buffer* → sodium chloride + sodium dihydrogen phosphate *weak acid*

Sodium hydroxide *Strong base* + sodium dihydrogen phosphate *weak acid of buffer* → water + disodium hydrogen phosphate *weak base*

10 The water potential of the blood is more negative than that of the water flowing over the gills. As the water flowing over the gills is continually replaced, water can continually diffuse into the blood.

Glossary

ABA – Abscisic acid A plant hormone with several functions, including the promotion of leaf fall and closing of the stomata during periods of water stress 160

Acetylcoenzyme A The compound formed when coenzyme A accepts the 2-carbon fragment produced by the oxidative decarboxylation of pyruvic acid during respiration 24

Acidosis A condition people can suffer from if they have too many hydrogen ions in the blood 215

Activation energy The minimum kinetic energy required to overcome the repulsion between molecules so that a reaction will take place between them 29

Active site The part of an enzyme where a substrate molecule is temporarily bound during a chemical reaction 30

Active transport The movement of materials across a membrane, by intrinsic protein molecules, requiring the transfer of energy from respiration 53

Acute renal failure A condition where the kidney suddenly stops working 208

Adenine One of the four bases in the nucleotides of DNA and RNA 80

ADH – Antidiuretic hormone A hormone involved in the control of the volume and water potential of urine 213

ADP – Adenosine diphosphate A molecule that links with inorganic phosphate to form ATP 19

Aerobic A situation where there is sufficient oxygen for respiration 170

Afferent fibres Nerve cells which transmit impulses from receptors to the brain/spinal cord 69

Aldosterone A hormone involved in the control of the sodium chloride content of the blood 214

Allele One of two or more different versions of a gene. Different alleles of a gene have slightly different sequences of nucleotide bases 85

Alveoli Tiny air sacs on the lungs where gaseous exchange takes place 171

Amino acids Monomers which join together in large numbers to form large molecules called proteins (polymers); each amino acid contains an amino group ($-NH_2$) and an acid group ($-COOH$) 10

Ammonia A nitrogenous excretory compound formed when the liver deaminates amino acids 208

Ammonification The conversion of nitrogen-containing compounds in the remains of living organisms into ammonium compounds by bacteria and a fungi 63

Amylase An enzyme which converts starch into sugars by hydrolysis 159

Anaemia A condition resulting in a low red blood cell count 200

Anaerobic A situation where there is insufficient oxygen for respiration 170

Angina A pain resulting from oxygen starvation of heart muscle 193

Angiotensin A hormone important in the control of the sodium chloride level in the blood 214

Antibodies Chemicals produced by the body to attack foreign chemicals, usually proteins 201

Anti-coagulant A substance which prevents blood clotting 202

Anticodon The sequence of three bases on a tRNA molecule which joins to a codon on a mRNA molecule during translation 89

Antigen A molecule, often a foreign protein, that stimulates the immune system of an organism to produce an antibody 121

Aortic body A group of chemoreceptor cells next to the wall of the aorta 174

Apoplast A pathway through plants comprising cell walls and intercellular spaces 163

Arid Dry 161

Arterioles Small blood vessels that subdivide to form capillaries 195

Asexual reproduction Form of reproduction in which a single parent organism produces offspring which are genetically identical to itself 94

Atheroma A fatty deposit in the wall of a blood vessel 193

Atom The smallest part of an element, usually consisting of a small central nucleus around which there are electrons 18

ATP – Adenosine triphosphate A molecule used as a temporary energy store in both photosynthesis and respiration. Energy is stored in a bond linking adenosine diphosphate and inorganic phosphate ($ATP \rightleftharpoons ADP + P_i + energy$) 19

Atrial systole Contraction of the muscles of the atria of the heart 194

Atrioventricular node A group of cells in the heart concerned with the beating of the heart 198

Atrioventricular valve A valve in the heart that prevents backflow of blood into the atria 193

Atrium An upper chamber of the human heart 193

Balloon angioplasty A technique to unblock blocked blood vessels 194

Base pair In a DNA molecule, the combination of two bases in complementary strands, either adenine and thymine, or cytosine and guanine 82

Bile A liquid produced by the liver 184

Bile canaliculi Tiny tubes in the liver into which bile is secreted 186

Biological control The use of a predator or parasite to kill a pest 148

Biomass The mass of materials in the bodies of organisms 57

Blastocyst A ball of cells resulting from several divisions of a fertilised egg cell 76

Blood plasma The liquid part of blood in which the blood cells are suspended 47

Bond The area of overlap of electron orbits between two chemically linked atoms 18

Bowman's capsule Part of the nephrons of a kidney 209

Breed A particular variety of a domesticated animal, such as a dog or cat, which has certain selected characteristics 133

Bronchiole A subdivision of the bronchus 171

Bronchus The large tube carrying air into and out of the lungs 171

Buffer system A mixture, usually consisting of a weak acid and a weak base, which maintains a relatively constant pH 215

Bulliform cells Cells which change shape and so cause leaves to roll or unroll in different levels of humidity 162

Bundle of His A collection of nerve fibres in the heart concerned with the beating of the heart 198

CAM – Crassulacean acid metabolism A special type of photosynthesis in which carbon dioxide is absorbed during the night, stored as malic acid, then utilised during the day 161

Capillaries Microscopic blood vessels found around tissue cells 195

Carbonic anhydrase An enzyme which speeds up the dissociation of carbonic acid 205

Cardioacceleratory centre A group of cells in the medulla oblongata of the brain which sends impulses to the heart to speed up the rate of heartbeat 199

Cardioinhibitory centre A group of cells in the medulla oblongata of the brain which sends impulses to the heart to slow down the rate of heartbeat 199

Carnivore An animal which eats other animals 58

Carotid body A group of chemoreceptor cells next to a carotid artery 174

Carotid sinus A group of stretch receptor cells in a carotid artery 199

Casparian strip A ring of endodermal cells around the xylem and phloem of the root that contains suberin 165

Catalyst A substance that, in effect, lowers the activation energy required for a reaction and remains unchanged at the end of the reaction 30

Central receptors Nerve cells in the brain which are sensitive to chemical changes 174

Centrifuge An instrument which spins samples round at high speed. It can be used to separate organelles, using the principle that organelles with a higher mass settle (sediment) at lower spinning speeds than those with lower masses 39

Centromere The point at which the two chromatids are joined during the early stages of cell division, and where the spindle fibres attach 94

Chemical digestion Hydrolysis of food polymers into monomers 183

Chemiosmotic channels A channel through a membrane which can transfer energy from moving molecules to other reactions in photosynthesis and respiration 19

Chemoreceptor A nerve cell(s) sensitive to chemical changes 174

Chlorophyll *a* A green-coloured molecule, found in most organisms which photosynthesise, which can trap light energy 17

Chloroplast A cell organelle in green plants in which the light-dependent reactions of photosynthesis take place 40

Cholecystokinin A hormone with a number of effects which promote digestion in the duodenum 188

Chromatid One of the two strands of a chromosome seen during the early stages of cell division 94

Chromatin The DNA molecules present in the nucleus of cells that are not dividing. It stains as a dark mass of material but without visible chromosomes 37

Chromosome One of the thread-like structures in a nucleus, consisting of a long chain of genes. Chromosomes become visible during cell division 93

Chylomicrons Droplets, resulting from the digestion of fats, containing triglycerides and phospholipids 186

Cilia Tiny hair-like projections on the surface of a cell 191

Class A large classification group comprising several orders 139

Climax community The community of organisms that develops in an area of land when it remains untouched by human activity. In most places in the UK this is forest 153

Clone Genetically identical cells or individuals produced by asexual reproduction 101

Codominant Two alleles that both produce a functional protein. Therefore the phenotype of the heterozygote may be different from that of either homozygote 105

Codon A sequence of three bases on a mRNA molecule to which a tRNA molecule attaches, thus assembling the amino acids in the correct order during protein synthesis 89

Coenzyme A A compound which accepts the 2-carbon fragment produced by the oxidative decarboxylation of pyruvic acid in respiration to form acetylcoenzyme A 24

Cohesion-tension mechanism The mechanism resulting in water being pulled up the xylem of a plant when water evaporates from the leaves 165

Collecting duct Part of the nephrons of a kidney 211

Community Populations of organisms living together in a particular habitat 146

Competitive inhibition Inhibition occurring when molecules with a similar shape to substrate molecules occupy the active sites of enzymes and so prevent access by substrate molecules 33

Compound A substance in which atoms of two or more elements are chemically combined 18

Concentration gradient A difference in concentration of a substance between two areas 48

Condensation A reaction in which two molecules are joined together by the loss of two hydrogen atoms and one oxygen atom (two hydrogen atoms and one oxygen atom are effectively one molecule of water) 8

Continuous variation Genetic variation in which a characteristic has a range of values on an unbroken scale, such as height or weight 122

Coordinator The part of the brain/spinal cord which receives impulses from receptors and transmits impulses to the appropriate effectors 69

Corpus luteum A group of cells in the ovary which secrete hormones after the release of an egg and during pregnancy 74

Countercurrent flow Two liquids flowing past each other in opposite directions to maximise the rate of exchange between them 177

Cristae Folds of the inner membrane in mitochondria. Cristae increase the surface area available for the proton pumps of respiration 42

Cytosine One of the four bases in the nucleotides of DNA and RNA 80

Cytosol The liquid part of cytoplasm in a cell 38, 185

Deamination Excess amino acids are converted to organic acids and ammonia in the liver 187

Denatured Changing the tertiary structure of a protein molecule and so its three-dimensional shape. This can cause proteins to come out of suspension and prevent substrates from binding to the active site of enzymes 31

Denitrification The breakdown of nitrogenous materials resulting in the release of nitrogen gas 63

Deoxygenated Having low oxygen and high carbon dioxide levels 194

Deoxyribose The sugar in the nucleic acid, DNA 80

Desiccation Drying out 158

Detritivores Animals which feed on dead material and excretory material 62

Diaphragm The layer of muscle below the ribs and above the gut 170

Diastole Relaxation of the heart muscle 194

Dicotyledonous A plant that germinates to produce two cotyledons 164

Differential centrifugation Using a centrifuge to separate particles of different masses by collecting sediments produced at different spin speeds 39

Differentially permeable membrane A membrane which allows some substances to pass through but not others 48

Diffusion The spread of particles from areas of high concentration to areas of low concentration. Diffusion is a passive process caused by the random movement of molecules 48

Dihybrid Cross between individuals which differ by two characteristics, e.g. tall, white-flowered plants and short, red-flowered ones 109

Diploid A nucleus with the chromosomes in homologous pairs (2n) 94

Disaccharide A sugar consisting of two single sugar molecules (monomers) joined together by a condensation reaction 8

Discontinuous variation Genetic variation in which a characteristic has a small number of distinct forms, e.g. blue and brown eyes 121

Dissociation curve A curve which shows the percentage of a substance which dissociates (breaks up) under varying conditions 204

Distal tubule Part of the nephrons of a kidney 211

DNA – Deoxyribonucleic acid The substance of which genes are made. DNA molecules carry the code for inherited information 80

DNA polymerase The enzyme that fits the nucleotides together in the replication of DNA 82

Dominant When an individual has two different alleles of the same gene, the dominant allele is the one that takes effect in the phenotype 104

ECG – Electrocardiograph An instrument which records the electrical impulses produced by the heart 198

Ecosystem An ecosystem is made up of one or more communities and the interactions between them and the environment 150

Effectors Parts of the body which bring about responses (to stimuli), e.g. muscles, glands 69

Efferent fibres Nerve cells that transmit impulses from the brain/spinal cord to effectors, e.g. muscles, glands 69

Electron microscope An instrument which uses electron beams and magnetic 'lenses' to produce a magnified image of an object. Sometimes abbreviated to EM 35

Electrons Very small, negatively charged particles orbiting the nucleus of atoms. Electrons are involved in the chemical reactions of atoms 18

Endocrine gland A gland which secretes hormones into the bloodstream 72

Endometrium The inner lining of the uterus which is shed during menstruation 76

Endopeptidase A protein-digesting enzyme which breaks proteins in two rather than removing the amino acids one by one 184

Endoplasmic reticulum A series of phospholipid membranes extending throughout most of a cell. Often abbreviated to ER 38

Endothelial cells Cells which line an internal tissue 172

Environment The conditions surrounding an organism 144

Enzyme A protein molecule that is able to catalyse reactions within living organisms 30

Enzyme–substrate complex The temporary compound formed when a substrate molecule links with an active site of an enzyme during a reaction 30

Epidermal Pertaining to the epidermis – the covering layer of cells 161

Epidermis The outer protective layer of the skin 129

Essential amino acid An amino acid needed in the diet since it cannot be made from other amino acids 10

Essential fatty acid A fatty acid needed in the diet since it cannot be made from other fatty acids 13

Eukaryotes Organisms with membrane-bound organelles inside their cells 43

Evolution The process by which living organisms change over a period of

time as they are modified by natural selection to changing conditions 138

Exopeptidase A protein-digesting enzyme which removes the final amino acid from the chain 184

Expiration Breathing out 170

Extracellular Anything that occurs outside a cell 184

Extrinsic membrane proteins Protein molecules on the outer surface of the plasma membrane 39

Facilitated diffusion Movement across a cell membrane facilitated by a specific, intrinsic protein molecule. No energy is required 52

FAD⁺ – Flavine adenine dinucleotide A compound which accepts electrons in the redox reactions of respiration, to be reduced to FADH 24

Fallopian tube A tube which conveys eggs from the ovary to the uterus 75

Family Classification group comprising a small number of related genera 138

Feeding current A current of water drawn into an animal, bringing with it suspended food particles 191

Fenestrations Gaps between adjacent cells allowing materials to pass easily between them 196

Fertilisation The fusing of the nuclei of two gametes during sexual reproduction 94

Fibrinogen A protein in blood concerned in the clotting process 202

Flagellum A long 'whip-like' structure used for locomotion by some single-celled organisms 43

Follicle cells Cells which surround a developing egg cell in the ovary 74

Food chain A diagram showing how energy passes from primary producers to the top carnivores in an area 58

Food web A diagram which shows the feeding relationships of the organisms in an area 59

FSH – Follicle-stimulating hormone A hormone, produced by the pituitary gland, which stimulates a group of follicle cells in the ovary to grow and divide 74

Gamete A sex cell, such as an ovum or sperm 94

Gaseous exchange The movement of gases, or dissolved gases, into and out of blood or cells 172

Gastrin An enzyme which encourages the stomach to produce acid and digestive enzymes 188

Gene mutation A change in the sequence of the nucleotide bases in the DNA of a gene, which causes a change in the genetic code 85

Genetic divergence Increasing differences in the genetic composition of isolated populations of a species due to the effects of different selection pressures 136

Genetic engineering Artificially changing an organism's genetic material, e.g. inserting a human gene into a bacterium 116

Genetic variation The variation in a population caused by different alleles 136

Genotype The allelic composition of the genes of an individual, either for one or more characteristics. For one pair of genes the genotype may be either homozygous or heterozygous 104

Genus (plural genera) Classification group comprising a small number of closely related species 138

Gills The respiratory organs in fish and some other animal phyla 177

Gland An organ in the body that produces a secretion 184

Global warming The increase in the mean temperature of the Earth probably brought about by increased 'trapping' of energy from the Sun by gases in the atmosphere. Sometimes called the 'greenhouse effect' 56

Glucagon A hormone produced by the pancreas, effective in raising blood sugar levels 188

Gluconeogenesis The break down of triglycerides and proteins to release glucose for respiration 188

Glyceraldehyde-3-phosphate A sugar molecule in the light-independent reactions of photosynthesis 21

Glycerate-3-phosphate A molecule in the light-independent reactions of photosynthesis 21

Glycogenesis The conversion of glucose to glycogen in the liver 188

Glycogenolysis The conversion of glyocgen to glucose in the liver 188

Glycolysis The first series of reactions in respiration. A molecule of glucose is eventually split into two molecules of glyceraldehyde 3-phosphate, each of which is then oxidised to pyruvic acid 24

GnRH – Gonadotrophin–releasing hormone A hormone, secreted by the hypothalamus, that stimulates the secretion of FSH in the pituitary gland 74

Granulosar cells Cells in the follicles, in the ovary, that secrete hormones such as oestrogen 74

Greenhouse gas A gas which, on entering the atmosphere, enhances global warming by 'trapping' heat energy 56

Guanine One of the four bases in the nucleotides of DNA and RNA 80

Guard cells Pairs of cells that surround stoma 158

Habitat The type of place where a particular species lives, such as pond, woodland, desert 144

Haemoglobin A chemical found in red blood cells involved in the transport of oxygen and carbon dioxide 204

Haemorrhaging Losing large amounts of blood from a wound 195

Hair erection Contraction of muscles attached to the roots of hairs which pulls the hair shaft upright 71

Haploid A nucleus with only a single set of chromosomes, one from each homologous pair (n) 94

HCG – Human chorionic gonadotrophin A hormone, produced by the placenta, with several effects during pregnancy 77

Heat gain centre A region in the hypothalamus of the brain which controls the processes which result in the body conserving heat 69

Heat loss centre A region in the hypothalamus of the brain which controls the processes which result in the body losing heat 69

Hemicellulose A complex carbohydrate that is a major component of primary cell walls 43

Herbivore An organism which eats plants 58

Heterozygous Having two different alleles of a particular gene 105

Homeostasis The processes which maintain a constant internal environment in organisms 68

Homogenate The suspension of organelles produced when cells are broken up in a homogeniser 40

Homogeniser An instrument used to break up cells so that all the organelles are brought into a suspension 40

Homologous chromosomes A pair of chromosomes with the same sequence of genes in a diploid nucleus 94

Homozygous Having two identical alleles of a particular gene 105

Hormones Chemicals, secreted by endocrine glands, which control processes in the body 72

HRT – Hormone replacement therapy A treatment involving giving hormones such as oestrogens to women who have ceased to produce them naturally 77

Humus Partially decomposed organic matter in the soil 151

Hybrid The offspring of a cross between closely related species or breeds 133

Hydrogencarbonate system A buffer system containing sodium hydrogencarbonate (a weak base) and carbonic acid (a weak acid) 215

Hydrolysis Breaking apart a large molecule to release smaller molecules by reacting it with water. The opposite process to condensation 29

Hydrophilic 'Water-loving' – a molecule or part of a molecule which can mix with water 13

Hydrophobic 'Water-hating' – a molecule or part of a molecule which will not mix with water 13

Hydrotropic Growth of a plant or part of a plant towards water 163

Hyperglycaemia High blood sugar levels 189

Hypertonic A solution that has a lower concentration of water molecules than another solution 48

Hyphae Strands of the fungal cell body 190

Hypoglycaemia Low blood sugar levels 189

Hypothalamus A region at the base of the brain important in controlling many homeostatic processes 68

Hypotonic A solution that has a higher concentration of water molecules than another solution 48

Hypoxia A condition in which the concentration of oxygen in the blood is too low 175

Inspiration Breathing in 170

Inspiratory Anything concerned with breathing in 173

Insulin A hormone produced by the pancreas, effective in lowering blood sugar levels 188

Interbreed To mate and reproduce sexually, usually between different breeds, occassionally between species 133

Intercostal Between the ribs, particularly the intercostal muscles which act between the ribs to raise and lower the rib cage 170

Interspecific competition Competition for resources between individuals of different species 146

Intracellular Anything that occurs inside a cell 185

Intraspecific competition Competition for resources between individuals within a species 145

Intrinsic membrane proteins Protein molecules held within a plasma membrane 39

Ionise To gain or loose electrons and so develop an electrical charge on an atom or molecule 19

Islet cells Groups of cells in the pancreas which synthesise insulin and glucagon 188

Isolation Separation of populations, either physically, e.g. on islands, or genetically so that there is no mixing of genes 136

Isotonic Two solutions are isotonic if they have the same water potential 47

Karyotype The number, appearance and arrangement of the chromosomes of an individual 94

Kinetic energy Energy present in a body due to the body's movement 29

Kingdom Living organisms are classified into five kingdoms: animals, plants, fungi, protoctists (including unicells and algae) and prokaryotes (including bacteria) 139

Krebs cycle A series of oxidative decarboxylation reactions occurring in cells during respiration 25

Lacteals Branches of lymph vessels which pass into the villi of the small intestine 186

Lactic acid A chemical produced during anaerobic respiration when pyruvic acid accepts NADH rather than being oxidatively decarboxylated 170

LH – Luteinising hormone A hormone, secreted by the pituitary gland, whose main function is to stimulate the release of an egg from a follicle 74

Ligase Enzyme used in genetic engineering techniques to link sections of DNA together, e.g. to insert a gene into a bacterial plasmid 116

Light microscope An instrument in which light rays are passed through lenses to produce a magnified image of an object 35

Light-dependent reactions A series of reactions of photosynthesis which provide the energy and electrons needed to reduce carbon dioxide to carbohydrate in the later, light-independent, reactions of photosynthesis. The light-dependent reactions only occur in the light 18

Light-independent reactions A series of reactions of photosynthesis in which energy and electrons, from the light-dependent reactions of photosynthesis, are used to reduce carbon dioxide to carbohydrate. The light-independent reactions can occur in dark and light conditions 21

Lignin A complex carbohydrate molecule used to strengthen the xylem vessels of woody plants 165

Linkage Genes that are on the same chromosome 113

Lipase An enzyme which hydrolyses lipids 184

Lipid A molecule produced by attaching molecules, including fatty acids, to glycerol molecules by condensation reactions 12

Locus The position on a chromosome occupied by a gene 104

Loop of Henle Part of the nephrons of a kidney 211

Lumen The space inside an enclosed area, e.g. the lumen of the mitochondria or the gut 42, 183

Lymph A fluid, derived from tissue fluid, which drains from the tissues into lymph vessels 202

Lymph vessels Vessels which help to drain tissue fluid and return it to the blood 186

Malpighian tubules Excretory organs found in insects 216

Maltase An enzyme that breaks down maltose into glucose 184

Mass flow hypothesis An explanation of the movement of organic materials through the phloem vessels of plants 167

Maximum breathing capacity The maximum amount of air that can be moved in and out of the lungs over a period of time 171

Mechanical digestion Breakdown of food into smaller pieces not involving chemical reaction 183

Medulla oblongata The part of the brain which controls many unconscious activities such as breathing and heartbeat 173

Meiosis The process of cell division, occurring during gamete formation, in which the number of chromosomes in the nucleus is halved. Each daughter nucleus has only one of each pair of homologous chromosomes 94

Melanin A black pigment found in skin and hair 129

Mesosomes Folds of cell membrane in bacteria which increase the surface area within the cell 43

Microfibrils Microscopic fibres made up from long polymers, e.g. cellulose microfibrils made up of cellulose molecules 43

Microvilli Tiny projections on the wall of a cell which increase its surface area 185

Mitochondria Organelles which are the site of many of the reactions which make up respiration in eukaryotes 41

Mitosis Cell division in which all the chromosomes are copied and each daughter cell has the same number of chromosomes as the parent cell 100

Monohybrid Cross between individuals which differ in a single characteristic, e.g. tall/short plants 108

Monomers Small molecules which join in large numbers to form large molecules called polymers 7

Monosaccharides Single sugar molecules (monomers) which can join together in large numbers to form large carbohydrate molecules called polysaccharides (polymers) 8

mRNA – Messenger RNA Strand of ribonucleic acid which copies the code in the DNA of a gene. mRNA then passes out of the nucleus to a ribosome, where it provides the coded information to make a section of protein 88

Mucosa The inner layer of the gut wall 183

Mutagen A substance or agent, such as radiation, which increases the rate of gene mutation 86

Mutualism A close relationship between different species in which both benefit 63

Myocardial infarction A heart attack, caused by a blockage in the blood supply to part of the heart muscle 193

NAD⁺ – Nicotinamide adenine dinucleotide A compound which accepts electrons in the redox reactions of respiration, becoming reduced to NADH 24

NADP⁺ – Nicotinamide adenine dinucleotide phosphate A compound which accepts excited electrons in the light-dependent reactions of photosynthesis, becoming reduced to NADPH. These electrons are then used to reduce carbon dioxide in the light-independent reactions of photosynthesis 19

Native population A population of a species that has been long established in a particular area or habitat, and that may be affected by the introduction of new species 122

Natural selection Darwin's theory that species evolve because individuals with favourable, inherited characteristics are more likely to survive than those with unfavourable ones 126

Negative feedback A system where the outputs tend to reduce the inputs. This tends to stabilise the system 75

Nephrons The microscopic working units of the kidney 208

Net primary productivity The amount of energy captured by plants in an ecosystem minus the amount of energy transferred by their respiration 61

Net productivity The amount of stored energy that is available to the organisms at higher trophic levels in an ecosystem 60

Neutrons Nuclear particles which have a mass of one atomic mass unit but no charge 18

Nitrification The conversion of ammonium compounds to nitrates by a chain of bacterial species 63

Nitrogen fixation The incorporation of nitrogen gas into nitrogen compounds 63

Non-competitive inhibition Inhibition occurring when molecules attach to enzyme molecules, at positions other than active sites, distorting the shape of the active sites and thus preventing the formation of enzyme–substrate complexes 33

Noradrenaline A hormone with a range of effects including heat control 72

Nuclear membrane The double-layered membrane surrounding the nucleus in eukaryotes 37

Nucleic acid DNA and RNA, the molecules that carry genetic information in long chains of nucleotides 80

Nucleoid The collection of DNA strands found in prokaryotes.

Prokaryotes do not have a membrane-bound nucleus 43

Nucleolus An area of the nucleus concerned with the production of RNA 37

Nucleotide One of the monomers in DNA or RNA, consisting of a sugar (deoxyribose or ribose), a phosphate group and a base 80

Nucleus An organelle containing the genetic information required to control the activities of the cell 37

Oestrogens Hormones, secreted by follicle cells in the ovary, which have several effects in the menstrual cycle 74

Omnivore An animal which can eat both plants and animals 59

Optimum pH The pH which produces the maximum rate of reaction 32

Optimum temperature The temperature which produces the maximum rate of reaction 31

Order Classification group comprising related families 138

Organ A structure in which the activities of a number of different tissues are integrated to carry out a particular process 35

Organelle An area in the cell which carries out a particular function 35

Organic A chemical containing hydrogen and carbon. Organic chemicals have typically been produced by living organisms 21

Ornithine cycle A series of reactions in the liver in which ammonia is converted into urea 208

Osmosis When water passes from a region of higher concentration of water molecules to a region of lower concentration of water molecules through a differentially permeable membrane 48

Ovum The female gamete 97

Oxidation A reaction in which electrons or hydrogen are taken away from or oxygen is added to an atom or compound 18

Oxidative decarboxylation A reaction in which both carbon dioxide and electrons are removed from a compound 24

Oxidised An atom or compound which has had electrons or hydrogen taken away or oxygen added 18

Oxygenated Having high oxygen and low carbon dioxide levels 194

Pectins A group of soluble polysaccharides which are important in plant cell walls 43

Pedicels The processes of podocytes that have gaps between them 209

Peptide A molecule made by joining at least two amino acid molecules (monomers) together by means of condensation reactions forming peptide bonds 10

Peripheral receptors Receptor cells in parts of the body other than the brain and the spinal cord 174

Peristalsis Muscular contractions in the gut wall that move food along the gut 183

Petioles The stalk that joins a leaf blade to the main stem 162

Phenotype The actual effect of the genes of an individual for one charateristic (or set of characteristics). The phenotype is determined by both the genes that an individual has and the environment in which it develops 104

Phloem A plant tissue mainly concerned with the transport of ions and organic substances 166

Phosphate system A buffer system containing the weak acid sodium dihydrogen phosphate and the weak base disodium hydrogen phosphate 215

Phospholipid A triglyceride molecule consisting of two fatty acid molecules and one phosphoric acid molecule joined to a glycerol molecule by condensation reactions 12

Phospholipid membranes Membranes consisting of two layers of phospholipid molecules which form the outer membranes of cells, the outer layer of many organelles and the endoplasmic reticulum 38

Phosphorylase An enzyme that converts sugars into starch by condensation 159

Photolysis The splitting of water using light energy during photosynthesis 19

Photosynthesis A process in which organisms use light energy to produce carbohydrates, usually from carbon dioxide and water 17

Phylogenetic classification A system in which organisms are grouped on the basis of the evolutionary history of each species 139

Phylum The largest classification group within the animal and plant kingdoms 139

Pituitary gland A gland at the base of the hypothalamus that secretes many different hormones 74

Placenta The organ that manages the exchange of materials between the mother and fetus 76

Plasmid A small, ring-shaped DNA molecule in the cytoplasm of bacteria 116

Plasmodesmata Minute strands of cytoplasm, passing through cell walls, which 'connect' the living parts of adjacent plant cells 163

Podocytes Cells that make up the inner layer of the Bowman's capsule 209

Polymers Large molecules formed when many small molecules, called monomers, join together 7

Polynucleotide Long chain of nucleotide monomers joined together, as in DNA and RNA 80

Polypeptide A polymer molecule consisting of large numbers of amino acids (monomers) joined by condensation reactions forming peptide bonds 11

Polysaccharide A polymer molecule made by joining large numbers of monosaccharides (monomers) together by condensation reactions 8

Population The group of individuals of the same species that live in a particular area 144

Positive feedback A system where the outputs increase the inputs. This can make the system unstable 75

Pressure potential The pressure exerted on cell contents by the cell membrane 50

Primary cell wall The cell wall laid down when a cell is produced by cell

division. It is made up largely of cellulose microfibrils and complex carbohydrates called hemicelluloses 43

Primary consumer An organism which eats plants 58

Primary oocyte Cells in the ovaries which have the potential to develop into egg cells 74

Primary structure of a protein The sequence of amino acids in a polypeptide chain 10

Producers The organisms in an ecosystem that fix atmospheric carbon dioxide to produce complex organic matter. Sometimes called primary producers 58

Productivity The rate at which energy entering an ecosystem is stored 60

Progesterones Hormones, secreted by follicle cells in the ovary, which have several effects in the menstrual cycle 75

Prokaryotes Organisms whose nucleic acid molecules are not contained inside a nuclear membrane, e.g. bacteria and cyanobacteria 43

Protease An enzyme which hydrolyses long polypeptide polymers into shorter polymers or into amino acids 29

Proton pumps Proteins in plasma membranes which can move protons across the membrane against a concentration gradient 19

Protons Particles in the nucleus that have a charge of plus one and a mass of one atomic mass unit. Hydrogen atoms with electrons removed are often regarded as protons 18

Protozoans Single-celled organisms 217

Proximal tubule Part of the nephrons of a kidney 210

Punnett square A chart to show the results of a dihybrid cross between heterozygotes 111

Purkyne fibres Fibres in the walls of the ventricles concerned with the control of the heartbeat 198

Race A population within a species that shares certain distinctive features, usually due to a small number of specific alleles 130

Receptors Cells which can sense changes in the environment 69

Recessive A recessive allele is one that only takes effect in the phenotype if the dominant member of the pair is not present 104

Redox When one atom is reduced another is usually oxidised. The pair of reactions is thus known as a redox pair 18

Reduced An atom or compound which has had electrons or hydrogen added or oxygen removed 18

Reduction A reaction in which electrons or hydrogen are added to an atom or compound or oxygen is removed 18

Renin A hormone important in the control of the sodium chloride level in the blood 214

Resolving power The power, e.g. of a microscope, to distinguish between two objects 35

Respiration A series of oxidation reactions in which energy is transferred from organic compounds, such as carbohydrates, to the temporary storage compound ATP 23

Respiratory surface Where oxygen passes into blood or cells, and carbon dioxide passes out of blood or cells 172

Restriction endonucleases Enzymes used in genetic engineering techniques to cut DNA molecules at specific points 116

Ribose The sugar in the nucleic acid RNA 88

Ribulose biphosphate An acceptor molecule used to fix carbon dioxide in the light-independent reactions of photosynthesis 21

Ribulose biphosphate carboxylase An enzyme which catalyses the fixation of carbon dioxide in the light-independent reactions of photosynthesis 21

RNA – Ribonucleic acid The single-stranded nucleic acid involved in the synthesis of proteins from the DNA in genes 88

RNA polymerase An enzyme that joins the nucleotides together and forms mRNA during transcription. The

nucleotides are assembled alongside a strand of the DNA of a gene 88

Saturated fatty acid A fatty acid in which all the carbon atoms in the carbon chain are joined to each other by single bonds 12

Secondary cell wall Additional layers to the primary wall laid down as cells mature, often containing other compounds such as lignin for additional strength 43

Secondary consumer An organism which eats primary consumers (herbivores) 58

Secondary lamellae The part of the gill in fish where gases pass into and out of the blood 177

Secondary structure of proteins The shape of a constituent polypeptide molecule, e.g. α helix or β pleating, maintained by weak chemical bonds, e.g. hydrogen bonds 11

Secretin A hormone which encourages the pancreas to produce digestive juices 188

Sedentary Staying in one place 191

Selective reabsorption Active uptake into the blood of substances needed by the body from the fluid filtered by the kidneys 210

Semi-conservative mechanism The process in which one strand of DNA is preserved during the replication of DNA, with a new strand being formed alongside it 83

Semilumar valve A valve in the heart that prevents the backflow of blood into the ventricles 193

Serum Blood plasma which has had the 'clotting' protein fibrinogen removed 202

Sex chromosome One of the X or Y chromosomes carrying the genetic information which determines whether an individual is male or female 93

Sexual reproduction Form of reproduction in which the genes from two individual organisms are combined, producing offspring that differ from the parent and each other 94

Sinoatrial node A group of cells in the wall of the right atrium of the heart which acts as a natural pacemaker 198

Sink The part of a plant that removes a particular product from circulation, usually to store it 166

Sinusoids Spaces through which blood flows through the liver from the hepatice portal vein and hepatic artery to the central vein 186

Solute A dissolved substance 48

Solute potential A measure of the concentration of solutes in a solution on the water potential of the solution. Solute potential always has a negative value 50

Source The part of a plant that manufactures a particular product 166

Speciation The evolution of two or more new species as a result of natural selection in isolated populations of one species 136

Species A group of organisms with similar features that can interbreed to produce fertile offspring and that do not normally interbreed with other groups 133

Sperm The male gamete 97

Spiracles Holes in the abdomen and thorax of insects concerned with ventilation 178

Stomata Holes in leaves which allow gaseous exchange with the atmosphere 158

Stretch receptor A nerve cell(s) that is sensitive to tension 173

Suberin A waxy chemical which acts as a waterproofer in plant cell walls 165

Submucosa The layer in the gut wall immediately below the mucosa layer 183

Substrate molecules The molecules which take part in a reaction 29

Succession The sequence of changes that occurs in a habitat when it is left untouched by human activity until a climax community develops 153

Succulent A tissue in a plant swollen with water, e.g. in a cactus 161

Supernatant When a suspension is spun in a centrifuge it separates into a sediment and an overlying liquid, the supernatant 40

Surface area to volume ratio The surface area of an organism divided by its volume 172

Surface tension The force tending to draw liquids into the smallest possible volume 172

Surfactant A substance that can reduce the surface tension of a liquid 172

Symplast A pathway through a plant involving cytoplasm and vacuoles 163

Territorial behaviour Defence of an area of habitat by an individual. Maintenance of a territory helps to ensure a sufficient supply of food and other resources 145

Tertiary consumers Organisms which eat secondary consumers 59

Tertiary structure of a protein The 3-dimensional shape of the whole protein molecule, held together by weak chemical bonds, e.g. hydrogen bonds and sulphur bonds 11

Thermal panting Increased rate and/or depth of breathing to cool the body, particularly in animals with thick fur coats 70

Thermoregulation Regulation of body temperature 72

Thorax The upper part of the main body, usually called the chest in humans 170

Thrombosis A blood clot blocking a blood vessel 193

Thylakoids The membranes that hold the chemicals needed for the light-dependent reactions of photosynthesis 40

Thymine One of the four bases in the nucleotides of DNA 80

Thyroxine A hormone that influences the rate of respiration 72

Tidal The flow of air in and out of the lungs 170

Tissue A group of similar cells with a common function 35

Tissue fluid A fluid derived from blood plasma which acts an intermediary between blood and tissue cells 201

Tracheae Air tubes in insects used in ventilation that branch to form tracheoles 178

Tracheids Water-conducting cells in woody plants 165

Tracheoles Microscopic tubules that enter the muscle cells of insects and are concerned with ventilation 178

Transamination Transfer of an amino group from one molecule to another 187

Transcription The process in which the genetic code in DNA is copied to produce mRNA 88

Translation The process in which amino acids are joined together to make a section of protein, using the code of mRNA. It takes place on the ribosomes 89

Transpiration Loss of water from a plant by evaporation, largely through the stomata 158

Triglyceride A molecule produced by joining three fatty acid molecules to one molecule of glycerol by condensation reactions 12

tRNA – Transfer RNA Small molecules of ribonucleic acid which join the correct amino acid to a codon on mRNA during protein synthesis 89

Trophic level A group of organisms within a food web that are equal numbers of stages away from primary producers. Trophic level two contains all primary consumers 59

True-breeding When the offspring are the same genotype as the parents 112

Turgid A cell that is full of water 48

Ultrafiltration Filtration brought about by blood pressure 209

Unsaturated fatty acid A fatty acid in which some of the carbon atoms in the carbon chain are joined together by double bonds 12

Uracil The base that replaces the thymine of DNA in the nucleotides of RNA 88

Urates Soluble salts of uric acid 216

Urea The principle nitrogenous waste compound formed from ammonia in the liver and excreted in the urine of mammals 208

Uric acid A relatively insoluble nitrogenous waste product excreted by many insects 216

Uterus The part of the female reproductive system in mammals where the embryo develops during pregnancy 75

Valves In blood vessels these prevent the backflow of blood 196

Vascular tissue Tissue used in

transporting materials, typically made of a collection of tubes 163

Vasoconstriction Constriction (narrowing) of blood vessels 71

Vasodilation Dilation (widening) of blood vessels 69

Vasomotor centre A region of the medulla of the brain involved with regulation of blood pressure 200

Ventilation The movement of air or water over a respiratory surface 170

Ventral group A group of receptor cells near the floor of the medulla oblongata 174

Ventricle A lower chamber of the human heart 193

Ventricular systole Contraction of the muscles of the ventricles of the heart 194

Venules Small blood vessels that join to form veins 195

Vessels The water-conducting cells of plants or any tubular system within an organism 165

Villi Extensions of the small intestine wall 183

Vital capacity The maximum amount of air that can be exhaled from the lungs in one breath 170

Water potential A measure of the ability of water molecules to move. By convention, pure water is given a value of 0 for its water potential and solutions are given a negative value 50

Water stress The situation when an organism is losing more water than it is absorbing 160

Xerophytes Plants adapted to living in very dry conditions 161

Xylem A plant tissue mainly concerned with the transport of water but also important in support 163

Zygote The cell formed when two gametes fuse during fertilisation; a fertilised egg 94

Index

abortion pill (RU486) 73, 76
abscisic acid 160
absorption of food/nutrients 52-3, *see also* reabsorption
  in gut/intestine 52-3, 185
  plants 53-4
acetylcoenzyme A 24
acid–base balance 205, 215, *see also* pH
acidification 154
activation energy 29-30
active transport 53
adenosine deaminase deficiency 118
ADH 213-14
adrenal gland and thermoregulation 72
aerobic respiration 170
agriculture/farming 150-2
  desert reclamation for 157, 168
aldosterone 214
alimentary tract (gut),
  digestion/absorption of food 52-3, 182-7, 189
alleles 85, 104
  animal breeding and 108, 110
  blood group 121
  codominant 105
  dominant 104
  HLA 122
  mutant *see* mutations
  recessive 104
  successful 136
alpha-1-antitrypsin 79, 116
alveoli 171, 172
Amazonia 55
amino acids (protein monomers) 7, 10
  essential 10
  genetic code for 87, 90
ammonia 208
ammonification 63
amylase 159
anaemia 200
anaerobic respiration 170
anaphase 100
angina 192, 193
angioplasty, balloon 194, 195
angiotensin 214
animals *see also specific animals*
  breeding 107-11, 112, 113
  cells of, structure/components 36, 44
  energy flow for individual 61
  grazing 143, 144, 146, 147, 152
  populations 143-56

ANP 207, 208, 214, 217
anticodon 89
antidiuretic hormone (ADH) 213-14
antigens
  blood group 121
  human leucocyte 122
aorta 196, 199
aortic body 174
apoplast 163, 165
arteries 196
arterioles 196
asexual reproduction 94, 97
atheroma 193, 195
athletes and exercise/training 169, 170, 171, 172, 174, 175
atmosphere and cyanobacterial photosynthesis 17
ATP 26
  production
    in photosynthesis 19, 20
    in respiration 25, 170
  role 26
atria 194
atrial natriuretic peptide (ANP) 207, 208, 214, 217

babies
  choosing sex of 99
  diets for 14-15
bacteria
  denitrifying 63
  in genetic engineering 79, 116
  nitrogen-fixing 63
  structure 44
balloon angioplasty 194, 195
Barr body 92, 93
bases of DNA 80, 81
  pairs 81, 82
bean caper 162
beetle, waste removal 216
bile 184, 186
biological control (of populations) 148-9
biomass 57, 60
Biston betularia 126-8
blastocyst 76
blood
  cleaning 208-17
  clotting *see* clotting
  composition 200-1
  flow/circulation 192-7

  kidney 209
  functions 200-01, 203-5
  pressure 195, 196
    receptors 199-200
  sugar (glucose) *see* glucose
  sweating and 47
  transfusion 202, 203
blood clotting disorder 115
blood groups 121-2
blood vessels 194-6
  thermoregulation and 69, 71
Bowman's capsule 209
brain *see* central nervous system
breast feeding 14
breathing 204, *see also* ventilation
  capacity, maximum 171
  definition 170
breeding 107-11
  animal 107-11, 112, 113
  plant 112, 113
bronchi/bronchial tree 171
brown fat 72
buffering 215

cancer 34, 35, 44-5
  cytological tests 35, 45
  mutation and 85
capillaries 194-6
carbohydrate 7, 8-9, 185
  dietary 181
    digestion 182, 185
  plants
    in photosynthesis, production 21
    sources and sinks 166, 167, 168
  in respiration, metabolism 23-5
carbon chains 7
carbon cycle 56-7, 58
carbon dioxide
  in blood, transport 205
  as greenhouse gas 56
  in plants 160
    photosynthetic reduction 18, 21
  ventilation and
    humans 174, 204-5
    insects 178
carbonic anhydrase 205
cardioacceleratory and cardioinhibitory centres 199
cardiovascular system 192-205
carnivores (secondary consumers) 58, 59

carotid body 174
carotid sinus 199
cat breeding 109-11
catalysts, enzymes as 11, 30
cell(s) 34-45
    absorbing 52-3, 185
    division *see* meiosis; mitosis
    organelles 35, 36, 37-42, *see also*
    specific organelles
cell wall, plant 43
cellulose 8, 9, *see also* hemicelluloses
    detritivores digesting 62
central nervous system (brain etc.)
    heartbeat rate and 199-200
    ventilatory control and 173, 174, 175
centrifugation
    cell homogenates 39-40
    DNA 83-4
centromere 94
cervical cancer 34, 45
    cytological tests 35, 45
chemoreceptors
    heartbeat regulation and 199
    ventilatory control and 174, 175
chest pain (angina) 192, 193
chlorophyll 17, 18, 19
chloroplasts 17, 40-1, 53
cholecystokinin 188
cholesterol 186
chorionic gonadotrophin, human 77
chromatids 94
    crossing-over 96, 97, 124
chromosomes 94-5
    in meiosis 94-5, 96
        independent assortment 96
    in mitosis 100
    mutations, variation due to 124
    sex *see* X chromosome; Y
    chromosome
chylomicrons 186
climax communities 153
cloning of organisms 101-2
clotting/coagulation 202
    disorders 115
coagulation *see* clotting
codominant alleles 105
codon 89
coenzyme A 24
cohesion-tension mechanisms 165
collecting duct/tubules 212
colon 182, 183
colour, skin 129-31
colour blindness 113, 114
communities 146, 153

climax 153
competition 144
    interspecific 146
    intraspecific 145, 146
competitive inhibition 33
concentration
    gradients of 48, 52
    substrate, enzyme activity and 32
condensation reactions
    amino acids 10
    fat 12
    sugars 8
conduction in heart 197-8
conservation 154-6
consumers
    primary 58, 59
    secondary 58, 59
    tertiary 59
contraceptive pill 73, 76, 77
control systems 66-78
coordinator in hypothalamus 69
coronary artery disease 193, 195
corpus luteum 74, 75, 76, 77
countercurrent flow 177
cristae 42
crops *see* agriculture
cross-breeding 108-11, 112
crossing-over 96, 97, 124
cultivation of land *see* agriculture
cyanobacteria, *see also* phytoplankton
    photosynthesis 16, 17, 19, 20, 21, 26,
    40
    structure 44
cystic fibrosis 80, 90, 105
cytosol 38

Darwin, Charles 126, 135
Darwin's finches 128-9, 135-6
deamination 208
decarboxylation, oxidative 24, 40, 42
decay processes in rainforest 62
deforestation 55, 64, 156
denitrifying bacteria 63
deoxyribose 80, *see also* DNA
desert reclamation 157-68
desiccation 158
detergents, enzymes in 28, 29, 31
detoxification *see* waste removal
detritivores 62
diabetes (mellitus) 118, 181, 186
    suitable foods 182, 189
dialysis 207, 217
diastole 194
dicotyledons

respiratory systems 179
    water movement 164
diet 6, *see also* food
    babies 14-15
diffusion 48-9
    facilitated 52
    gases, respiratory systems 172, 176-9,
    205
digestion of food 182-7, *see also*
    absorption
    fungi 190
    humans 182-7, 188
dihybrid inheritance 109-11, 113
diploid number of chromosomes 94, 95
disaccharides 8
divergence, genetic 136
DNA 37, 79-91, *see also* genes
    manipulation (in genetic engineering)
    79, 90-1, 116-19
    replication 82, 83-4
        mistakes (mutations caused by) *see*
        mutations
    species differences 137
    structure 80-1
    transcription 88
DNA polymerase 82, *see also*
    polymerase chain reaction
dominant alleles 104
duodenum, 186 *see* small intestine

ECG 198
ecosystems 55-65, 150, 151
effectors and thermoregulation 69
efferent fibres and thermoregulation 69
electrocardiogram 198
electron(s)
    in photosynthesis 18, 19, 20
    in respiration 25, 41
electron microscope 35-7
embryos, human, cloning 102
endocrine system *see* hormones
endodermal cells around xylem 165
endometrium 76
endoplasmic reticulum 38
endothelial cells, alveolar 172
energy
    activation 29-30
    flow/transfer
        in ecosystems 59, 60, 61
        thermoregulation 67, 68, 69, 70
    pyramid of 60
energy metabolism 16-27
environment
    of a species (=habitat) 144

variation affected by 122-3, 124
enzymes 11, 28-33
  activity
    factors affecting 31-2
    inhibitors 33
  digestive 184, 186, 188
  in DNA replication 82
  starch–sugar interconverting, in
    plants 159
  structure 30
epidermal cells of xerophytes 161
eukaryotes, prokaryotes compared with
  43, 44
evolution of new species 134-7
excretion in kidney 209, 212-14, 216-17
exercise/training 169, 170, 171, 172,
  174, 175
expiration 170, 171

facilitated diffusion 52
factor VIII 115
FAD$^+$/FADH 24, 25
fallopian tubes, oocyte release into 75
farming see agriculture
fat see brown fat; lipid
fatty acids 12, 13
  essential 13
females
  equal balance of males and 99
  hormone replacement therapy 77
  sex tests 92, 93
  sexual reproduction 73-6
fertilisation (gamete fusion) 94-5, 97
  random 96, 124
fertilisers 151, 152
fibrinogen 202
fibrous proteins 11
filtration in kidney 209-10
finches, Darwin's 128-9, 135-6
fish
  respiratory system 176-7
  waste removal 216
flagellum 43, 44
flavine adenine dinucleotide 24, 25
fluid 46-54, see also water
  balance 46-54
  loss by sweating 47, 67, 68
    replacement 69-70
  tissue 201-2
follicle cells 74
follicle-stimulating hormone 74-6
follicular phase of menstrual cycle 74-5
food 6-15, 181-91
  digestion/absorption see absorption;

digestion
  production 150-2
  types 7
food chains and webs 58-9
forests
  destruction 55, 64, 156
  rain see rainforest
fungi
  mycorrhizal 154
  nutrition 190

Galapagos finches 128-9, 135-6
gametes see fertilisation; ovum; sperm
gas exchange, respiratory systems 172,
  179-80, 193
gastrin 188
gastrointestinal tract (gut),
  digestion/absorption of food 52-3,
  182-7, 188
genes 80, 82, 103-19, see also DNA
  independent 112-13, 124
  linked see linkage
  mutations see mutations
  proteins synthesised from 87-9
genetic code 87, 88, 90
genetic counselling 114-15
genetic diseases 80, 86, 103-19
  treatments/cures 79, 86, 103, 116,
  118, 119
genetic divergence 136
genetic engineering 79, 90-1, 116-19
genetic variation 96-7, 120-31
  new species and 136
  in sexual reproduction 96-7, 99
genotype 104
gills 177, 216
glands
  digestive 184, 188
  endocrine, secretions see hormones
global warming 56-7, 156
globular proteins 11, 30, see also
  enzymes
glucagon 188, 189
gluconeogenesis 188
glucose 7, 8
  in blood (=blood sugar) 185, 186,
  188-9
    levels 181, 188-9
  in intestine, transport/absorption 53,
  185
  in respiration 24
glyceraldehyde-3-phosphate 21
glycerate-3-phosphate 21
glycogen 9

glycogenesis 188
glycogenolysis 188
glycolysis 24
gonadotrophin, human chorionic 77
gonadotrophin-releasing hormone 74,
  75
granulosa cells 74, 75
grasses 162
grassland, energy flow 61
grazing animals 143, 144, 146, 147,
  152
greenhouse gases 56, 156
growth hormone, manufacture 117
guard cells 158, 160
gut, digestion/absorption of food 52-3,
  182-7, 188

habitat 144
haematology 200
haemoglobin 204-5
  abnormal (of sickle-cell disease)
  105-7, 130
  function 204-5
haemophilia 115
haemorrhaging 195
hair erection 71
haploidy in meiosis 94
heart 193-4, 197-200
  attacks 192, 193, 198
  pacemaker 197-200
    artificial 197, 199
    natural 197-200
  rate, modification 199-200
  'secondary' 196-97
  structure/function 193-4
heat control mechanisms 67-72
hemicelluloses 43
Henle, loop of 212
herbicides 151, 152
herbivores (primary consumers) 58, 59
heredity see genes; inheritance and
  entries under genetic
heterozygosity 105
HLA 122
homeostasis in mammals 68
homogenisation of cells/tissues 39-40
homozygosity 105
hormone(s) (and endocrine system)
  food and 188-9
  kidney-regulating 213-14
  oestrous/menstrual cycle and 73-6,
  76
  pregnancy and 77
  thermoregulation and 72

hormone replacement therapy 77
human(s)
    embryos, cloning 102
    populations 149-52, 153
human chorionic gonadotrophin 77
Human Genome Project 86
human leucocyte antigens 122
humus 151
Huntington's disease 103, 114, 119
hybrids 133
hydrogen ions see pH; protons
hydrogencarbonate system 215
hydrolysis, starch 9, 182, 185
hydrophilic end of phospholipid 13
hydrophobic end of phospholipid 13, 38
hyperglycaemia 189
hypertonic solutions 48
hyphae 190
hypoglycaemia 189
hypothalamus
    kidney function and 213-24
    menstrual cycle and 74
    thermoregulation and 68-9, 70
hypotonic solutions 48
hypoxia 175

ileum 182, 183, see also small
    intestine
independent genes 112-13, 124
infants see babies
infertility, female 75
inheritance 103-19
    dihybrid 109-11, 113
    of disorders see genetic diseases
inhibitors, enzyme 33
insects
    respiratory systems 178
    waste removal 216
inspiration 170, 171
inspiratory cells 173, 174
insulin 181, 188, 189
    manufacture/use 116-17, 117, 118
interphase 100
intestine
    absorption 52-3, 185
    large (colon) 182, 183
    small 184, 185, see also duodenum;
    ileum
ion transport
    intestinal 53
    kidney 211-12
    plants 54
islet cells 184, 188

isolation, new species arising by 136
isotonic drinks/fluids
    for horses 70
    in sport 46, 47, 51

kidney 207-217
    failure 207
        acute 208, 217
Krebs cycle 24, 25, 40

lacteals 186
lactic acid 170
lamellae, secondary 177
large intestine (colon) 182, 183
leaves
    transport processes 53, 166, 168
    water loss 158-60
leg muscles as secondary heart 196-7
leucocyte antigens, human 122
light-dependent reactions of
    photosynthesis 18-20, 22, 40
light microscope 35
lignin 43
linkage 113, 114
    sex 113, 114, 115
lipase 186
lipid (fat) 12-13, 186
    cell membrane 38-9, 52
    digestion 186
liver function 184, 186-7
loop of Henle 212
lung function 170-5, 193, 204
luteal phase of menstrual cycle 75-6
luteinising hormone 74-6
lymph vessels 186, 201-2

magnesium and plants 62
malaria and sickle-cell allele 130
males
    equal balance of females and 99
    sex tests 92, 93
malpighian tubules 216
mammals, control systems 66-78
mass flow hypothesis 167
maximum breathing capacity 171
medulla oblongata
    heartbeat rate and 199-200
    ventilation and 173, 174, 175
meiosis 94-5, 96-7
melanin 129-30
membranes
    cell 38-9, 52
    chloroplast (=thylakoids) 40, 41
menstrual cycle 74-5, 76

mesophyll 54, 179
mesosomes 43, 44
messenger RNA 88, 89, 90
metaphase 100
microfibrils 43
microscopy 35-7
microvilli of small intestine 185
minerals in diet 15
mitochondria 40, 41-2
mitosis 100-1
monohybrid crosses 108
monomers 7
    nucleic acid 80
    protein see amino acids
    sugar (monosaccharides) 7, 8
moth, peppered 126-8
mucosa of gut 182, 183
mule 133
muscle(s)
    fatigue 170
    heart 193, 194
    leg, as secondary heart 196-7
    respiratory 171, 173, 175
mussels 191
mutagenic agents 86
mutations/mutant alleles 85-6, 88
    disorders caused by 80, 85-6, 103-19
    successful 136
    variation due to 124
mutualism 63
mycorrhizal fungi 154
myocardial infarction (heart attacks)
    192, 193, 198
myxomatosis 143, 144, 148

NAD$^+$/NADH and respiration 24, 25
NADP$^+$/NADPH and photosynthesis 19, 20
natural selection (theory of) 126-31, 145, 146
    new species and 136
negative feedback
    in ADH production 213
    in menstrual cycle 75
nephrons 208
nervous system
    heartbeat rate and 199-200
    ventilatory control and 173, 174, 175
net productivity 60, 61
neural mechanisms see nervous system
nicotinamide adenine dinucleotide
    (phosphate) see NAD; NADP
nitrification 63
nitrogen 63-4

fixation 63
nitrogen cycle 64
nitrogenous waste 208, 216-17
non-competitive inhibition 33
nucleic acids *see* DNA; RNA
nucleotides 80
nucleus 37
  transfer (in cloning) 102
nutrient cycles 62-4
nutrition *see* diet; food

oesophagus 182, 183
oestrogen
  menstrual cycle and 74-6, 76
  pregnancy and 77
oestrous cycle, control 73-6
omnivores 59
oocyte, *see also* ovum
  maturation 74
  release 74, 75
oral contraceptive (pill) 73, 76, 77
organelles 35, 36, 37-42
ornithine cycle 208
osmosis 48-9
osteoporosis 77
ovulatory phase of menstrual cycle 75
ovum 98
  fertilisation 94-5, 97
oxidation reactions 18
  in respiration 23, 24, 25
oxygen
  in blood, transport 193-4, 202-05
  in breathing/ventilation
    humans 172, 175
    other organisms 176, 177, 178, 179
  photosynthetic release 20

pacemaker *see* heart
pancreas 184, 188
parasitic food chains 60
pea crosses 112
pectins 43
peppered moth 126-8
peptides 10, *see also* polypeptides
peripheral receptors in ventilatory
  control 174, 175
peristalsis in gut 183
pH
  enzyme activity and 32
  regulation 205, 215
phenotype 104
phloem 166-7, 168
phosphate system 215
phospholipid 12-13, 186

cell membrane 38-9, 52
phosphorus and plants 62
phosphorylase 159
phosphorylation, oxidative 25
photolysis 19
photosynthesis 18-22, 26, 40-1, 159
  cyanobacteria 16, 17, 19, 20, 21, 26
  global CO_2 content and 56-7
  light-dependent reactions 18-20, 22,
  40
  light-independent reactions 21, 22
  respiration compared with 23
  xerophytes 161
phytoplankton 56-7
  ecosystems based on 60
pigmentation, skin 129-31
pituitary
  kidney function and 213-14
  menstrual cycle and 74-5
placenta 76-7
plants 18-22, 157-68
  absorbing cells 53-4
  breeding 112, 113
  carbohydrate *see* carbohydrate
  cells, structure/components 36, 43,
  44
  crop *see* agriculture
  desert 161-3
  grazing on 143, 144, 146, 147, 152
  photosynthesis *see* photosynthesis
  respiration 159, 179
  transport processes 53-4, 158-68
  water in *see* water
plasma 201, 202
  sweating and 47
plasmodesmata 163
ploughing 152
polymer(s) 7
  amino acid *see* peptide; polypeptide;
  protein
  carbohydrate (polysaccharides) 8, 9
  nucleotide (polynucleotide) 81
polymerase chain reaction (PCR) 83, 86
polypeptides 11
populations 143-56
  animal 143-56
  cycles 145-6
  growth/size 144-9
    control 148-9
  human 149-52, 153
positive feedback in menstrual cycle 75
potassium pump 160
pregnancy 76-7
  oral contraceptives preventing 73,

76, 77
pressure, blood *see* blood
pressure potential 50, 51
producers 58
productivity 60, 61
progesterone
  menstrual cycle and 75-6, 76
  pregnancy and 77
prokaryotes 43, 44
  eukaryotes compared with 43, 44
prophase 100, 101
proteases
  temperature effects 31
  uses 28, 29
proteins 7, 10-11, *see also* enzymes
  cell membrane 39, 52
  dietary, digestion 185
  structure 10-11
  synthesis from genes 87-9
protons (H^+ ions), *see also* pH
  photosynthesis and 19, 20, 41
  pumping 41
protozoans, waste removal 217
Punnett square 111
pyramids, ecological 59-60

rabbit populations 145
  control 143, 144, 147, 148
racial differences 129-31
rainforest 55, 56, 62-5
  destruction 55, 64
  energy flow 61
  importance 56
  nutrient cycles 62-4
  use 64-5
reabsorption in kidney 210, 213
receptors
  in heartbeat regulation 199-200
  in temperature regulation 69, 70-1
  in ventilatory control 173, 174, 175
recessive alleles 104
redox reactions 18
reduction 18
renin 214
reproduction 73-7, 94-102
  asexual 94, 97
  sexual *see* sexual reproduction
respiration (cellular) 23-5, 26, 40
  aerobic vs anaerobic 170
  global CO_2 content and 56, 57
  plants 159, 179
respiration (gas exchange in body) *see*
  gas exchange; ventilation
respiratory organs/systems 170-9

humans 170-6
  surfaces (=alveoli) 171, 172
  other animals 176-9
  plants 179
restriction endonuclease 117
ribose 80, *see also* RNA
ribosomes 38
ribulose biphosphate 21
RNA 37, 88-90
  messenger 88, 89, 90
  structure 88
  transfer 89, 90
roots
  as carbohydrate sources/sinks 166, 167
  water movement and 165
  xerophytes 163
RU486 73, 76

salivary glands 184
saturated fats 12
secretin 188
serum 202
sex
  alligators, temperature determining 123
  child's, choosing 99
  tests/methods of determination 92, 93
sex chromosomes *see* X chromosome; Y chromosome
sex linkage 113, 114, 115
sexual reproduction 94-9
  females 73-7
  genetic variation in 96-7, 99
shivering 71
sickle-cell anaemia and trait 105-7, 130
sinoatrial node 197-9
skin colour 129-31
small intestine 184, 185, *see also* duodenum; ileum
sodium chloride in kidney 211-14
soil acidification 154
solute, movement in plants 166-8
solute potential 50
soy bean-based baby feed 14, 15
speciation 136
species 133-42
  competition between 146
  competition within 145, 146
  conservation 154-6
  defining/distinguishing 133-4
  new, development 134-7
sperm 98

ovum fertilised by 94, 95, 97
sports drinks 46, 47, 57
SRY gene 93
starch 9
  in humans, digestion (hydrolysis) 9, 182, 185
  in plants, interconversion with sugar 159-60
stomach 182, 183, 186
stomata 158, 159, 160
  xerophyte 171
stretch receptors in ventilatory control 173
suberin 43, 165
submucosa of gut 182, 183
succession 153
sucrose 8
  transport in plants 167
sugars 8, 9
  in humans *see* glucose
  in plants
    starch and, interconversion 159-60
    transport 53, 54
supernatant 40
surface area–volume ratio 172, 179-80
surface tension in lung 172
surfactant 172
sweating 47, 67, 68
symplast 163
systole 194

telophase 100
temperature
  enzyme activity and 31
  regulation 67-72
  sex determination and 123
territorial behaviour 145
thermoregulation 67-72
thrombosis 193
thylakoids 40, 41
thyroid gland and thermoregulation 72
tigers 154-6
tissue fluid 201-02
toxins *see* waste removal
training by athletes 169, 170, 171, 172, 174, 175
transcription of DNA 88
transfer RNA 89, 90
transpiration 158, 159
transplanted organs 132
transport processes 52-4
  cardiovascular 193-4, 200-3
  kidney 207-17
  plants 53-4, 158-68

triglycerides 12, 186
trophic levels in ecological pyramids 59-60
tropical rainforest *see* rainforest
trout 216
Tubifex 204
tubules
  kidney
    collecting 213
    distal 213
    proximal 210
    malpighian 216

ultrafiltration in kidney 209
unsaturated fats 12
urea 208
uric acid 216
urine 211-13
uterus 76-7
  hormones affecting 76-7
  oocyte passage towards 75

variation 96-7, 120-31
  causes 124
  continuous 122-3
  discontinuous 121-2
  genetic *see* genetic variation
vasculature *see* blood vessels; lymph vessels
vasoconstriction 71
vasodilation 69
veins 196
ventilation 170-1, 172, 173-5, *see also* breathing
  control 173-5
  definition 170
  fish 176, 177
  humans 170-1, 172, 173-5
  insects 178, 179
ventral group and ventilatory control 174
ventricles 193-4
villi of small intestine 185
viruses in genetic engineering 117, 118
vital capacity of lungs 170
vitamins 15
  fat-soluble 12
volume–surface area ratio 172, 179-80

washing powder enzymes 28, 29, 31
waste removal
  in animals 216-17
  in humans by kidney 208-10
water 158-65, *see also* fluid

blood/tissue balance 201-2
intestinal transport 52
kidney handling 211-13
in plants 158-65
    conservation in arid conditions
161-3
    loss 158-60
    photosynthesis and 18-19
    transport 54, 163-5, 168
water potential 50-1, 54
  plants 158, 165
water stress 160
white blood cells 2201
whiteflies 148
women *see* females

X chromosome 93
    choosing sex of baby and 99
    genes on 113, 114, 115
    sex tests and 92
xerophytes 161-3
xylem 43, 163-5, 168

Y chromosome 93
    choosing sex of baby and 99
    sex tests and 92

zygote 94, 95